Let us be HONEST AND MODEST

Let us be HONEST AND MODEST
Technology and Society in Canadian History

Edited by
Bruce Sinclair
Norman R. Ball
and
James O. Petersen

Toronto
Oxford University Press
1974

Cover design by
FRED HUFFMAN

ISBN-0-19-540222-7

Printed in Canada by
THE BRYANT PRESS LIMITED

Acknowledgements

We owe a debt of gratitude to past members of the seminar in the History of Technology at the University of Toronto's Institute for the History and Philosophy of Science and Technology. Their investigations into varied aspects of the history of Canadian technology have provided us with both ideas and sources of information. We are grateful also to librarians at the University of Toronto, the Toronto Public Library, and the Public Archives and National Library in Ottawa, for their aid and for the permission to reproduce materials included in this book. We should like also to express our thanks to Massey-Ferguson Industries, Ltd., for permission to reproduce the letters of Hart Massey.

B.S.
N.R.B.
J.O.P.

Contents

INTRODUCTION   1

1 DISCOVERING THE NEW WORLD   4

VISIONS OF THE NEW WORLD

A Bounty from the Sea
N. Denys, *The Natural History of the People, . . . of
North America*, 1908   5

A Fair and Fruitful Land
R. Whitbourne, *A Discourse and Discovery of
Newfoundland, . . . , 1620*   8

As God Made It
M. Lochinvar, *Encouragements for Such as Shall Have
Intention to bee Under-takers . . . , 1625*   10

NATIVE AMERICAN TECHNOLOGY

They Go Quite Naked
H.P. Biggar, ed., *The Voyages of Jacques Cartier*, 1924   13

The Techniques of an Agricultural Community
H.P. Biggar, ed., *The Voyages of Jacques Cartier*, 1924   15

A Symbiotic Relationship
J. Marshall, ed., *Word from New France*, 1967   16

Transportation, Native Style
The Hargrave Correspondence, 1821-1843, 1938   17

Domestic Arts on the Pacific Coast
W.C. Hazlitt, *British Columbia and Vancouver Island*, 1858   18

THE TRANSFER OF TECHNOLOGY

A Report from New France *ca.* 1736
'Mémoire sur le Canada', PAC   20

The Ironworks at Three Rivers, 1752
J.H. Bartlett, 'The Manufacture of Iron in Canada', 1885-6   23

The Ironworks at Three Rivers, 1749
Peter Kalm's Travels in North America, 1964   24

The Need for British Agricultural Methods
J. Robinson and T. Rispin, *A Journey through Nova Scotia*, 1774   26

2   SETTLING THE LAND   29

A GARLAND OF PROMISES

The Prospect for Agriculture in Newfoundland
W. Carson, *Reasons for Colonizing the Island of
Newfoundland, . . . ,* 1813   30

Letter of Reassurance
C. Barclay, *Letters from the Dorking Emigrants, . . . ,* 1833   32

Making Light of Locusts
A. Begg, *Practical Hand-Book and Guide to Manitoba
and the North-West,* 1877   35

THORNS AMONG THE ROSES

The Anguish of First Settlement
J. MacGregor, *Historical and Descriptive Sketches
of the Maritime Colonies of British America,* 1828   37

A Contrary View of Emigration
J. Mactaggart, *Three Years in Canada,* 1829   37

Bad Managers in Nova Scotia
J. Robinson and T. Rispin, *A Journey through Nova Scotia,* 1774   38

CULTIVATION AND LAND MANAGEMENT

An Appeal for Improvement
Papers and Letters on Agriculture, . . . , 1790   39

A Novel Proposal for Clearing the Land
J. Mactaggart, *Three Years in Canada,* 1829   40

Draining the Land
'Land Drainage', *The Canadian Agriculturist, . . . ,* 1860   41

Tile
J. Miner, 'Tile', in R.W. Irwin, *A Review of Land
Drainage in Ontario,* 1961   44

THE COMFORTS OF ACCOMPLISHMENT

Farm Life in the Selkirk Colony
R.G. MacBeth, *Farm Life in the Selkirk Colony,* 1897   45

Stagnation in Lower Canada
H.Y. Hind, et al., *Eighty Years' Progress in British
North America,* 1863   48

Progress in Upper Canada
H.Y. Hind, et al., *Eighty Years' Progress in British
North America,* 1863   49

3   THE CONQUEST OF SPACE AND TIME   52

ROAD BUILDING
A Governor's Proclamation
Proclamation of Guy Carleton, Concerning Winter Roads, 1776   54
Corduroy Roads
J. Mactaggart, *Three Years in Canada*, 1829   55
The Want of Good Roads
T. Roy, *Remarks on the Principles and Practice of
Road-Making, . . . , 1841*   56
The Great Democratic Highway
H.Y. Hind, et al., *Eighty Years' Progress in British
North America*, 1863   59

CANALS
A Tidy Plan
Sketches of Plans for Settling in Upper Canada, . . . , 1822   60
An Appeal to British Capitalists
O. Creighton, *General View of the Welland Canal*, 1830   63
The Welland Canal: A report from its directors
Welland Canal Company. Director's Report, 1852   65
The Welland Canal: A dissenting view
J. Mactaggart, *Three Years in Canada*, 1829   66
Old and New World Engineering Practices
D. Stevenson, *Sketch of the Civil Engineering of
North America*, 1838   69
An American View of the Canadian Threat
'Report . . . on the Petition of the Inhabitants of the
County of Oswego', 1842   70
Towards the 'Grand Canadian Canal'
J. Mactaggart, *Three Years in Canada*, 1829   72

THE RAILROAD
The Agent of Civilization
T.C. Keefer, *Philosophy of Railroads*, 1850   73
A Railroad Proposal, 1847
*Engineer's Report, and Statistical Information Relative to
the Proposed Railway from Port Hope to Peterboro*, 1847   76
Utility *vs* Appearance
W. Shanley, *Reports on the Preliminary and Locating
Surveys of the Bytown and Prescott Railway*, 1853   79
Track and Gauge
W. Shanley, *Reports on . . . the Bytown and Prescott
Railway*, 1853   80

The Canadian Gauge
H.Y. Hind, et al., *Eighty Years' Progress in British North America*, 1863   81

Credit Where Credit Is Due
The Canadian Engineer of the Victoria Bridge, ... , 1860   83

The Railway and Western Industrial Development
'Preface', *Manufacturing and Business Opportunities in Western Canada* ... , 1911   86

Contracts and Construction on the Transcontinental
E.W. Bradwin, *The Bunkhouse Man*, 1928   89

A Bridge to the Future
C. Legge, *A Glance at the Victoria Bridge* ... , 1860   93

ELECTRIC COMMUNICATION

A Proposed Telegraph System in New Brunswick
Report and Estimate Concerning an Electro-Magnetic Telegraph Between Fredericton and St John, 1847   95

Maintaining a Western Telegraph
J.S. Macdonald, 'The Dominion Telegraph', 1930   99

Railroads and Northern Exploitation
C. Baillargé, *La Baie d'Hudson*, 1895   101

Electricity for Transportation
T.C. Keefer, 'Presidential Address', *Trans. Roy. Soc. Can.*, 1899   103

4   THE VICTORIAN DREAM: TECHNOLOGY AND PROGRESS   104

INSTITUTIONS FOR ADVANCEMENT

A Rationale for the Past
'The President's Address', *The Canadian Journal*, 1853-4   106

Knowledge, Power, and Godliness
J. Dallas, *A Lecture on the Aims and Usefulness of Mechanics' Institutes*, 1865   108

The Importance of Mechanical Knowledge to the Working Classes
J.C. Gallaway, *The Claims of Mechanics' Institutes*, 1844   109

To Lighten the Mechanics' Labours and Inform the Manufacturer
The Canadian Journal, 1852   112

Progress as a Race
R.B. Sullivan, *On the Connection between the Agriculture and Manufactures of Canada*, 1848   115

TO DISPLAY THE FRUITS OF PROGRESS

The Moral Effect of Industrial Exhibitions
C.D. Day, *Address Delivered at the Provincial Industrial Exhibition, Montreal, on Saturday, Oct. 19, 1850*, 1850   117

Lessons from an Exhibition
The Canadian Journal, 1852   120

The Miscellany of Progress
Provincial Exhibition, Toronto, 1858   121

Canada at the Crystal Palace, London, 1851
Tallis's History and Description of the Crystal Palace, . . . , 1851   123

Let us be Honest and Modest
J.A. Chisholm, ed., *The Speeches and Public Letters of
Joseph Howe*, 1909   124

To Go or Not To Go: The American Centennial Exhibition, 1876
The Monetary Times and Trade Review, 1875   125

Kudos from Philadelphia
F.A. Walker, *The World's Fair. Philadelphia, 1876*, 1878   127

MEASURING NATIONAL PROGRESS

Science and the Farmer
The Canadian Farmer, 1847   128

An Elementary Catechism
Manuel Elémentaire et Pratique de l'Art Agricole, . . . , 1853   129

An 1865 Plea for Educational Reform
A. Buies, *Textes présentés et annotés*, 1959   131

The Creamery as Symbol of Progress
F.E.A. Gagnon, *Choses d'Autrefois, feuilles éparses*, 1905   133

A Summary of Canadian Progress
C. Legge, *A Glance at the Victoria Bridge and the Men
Who Built It*, 1860   134

5   THE GROWTH OF INDUSTRY   139

AGRICULTURAL IMPLEMENTS

Machines for the Farmer
The Canadian Agricultural Reader, 1845   140

An Improved Sawing Machine
Canadian Illustrated News, Nov. 22, 1862   142

Two Canadian Implement Manufacturers
Canadian Illustrated News, Oct. 3, 1863   143
Canadian Illustrated News, Nov. 21, 1863   144

The Details of Business
Hart A. Massey Correspondence   147

IRON AND STEEL MANUFACTURE

The Difficulties of Transplanting Iron-Making Technology
R. Gourlay, *Statistical Account of Upper Canada*, 1822   149

Early Iron Smelting
Elijah Leonard, *A Memoir*, 1894   151

The Marmora Ironworks
W.H. Smith, *Canada: Past, Present and Future*, 1851   152

The Case for a Nickel Steel Industry in Ontario
'Statement of Samuel J. Ritchie', 1892   153

The Age of Steel
Iron and Steel of Canada, 1918   156

STEAM POWER

Steam Boats on the St Lawrence
D. Stevenson, *Sketch of the Civil Engineering of North America*,
1838   157

Early Steam Engine Building in Toronto
Colonial Advocate, 1833   158

Pioneer Engine Building in London
Elijah Leonard, *A Memoir*, 1894   160

Workshops of the Great Western Railway in Hamilton
Canadian Illustrated News, Feb. 14, 1863   162

TARIFFS AND TECHNOLOGY

Protection: The Canadian manufacturer's answer
Letters to the People of Canada, . . . , 1858   166

A Furniture Factory
Canadian Illustrated News, Jan. 17, 1863   170

Manufacturers, Machines, and the National Policy
Canada, *Sessional Papers*, 1885   172

6   DEVELOPING NATURAL RESOURCES
ON A NATIONAL SCALE   177

A WEALTH OF WOOD

Timber Rafts
D. Stevenson, *Sketch of the Civil Engineering of
North America*, 1838   179

Making Withs
T.C. Keefer, 'Rafting on the Ottawa', June 27, 1863   180

Woods and Forests
A Few Words on Canada, . . . , 1851   182

Making Matches
The Lumber Trade of the Ottawa Valley, 1871   184

Running a Timber Slide
Memoirs of Robert Dollar, 1927   185

The Waste of Timber Reserves
Robert Bell, *The Forests of Canada*, 1886   187

Timber on the West Coast
H.N. Whitford and R.D. Craig, *Forests of British Columbia*, 1918   190

The Pulp Industry
D.L. McGibbon, *The Pulp Industry in Canada*, 1912   191

MINING

Protecting a Native Claim
British Columbia and Vancouver's Island   194

Gold Everywhere
British Columbia and Vancouver's Island   195

Mining Techniques in the Yukon
W.B. Haskell, *Two Years in the Klondike and
Alaskan Gold-fields*, 1898   196

A Burning Question
W.H. Ogilvie, *Early Days on the Yukon*, 1913   198

Investors and Engineers
The Canadian Mining Review, 1897   199

A Survey of Canada's Mineral Resources
G.M. Dawson, 'Canada as a Field for Mining Investment', 1896   200

A Plea for Mineral Development in Ontario
Ontario Development of Mines, *Annual Report*, 1892   204

The Discovery of Nickel
Report of the Royal Ontario Nickel Commission, 1917   206

Gold Mining in Central Canada
A.H.A. Robinson, *Gold in Canada 1935*   212

THE ELECTRICAL AGE

The Significance of Electric Power
T.C. Keefer, 'Presidential Address', *Trans. Roy. Soc. Can.*, 1899   213

Power from a National Heritage
Hydro-electric Power Commission of Ontario, *Genesis of the
Power Movement*   215

Ontario Hydro: The great experiment
R. Pelham, *An Expensive Experiment, . . . ,* 1913   216

Steam vs Electricity on Railways
S.J. Dodd, *Electrification of Railways*, 1918   218

7   ENGINEERS AND RATIONAL TECHNOLOGY   221

Americans on the Great Western
A.G. Bogue and L.R. Benson, eds, 'An Engineer on
the Great Western', 1952   223

An Alien Engineer
The Canadian Engineer, 1899   224

A Success Story
A. Somerville, 'Memoir of Charles Legge, Esq., . . . ', 1864   224

A Course in Civil Engineering
A.G. Bailey, ed., *The University of New Brunswick
Memorial Volume*, 1950   228

Should a Young Country Provide Technical Education?
J.G. Hodgins, ed., *Documentary History of Education in
Upper Canada*, 1908   229

The Canadian Institute
The Canadian Journal, 1852-3   231

A Free Field and No Favors
'President's Address', Canadian Society of Civil
Engineers, 1887   233

A Plea for Regulation
A. Macdougall, 'A Plea for a Close Corporation', 1892   234

Engineering Arrogance
The Canadian Mining Review, 1897   235

Engineers and the Public Interest
'President's Address', Canadian Society of Civil
Engineers, 1909   236

A Vote for Disinterestedness
'Report of Annual Meeting, 1911', Canadian Society of
Civil Engineers, 1911   238

8   TECHNOLOGY AND THE CITY   242

PROTECTION FROM DISEASE AND FIRE
Sanitation and Sobriety
A. Brunel, *Report of the City Engineer . . .* , 1859   244

The Health of Towns and Cities
'Health of Towns and Cities', *The Canada Lancet*, 1873   246

Sewage Disposal in Hamilton
*Sixth Annual Report of the Provincial Board of Health of
Ontario, . . .* , 1888   247

Sanitary Engineering
S. Keefer, 'President's Address', Canadian Society of Civil
Engineers, 1889   248

FIRE IN THE CITY
Conservation and Fire Loss
J. Grove Smith, *Fire Waste in Canada*, 1918   249

A Destructive Fire
J. Grove Smith, *Fire Waste in Canada*, 1918   251

The Need for Research
J. Grove Smith, *Fire Waste in Canada*, 1918   251

MUNICIPAL IMPROVEMENTS

The Hamilton Water Works
'Hamilton and its Water Works', *Canadian Illustrated News*,
Sept. 26, 1863   252

The Engine That Couldn't
C. Martin, *To the Citizens of Toronto* . . . , 1886   255

Street Railways
H.Y. Hind, *et al.*, *Eighty Years' Progress in British
North America*, 1863   257

Pioneer Electric Lighting in Montreal
J. Smillie, 'Pioneer Electric Lighting in Montreal', 1894   258

9   FROM THE GREAT WAR TO THE GREAT DEPRESSION   261

CONSERVATION

Conflicting Views on Water Pollution
Sessional Papers, 1873   263

Fernow Describes His Task
'The Chair of Forestry at Toronto University', 1907   267

Robert Laird Borden Introduces a Conservation Bill
*Official Report of the Debates of the House of Commons of the
Dominion of Canada*, 1909   269

WORLD WAR I

Industrial Research: A national asset
G. Bryce, 'The Crying Need of Industrial Research in Canada',
1909-1912   271

Ploughshares Into Swords
H.H. Vaughan, 'The Manufacture of Munitions in Canada', 1919   274

War and the Movement for Home Industry
Report of the Royal Ontario Nickel Commission, 1917   276

The Honorary Advisory Council for Scientific and
Industrial Research
F.D. Adams, *The Need for Industrial Research in Canada*, 1918 278

AVIATION

When Flying Was In 'The Air'
Canadian Aviation, 1933   281

Aviation Revolutionizes Canadian Mining
E.L. Chicanot, 'The Aeroplane Revolutionizes Canadian
Mining', 1928   284

Canada's Place in an International Air Network
J.F. Grant, 'Definite Air Policy Required', 1933   287

THE AUTOMOBILE

The Greatest Invention Since the Locomotive
*Official Report of the Debates of the House of Commons
of the Dominion of Canada*, 1926   289

A Menace to Our Railways
*Official Report of the Debates of the House of Commons
of the Dominion of Canada*, 1926   292

Good Roads and the Home
Canadian Good Roads Conference, 1921, 1921   293

AGRICULTURE BETWEEN THE WARS

Marquis Wheat
C.E. Saunders, 'Cereal Breeding on the Dominion
Experimental Farm During the Past Decade', 1913   295

The Problem of Rural Depopulation
W.C. Good, *Production and Taxation in Canada, . . .* , 1919   297

Mechanization as a Solution to Depression
Agricultural Problems
A. Stewart, 'The Economy of Machine Production in
Agriculture', 1931   300

An Agricultural Corporation
G.L. Smith, 'The Grievous Plight of Canadian
Agriculture', 1932   303

A BRIEF GUIDE TO FURTHER READING   307

Illustrations

All illustrations are reproduced by courtesy of the Metropolitan Toronto Central Library

Victoria Bridge. James Hodges, *Construction of the Great Victoria Bridge in Canada*, 2 vols (London, 1860).   FRONTISPIECE

The Beginning. H.Y. Hind, *et al.*, *Eighty Years' Progress in British North America* (Toronto, 1863)   28

La Chine Rapids. *Eighty Years' Progress* . . .   61

The Bay and River Steamer 'Charlotte' Built at Ernest Town, U.C., 1818. *Eighty Years' Progress* . . .   71

Building the Victoria Bridge: Machine for Dredging Puddle Chambers. *Construction of the Great Victoria Bridge* . . .   85

Victoria Bridge: View from Below the South Abutment. *Construction of the Great Victoria Bridge* . . .   94

Mr Good's Locomotive Engine, Toronto. *Canadian Illustrated News*   138

Noxon's Improved Sawing Machine. *Canadian Illustrated News*   142

Pitt's Horse Power with Watson's Improvement. *Canadian Illustrated News*   143

Improved Eight or Ten Horse Separator. *Canadian Illustrated News*   144

Agricultural Implement Manufactory of Messrs. L. & P. Sawyer, Hamilton C.W. *Canadian Illustrated News*   145

Workshops of the Great Western Railway in Hamilton. *Canadian Illustrated News*   162-3

Steam Forging Hammer, Great Western Railway Works. *Canadian Illustrated News*   165

Cabinet Factory of G.P. Walter, Bowmanville. *Canadian Illustrated News*   171

Raft Building, and 'With' Twisting Machine, on Lake Ontario, 1863. *Canadian Illustrated News*   181

Timber Slide. *Eighty Years' Progress* . . .   186

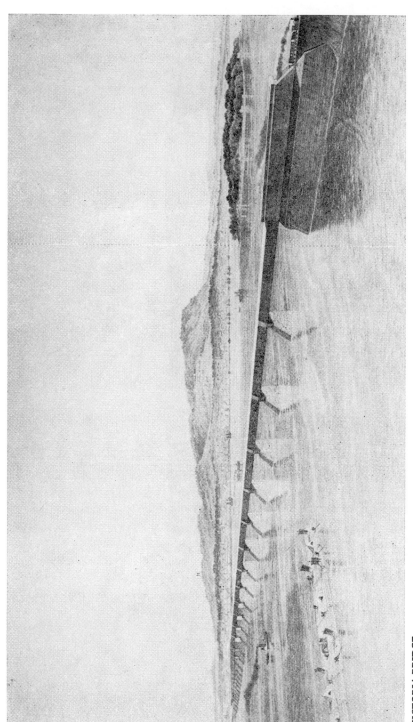

VICTORIA BRIDGE

Introduction

In the summer of 1854 Joseph Howe travelled to Paris to see the great industrial exhibition. Ever since England's Crystal Palace exposition three years earlier, massive international displays of art and industrial progress had captured the public's imagination, and Howe was fascinated by the spectacle. 'I could scarcely conceive that the civilization of the globe had risen to so high a pitch', he reported. But in contrast to the lavish displays of other nations, when he arrived at the New Brunswick and Nova Scotia booths Howe felt only pained embarrassment at the meagre samples of Canadian skill. At the next world's fair, he advised his countrymen, 'let us be honest and modest'.

Howe's words might well be taken as a motto for the history of Canadian technology. It appears to have few outstanding men or moments, and in comparison with the accomplishments of other nations, Canadians have long been diffident in advancing their own claims.[1] One could write the history of British technology because there was James Watt and John Smeaton, Joseph Whitworth and Henry Bessemer. Their achievements ensure them a place in the annals of the past.

But no one would expect to find any creative activity in Canada's past, especially any activity that required institutions, financial support, and a community of like-minded spirits. The land was sparsely populated and its people wholly engaged with a struggle for survival in a hostile environment. Against that background, the historian could expect to find only pale imitations of European culture, the stunted off-shoots of an under-nourished soil. That view is a popular one and has its own history. Canadians of the nineteenth century also bemoaned the lack of genius in the arts or sciences, and excused it for the same reasons.

Paradoxically, there was and still is a tendency to reason in the opposite direction. In its most virulent form, the argument is that our contributions

---

[1] A recent account in the *Globe and Mail* (June 14, 1973), p. 45, of a machine for cleaning up oil slicks illustrates the persistence of that attitude. The device, a Canadian invention 'pure and simple', was being marketed by the Japanese because the Canadians had not been aggressive enough in securing adequate patent protection. As the head of Canadian Patents and Development, Ltd put it, 'Canada's blown it again'.

to science and technology have been great, even out of proportion to our population, but that a combination of conservatism, capital, and cunning —our conservatism, their capital and cunning—has robbed Canada of its rightful place in the history of inventions.[2] The best scientists and engineers, or at least their ideas, always go somewhere else.

Neither of these approaches is satisfactory. Canadians did build bridges, canals, railroads, automobiles, and airplanes. As Professors Levere and Jarrell have shown in a companion volume to this book, Canadians also pursued the study of science and its applications. They extended the cultivation of wheat into areas where it had previously been impossible. They mechanized their agriculture with equipment that they manufactured themselves. They developed a sophisticated mining and minerals exploration industry. They designed and built factories and harnessed the energy of water, steam, and electricity to drive them. Obviously there was a Canadian technology.

Just as obviously, it does not lie in a search for the long-forgotten Canadians who anticipated the discoveries of others, but failed to get the credit. The history of invention is a poor substitute for the history of technology. For example, it is often said that Gutenberg 'invented' printing with moveable type. But the word misinforms us of Gutenberg's actual contribution and of the process that stimulated its creation. Indeed, even if one could isolate the act of invention, a difficult job in itself, the significance of the event depends on its social setting. The Chinese, after all, developed the art of printing with moveable type centuries in advance of the west, but chose not to exploit the new technique.

It is our intention to deal with the social history of technology. We see the subject as a process of adaptation. Nothing more strongly characterizes the Canadian situation than the continual selection of techniques from other societies. Nor was that a bankrupt approach. The ability to adapt is just as critical as the ability to originate. Britain imported most of the technology upon which its eighteenth-century industrial prowess was based. The United States did the same in the nineteenth century, and so did Japan in the twentieth century. In reality, the transfer of technology is itself a creative process. British engineers who visited Canada in the nineteenth century could see immediately that things were not done in the English manner. Some described the difference as shoddiness instead of substantiality. David Stevenson, however, was able to see beyond the 'apparently unfinished state' of engineering projects here and to discern the skill with which Canadians devised technical solutions in harmony with their environment.[3]

---

[2] See, for example, J. J. Brown's attempt to rescue the history of Canadian invention in his *Ideas in Exile* (Toronto, 1967).
[3] See below, p. 69.

The same adaptive talents were at work in agriculture, industry, and in the institutions that people created to express their technological ambitions. Canadians have long been sensitive to the relationship between techniques, the great natural wealth of the land, and the country's future. Almost from the outset, Canada's history has been inextricably linked with technology.

Yet, curiously enough, the subject has been little studied. We accept without question the critical role of technology in our daily lives, and understand that Canada is one of the world's major industrial powers. But beyond a vague memory that the transcontinental railway had something to do with confederation, and an intuitive perception that successive waves of emigrants were motivated by dreams of material advancement, we have neglected to imagine that there was a connection between past and present. Canadians know more of prime ministers than they do of the creation of the technological structure that is the framework for the nation's economic and social life.

We have attempted to gather a representative selection of documents, mainly from printed sources, to indicate some of the ways in which Canadians have dealt with their material environment over the past three and a half centuries. Some of the selections will already be familiar to students of Canadian history, and we have undoubtedly missed others that would have been more pertinent. In a book of this size, many relevant topics have not been included and the techniques themselves have been sketchily treated. Our aim is primarily to introduce the subject, in the conviction that technology lies close to the centre of the Canadian experience.

The subject is full of colour and drama. As Edmund Bradwin pointed out from his railway-building experiences, Canada's frontier civil-engineering campaigns were as daring and heroic as any great military action. Even at a more prosaic level, the study of technology promises to enrich the texture of Canadian history, to provide new insight into regional differences and into those common ingredients that distinguish a nation. In the spirit of Joseph Howe's words, we hope this book may prove a beginning.

1 | Discovering the New World

The ocean's riches first drew Europeans to these coasts. Cod from the Grand Banks fishery offered a seemingly inexhaustible supply of food, and it could be exploited with relative ease by well-established methods. Inevitably, Europeans were also drawn to the land. Nicholas Denys, who held a large grant from the Company of New France along the south shore of the Gaspé, described the cod-fishery in 1672 as only one of the New World's natural resources.

Most of the early accounts of Canada pictured it as a vast natural cornucopia, a land of clean water and wholesome air, stored to abundance with animal, vegetable, and mineral resources. At the same time, it was seen as a field ready for the application of European techniques, a country that wanted only the art and industry of the Old World to render it habitable. Without any sense of contradiction, the first Europeans described an Eden — the world as God had made it — as a place that required man's civilizing hand.

Settlement was never as easy as the early writers made it sound. They nearly always underestimated the severity of the weather and were unaware of problems inherent in the transfer of technology. Europeans also failed to appreciate the technical skills of the native peoples. Conditioned by the technology of their homeland as well as by their cultural background, they regarded the native Americans as crude savages.

Cartier's travel accounts reflected that view, but almost unconsciously he described a set of techniques well-adapted to an agricultural community. Indeed, just as in other parts of the New World, Europeans frequently came to depend on native ways of doing things for their own survival. In subsequent stages of western exploration, the same process was repeated; white men discovered a novel but well-established technology that often answered their own needs, if not their tastes.

The early history of Canadian technology is thus characterized by two processes that unfold simultaneously; the assimilation of native technology and the transfer of European technology. The fur trade is an example of the first process. Initially trapping, dressing, and shipping furs were carried on by the natives who delivered them to the coast where they were picked up by European traders. As the Europeans moved inland, they borrowed heavily from native American technology. Snowshoes, canoes, packs with tumplines, the fur-trade routes with their portages, and foodstuffs were all part of a technology that had been developed long before the Europeans came, by generations of men and women who had experimented with the materials and conditions available to them.

Technologies are highly adapted to the social environment in which they operate. If the Europeans were to make a successful application of their technique, they had also to recreate their own society in the new land. The absence of skilled craftsmen in New France, as the anonymous author of *Mémoire sur le Canada* (ca. 1736) pointed out, had stimulated a certain ingenuity with the axe and in the production of simple domestic goods. But more complex technical activities, such as shipbuilding or the exploitation of mineral resources, depended on the transplantation of technology. When the rate of transfer exceeded the rate of growth of the new communities, transplanted industries languished and could only survive if the state injected large amounts of capital. The furnace and forges of St Maurice at Trois Rivières illustrated one such enterprise and the difficulties in recreating Old World methods. Agriculture, particularly wheat growing, also rested on European practice. John Robinson and Thomas Rispin, two English farmers who toured Nova Scotia in the eighteenth century, came explicitly with the idea of introducing established techniques. In the long run, however, North America was to evolve a new approach towards technology, which had as its focus the conservation of labour.

VISIONS OF THE NEW WORLD

A BOUNTY FROM THE SEA

Nicholas Denys, *The Natural History of the People, of the Animals, of the Trees and Plants of North America* (Toronto, 1908), pp. 258-63.

I will commence with the green Cod, which is that eaten at Paris, and which is caught upon the Grand Bank of Newfoundland. The Bank which is thus called is a great elevation, lying in the sea but under water, distant twenty-five leagues or thereabouts from the Island of Newfoundland; from it the green Cod takes its name. This bank is about a hundred and fifty leagues from one extremity to the other, and some fifty leagues in its greatest breadth. This elevation in the sea has on its top at its highest part twenty-five fathoms of water, and in other places thirty, thirty-five, forty, fifty, and sixty fathoms of water. All around it is cut almost vertically, and around its circumference one cannot find bottom with twelve to fifteen hundred fathoms of rope. From that you can judge of the height of the elevation, which is of rock. All its top is flat, although it slopes off to greater depths.

This is where the Cod is caught, and it finds there plenty of shellfish of several sorts, and other fish for its sustenance. This fish is a great glutton, and its gourmandising embraces everything, even to those of its own species; and often one catches those which, despite the fact that they are caught on the hook, during the time they are being drawn up half swallow one of their own kind if it is met with on the way. They find nothing too hard; sometimes the fishermen let their knives fall, or their mittens, or other things; if a Cod comes across them it swallows them. Very often they catch the very Cod which has swallowed something which has fallen overboard, and they find it in its stomach, which the sailors call *gau*. This fish has also a peculiarity which is this, that if it swallows anything which it cannot digest, it ejects it from its stomach, which it everts out of its mouth, and thus gets rid of everything which injures it, after which it draws in again, and reswallows, its stomach. Those who go, as a rule, to make this fishery are the Normans from the harbour of Honfleur, from Dieppe, and from other little harbours of Normandy, likewise from Boulogne and from Calais, from Brittany, from Olonne, and from all the country of Aulnis. All those make up the number of two hundred to two hundred and fifty fishing vessels every year. All their fishery is almost solely for Paris, at least three quarters. There are ships which bring as much as thirty, forty, and fifty thousands of Cod. One ship of a hundred tons, for example, will have, counting even the captain, only fifteen or eighteen men at the most in her crew, and she will bring back twenty and even twenty-five thousands of fish.

It is necessary that a captain who sets out from France for this fishery should make preparation in provisions for six months at least for all his crew, which is of more or fewer men according to the size of his vessel. After that they go to take on their salt at Brouage, Oleron, Ré, or Brittany; this is worth ten, eleven, and twelve livres per hogshead, which is of twenty-eight heaping minots of salt, [which makes up] almost all the rest of that which the ship can carry. This fishery consumes much salt. There is need, further, of lines as large as quills, of eighty fathoms in length; eight to ten are needed for each man, and sometimes as many as twelve. A much larger number of hooks is required, for they are lost by the Cod carrying them off. There is also needed for each man twelve to fifteen leads, of six pounds weight each, which are attached at the end of the line to carry it to the bottom; [also] knives for opening the Cod, and others for dressing it, that is, splitting it down to the tail, as it is seen in Paris. After she is equipped in this fashion, she sets sail and goes by the grace of God to find the Grand Bank. Having arrived there, all the sails are furled, and the ship is prepared for this fishery. The tiller of the rudder is attached on one side, so that the vessel remains almost as if she were at anchor, though she drifts, nevertheless, when there is a wind. After that some throw overboard the lines into the sea to find whether the fish are biting, while others work at building a staging along one side of the vessel [and] outside, that is to say, unless good weather had allowed the crew to build it during the voyage or in approaching the Bank. Upon this staging are placed the barrels; these are half hogsheads, which reach to the height of the waist. Each fisherman places himself inside his own. They have also a large leather apron which extends from the neck to the knees. The lower end of the apron is placed over the barrel outside, in order to ensure that the water, which the line brings with it in drawing up the Cod from the bottom of the sea, shall not run into the barrel. The fisherman having sounded the depth, attaches his line to the barrel in which he stands, in such a manner as is necessary to ensure that the lead may not touch the bottom by about two fathoms. And it is also necessary to allow a fathom that the end of the line where the hook is, which is attached near the lead, also may not touch. He catches only a single Cod at a time, and in order to know the number that he takes, each fisherman has a little pointed iron near him, and at the time when he removes the hook from the Cod, he cuts the tongue from it and strings it upon this iron. Each fisherman has two lines, and whilst he is drawing up one he throws over the other, which descends to the bottom; [this he does] when there is abundance of fish in the place where the ship is.

A good fisherman is able to take as many as three hundred and fifty to four hundred [per day], but that greatly tires the arms. The Cod is heavy, besides which it resists, and then thirty, forty, and, according to the depth, up to sixty fathoms of lines are not so quickly drawn up. If they did this every day they would not be able to stand it. There are, indeed, days when they take nothing; at other times they only catch twenty-five, thirty, forty, a hundred, or two hundred each per day—it is all a matter of chance. As to the *boite* for the Cod, it is the bait which one places on the hook, on the point of which is stuck a piece of Herring; of this the skin has a certain lustre which glistens in the sea. When the Cod perceives this it rushes to it. Besides this they cover the hook entirely with the entrails of the Cod, in a mass as large as the two fists. But when they find in the *gau* or stomach of the Cod, shellfish or other fish which are not digested, they use them in place of Herring.

There are ships which will be fortunate enough to complete their fishery in a month or six weeks, whilst others will be three, four, and five months in achieving this. That depends upon good luck. None of the fishing vessels ever anchor upon the Grand Bank. By day they have a little square sail upon the sterns of their ships, which they call ring-tail [*tapecul*], in order to keep them up to the wind and to prevent the drift; that is, that the ship may not move to one side. If they were to move thus, the lines would trail out too far from the ship, and would not be able to reach the bottom, where the Cod is.

For the night they set their mainsail, and all those [vessels] which are upon the Bank set them always upon the same side in order that the vessels may make their drift all alike, and by this means avoid collisions with one another. Otherwise they would run a risk of being lost, since the vessels might come together with a crash.

Further, it is necessary to know that the Grand Bank is rarely without a mist or fog, which is sometimes so thick that one cannot see from one end of the ship to the other. It is this which obliges them to take this precaution to avoid shipwreck.

When the fishermen who are upon this Grand Bank see that Lent is approaching, those who have the half or two-thirds of their fish set out to endeavour to be the first to arrive for the sale, which is better than at any other time.

In spring they set out also with less cargo, for those who arrive first find still the best sale, the trade therein being well assured in Paris. It is this which is called the New Cod.

This diligence brings them yet another advantage, which is that of undertaking a second voyage in the same year as soon as they are unloaded. And if they make a good hit of fish upon the bank, they are able still to arrive in time for the Lenten sale. But all these advantages are accidental. Happy is he who meets with them. Yet there is much trouble and ill to be endured, for this reason, that upon the Grand Bank it is colder in the month of June than it is in France in September.

This is all the time they can have there, since the three months of summer are nearly always filled with a thick and rather cold fog.

A FAIR AND FRUITFUL LAND

Richard Whitbourne, *A Discourse and Discovery of Newfoundland, With Many Reasons to Prove How Worthy and Beneficial a Plantation May There be Made, After a Far Better Manner Than Now It Is* (London, 1620), pp. 3-11.

It is to be seene by the *Cosmographers* Maps; and well approued, that the

New-found-land is an Iland, bordering vpon the Continent of *America*, from which it is diuided by the Sea; so farre distant, as *England* is from the neerest part of *France*, & lieth betweene 46 and 53 degrees North-latitude: It is neere as spacious as *Ireland*, and lyes neere the course that ships vsually hold in their return from the *West-Indies*, and neere halfe the way betweene *Ireland* and *Virginiea*.

I shall not much neede to commend the wholesome temperature of that Countrey, seeing the greatest part thereof lieth aboue 3 degrees neerer to the South, then any part of *England* doth.

And it hath bin wel approued by some of our Nation, who haue liued there these many yeeres, that euen in the winter it is as pleasant and healthfull, as *England* is.

The soyle of this Countrey in the valleys and sides of the mountaines, is so fruitfull, as that in diuers places, there the Summer naturally produceth out of the fruitfull wombe of the earth, without the labour of mans hand, great plenty of greene Pease and Fitches, faire, round, full and wholesome as our Fitches are in *England*: of which I haue there fed on many times: the hawmes of them are good fodder for cattel and other beasts in the winter, with the helpe of Hay; of which there may be made great store with little labour in diuers places of the Countrey.

Then haue you there faire Strawberries red and white, and as faire Raspasse berries, and Gooseberries, as there be in *England*; as also multitudes of Bilberries, which are called by some, Whortes, and many other delicate Berries (which I cannot name) in great abundance.

There are also many other fruits, as small Peares, sowre Cherries, Filberds, &c. And of these Berries and fruits the store is there so great, that the mariners of my Ship and Barkes company, haue often gathered at once, more than halfe an hogshead would hold; of which diuers times eating their fill, I never heard of any man, whose health was thereby any way impaired.

There are also herbes for Sallets and Broth; as Parsley, Alexander, Sorrell, &c. And also flowers, as the red and white Damaske Rose, with other kinds; which are most beautifull and delightfull, both to the sight and smell.

And questionles the Countrey is stored with many Physicall herbs and roots, albeit their vertues are not knowne, because not sought after; yet within these few yeeres, many of our Nation finding themselues ill, haue brused some of the herbes and strained the iuyce into Beere, Wine or *Aqua-vitae*; and so by Gods assistance, after a few drinkings, it hath restored them to their former health.

The like vertue it hath to cure a wound, or any swelling, either by washing the grieued places with some of the herbes boyled, or by applying them so thereunto (plaister-wise) which I haue seene by often experience.

This being the natural fruitfulnes of the earth, producing such varietie of things, fit for food, without the labour of man; I might in reason hence inferre, that if the same were manured, and husbanded in some places, as our grounds are, it would be apt to bear Corne, and no lesse fertill than the *English* soyle.

But I need not confine my selfe to probabilities; seeing our men that haue wintred there diuers yeeres, did for a triall and experiment thereof sowe some small quantities of Corne, which I saw growing very faire; and they found the increase to be great, and the graine very good; and it is well knowne to me, and diuers that trade there yeerely, how that Cabbage, Carrets, Turneps, Lettice, and such like, proue well there.

In diuers parts of the Countrey, there is great store of Deere, and some Hares, many Foxes, Squirrels, Beuers, Wolues, and Beares, with other sorts of beasts, seruing as well for necessitie, as for profit and delight.

The fresh waters and Springs of that Countrey, are many in number, and withall very pleasant, delightfull and wholesome, that no Countrey in the world hath better. And Fewell for fire is so plentifull, that there is neuer like to be want of that commoditie.

In like manner there is great abundance of Trees fit to be imployed in other seruiceable vses: There are Firre and Spruce trees, sound, good, and fit to mast Ships withall; and as commodious for boords and buildings as the Spruce and Firre trees of *Norway*; and out of these came abundance of Turpentine. No Countrey can shew Pyne and Birch trees, of such height and greatness as those are there; and doubtlesse, if some store of your Maiesties subiects do once settle there to liue, & would be industrious to search further, and more throughly into the Countrey, then as yet it hath been, there might be found many other commodities of good worth. Amongst the which I may not omit, that there is much probabilitie of finding Mines, and making of Iron and Pitch.

AS GOD MADE IT

Mee Lochinvar, *Encouragements for Such as Shall Have Intention to bee Under-takers in the New Plantation of Cape Briton, Now New Galloway in America* (Edinburgh, 1625), pp. 16-18.

I have therefore heere taken a view that you may generallie knowe and learne, what the Countrie is, and her commodities: the temperature of the climate: nature of the natives: and the easinesse of the passage; all which I shall briefly runne over; only to remove from before your feete the stumbling blocks of impossibilitie that may affright vs.

The Countrie it is called by the name of Cape Briton, now *New Galloway*: new, not in respect of the discoverie thereof, which to the judgment of men of knowledge and understanding is not new, but old; for the much hath been written thereof, yet new, not olde, because of our new vndertaking of that plantation. It is situated betwixt the degrees of 45. and 57. an Yland within the Sea, but vpon the maine, severed by the distance of foure leagues in some parts, of two or three at other parts: and at others, lesse.

The Yland is in length some 120. myles, and in breadth 80. myles or thereby: standing South-east, and North-west to *New Scotland*; vvhere the great river *Canada* ingorgeth her selfe in the maine Ocean. Harbours there bee exceeding good on all sides, in most part vvhereof are ancorage for shippes of all burthen. Yles there be about over-grovvn vvith good timber of diverse sorts of vvood; all as yet not discovered except the Yle *Sablon*, vvhich is full of vvoodes and vvilde beastes, but vvithout any people. The Land is vvatered by foure maine rivers, full of Salmond, and diverse other sortes of fishes. It hath plentie of springes of svveete vvaters. Tovvards the North-east, *Mountainous*: and tovvard the South-west *Caimpainge*: promising as rich entralles as anie other Kingdome to whom the Sunne is no neare neighbour. The ground in it self so fertile and good as may equalize any of the Kingdomes that lyeth in the hight of 45. 46. 47. Onlie this advantage I find in nature, that they haue above this: they are bewtified by the long labour & diligence of industrious people & airt: & this is only as God made it, when he created the world, vncultured, planted & manured by men of industry, judgment & experience.

The commodities which we shal reape from thence shall be great, for the Sea shall sweeten our labours with her benefites, as the Land, and the Land as well as the Sea. The Sea shall reach vs vp her Whale, her turbot, her sturgion, cod, haddocke, small ling, makkerell, herring, mullet, pearch, Eele, crab, lobster, muskle, wilk, oyster, and infinite others. Fish is the maine Staple, from whence is to be extracted, a present commoditie to produce the rest: which howsoever it may seeme meane and base, yet it is the Mync, and the Sea is the source of these silvered streames of all these vertues, which hath made the *Hollanders*, the miracle of industrie, & patterne of perfection for these affaires: and the benefite of fishing, is that *Primum mobile* that turneth all the Spheare to this hight of plentie, strength, honour, and admiration.

The ground it will yeeld vs an admired varietie; some wee shall haue that are merchantable, which, by the serving for ordinarie necessars of the planters & inhabitants, may yeeld a superplus sufficient, by way of traffick and exchange with other nations, to enriche our selves the provyders; such as flaxe, hempe, which the Soyle doth yeeld of it self not planted. For pitch, tarre, rozen and turpentine, there bee these kind of trees there, which yeeld them aboundantlie. Sassafras, called by the natives, winauk, a kind of wood of sweet smell, and of rare vertues in Physick. The Vine, it groweth there wild. Oyle there may be there of two sortes: one of walnuts; and another of beries, like the ackornes which the natives vse. Furres of manie and diverse kinds; such as the marterne, the otter, the black foxe, the luzernes, Deere skins, bevers, wildcat, and manie others. Sweet gummes of diverse kinds, and many other Apothecarie drugges. Dyes of diverse sortes: such as shoemake, for blacke: the seede of an hearbe called vasebur, and a litle small roote called chappacor, for red: & for blew, the herbe woad, a thing of great vent and vse at home for Dyers, and many other commodities merchantable, which by planting may be raised.

Other commodities there are, which the ground doth yeeld vs for victuall and sustenance of mans life, and vsuallie fedde vpon by the naturall inhabitants: for it is knowne to bee so fertile, as without question capable of producing of any graine, fruite, or roote, or feede you will sowe, of plant, growing in any other region of the same hight. The graines are maze, which we call Guinie wheat, according to the countrie from whence the like hath beene brought, and this graine is much about the bignesse of our ordinary pease. There is also beanes, called of the natives Oknigier: and pease called by them, Wickonzour. They haue pompions, millons, and gourds, and an herbe called melden, growing foure, or five foote high, of the seede they make a thicke broth, and potage of a good taste, and of the stalke, by burning it in ashes they make a kinde of salt earth, wherewith they season their brothes, other salt they know not. They haue the hearbe Tobacco, called by the natives Vppowoe, in great plentie. Fruites they haue of sundrie sorts: as ches-nuts, walnuts, grapes, medlars, mulberries, goose-berries, respices, straw-berries, plummes, currans, or a fruite like currans. Rootes they haue of diverse kindes; Openauk, a kinde of roote, or a round forme and bignesse of walnuts, which beeing boyled or sodden, are verie goode meate: Okeepauke, another roote found in drye ground, which they eate with fishe or flesh: Tsinaw, a roote like the china-roote, growing together in clusters, of this roote they make bread. Of beasts; they haue Deere red, and fallow, conies, black foxes, and others, bevers, beares, wildecats, otters, marternes, luzernes, allanes, wolves, squirrels, and a beast called Moos, bigger than a Stagge. For fowle, they haue the turkie, the goose, the ducke, the skeldrake, the cran, the teale, Eagles, Falcons, marlin-hawkes.

And finallie are those other commodities, as are behovefull for those which shall plant and inhabite to know of: such as oakes, ashe, elme, firre, the pine, and ascopo: which is a kinde of tree like the Laurell, the barke whereof, is hotte in taste, and spycie; hazell, plume-tree, walnut-tree, chesnut-tree, and manie others, which I omitt to rehearse. For to make mention of the severall beastes, birdes, fishes, fruites, flowres, gummers, rootes, sweete woodes, trees, hearbs, and other commodities, wherewith the ground is so naturallie, and so plentifullie enriched, and stored withall; I should fill vp Decads: but referring these to the relations of such as hath fullie collected the varieties of them, I come to the temperature of the climat.

The nature of the Climate wee maye easilie conclude from the hight whereinto it is situated; beeing in the 45. 46. and 47. which is as temperate, and as fruitfull as anie other paralell in the World; and answerable to these fruitfull partes in *France*, which are accompted the garden of *Europe*; *Poictou*, and *Anjou*: and where is that famous river of *Loyre*, adorned with so manie faire, so ancient, and populous Cities: and manie other notable, and famous Kingdomes: as you maye looke in the vniversall Mappe, because I meane not to bee tedious: and so having there such excellent temperature of the aire at all seasons, much warmer than heere, and never so vehementlie hotte as it is vnder, and betwixt the Tropicks, or neere them, wee neede not thinke of vnwholesomenesse.

NATIVE AMERICAN TECHNOLOGY

THEY GO QUITE NAKED

H. P. Biggar, ed. and trans., *The Voyages of Jacques Cartier* (Ottawa, 1924), pp. 60-5.

On account of the continuous bad weather with over-cast sky and mist, we remained in that harbour and river, without being able to leave, until [Saturday], the twenty-fifth of the said month [of July]. During that time there arrived a large number of savages, who had come to the river [Gaspé basin] to fish for mackerel, of which there is great abundance. They [the savages] numbered, as well men, women as children, more than 300 persons, with some forty canoes. When they had mixed with us a little on shore, they came freely in their canoes to the sides of our vessels. We gave them knives, glass beads, combs and other trinkets of small value, at which they showed many signs of joy, lifting up their hands to heaven and singing and dancing in their canoes. This people may well be called savage; for they are the sorriest folk there can be in the world, and the whole lot of them had not anything above the value of five sous, their canoes and fishing-nets excepted. They go quite naked, except for a small skin, with which they cover their privy parts, and for a few old furs which they throw over their shoulders. They are not at all of the same race or language as the first we met. They have their heads shaved all around in circles, except for a tuft on the top of the head, which they leave long like a horse's tail. This they do up upon their heads and tie in a knot with leather thongs. They have no other dwelling but their canoes, which they turn upside down and sleep on the ground underneath. They eat their meat almost raw, only warming it a little on the coals; and the same with their fish. On St. Magdalen's day, we rowed over in our long-boats to the spot on shore where they were, and went on land freely among them. At this they showed great joy, and the men all began to sing and to dance in two or three groups, exhibiting signs of great pleasure at our coming. But they had made all the young women retire into the woods, except two or three who remained, to whom we gave each a comb and a little tin bell, at which they showed great pleasure, thanking the captain by rubbing his arms and his breast with their hands. And the men, seeing we had given something to the women that had remained, made those come back who had fled to the woods, in order to receive the same as the others. These, who numbered some twenty, crowded about the captain and rubbed him with their hands, which is their way of showing welcome. He gave them each a little tin ring of small value; and at once they assembled together in a group to dance; and sang several songs. We saw a large quantity of mackerel which they had caught near the shore with the nets they use for fishing, which are made of hemp thread, that grows in the country where they ordinarily reside; for they only come down to the sea in the fishing-season, as I have been given to understand. Here likewise grows Indian corn like pease, the same as in Brazil, which they eat in place of bread, and of this they had a large quantity with them. They call it in their language, *Kagaige*. Furthermore they have plums which they dry for the winter as we do, and these they call, *honnesta*; also figs, nuts, pears, apples and other fruits, and beans which they call, *sahé*. They call nuts, *caheya*, figs, *honnesta*, apples ... If one shows them something they have not got and they know not what it is, they shake their heads and say, *nouda*, which means, they have none of it and know not what it is. Of the things they have, they showed us by signs the way they grow and how they prepare them.

THE TECHNIQUES OF AN AGRICULTURAL COMMUNITY

II. P. Biggar, ed. and trans., *The Voyages of Jacques Cartier* (Ottawa, 1924), pp. 153-8.

When this was done we marched on, and about half a league thence, found that the land began to be cultivated. It was fine land with large fields covered with the corn of the country, which resembles Brazil millet, and is about as large or larger than a pea. They live on this as we do on wheat. And in the middle of these fields is situated and stands the village of Hochelaga, near and adjacent to a mountain, the slopes of which are fertile and are cultivated, and from the top of which one can see for a long distance. We named this mountain "Mount Royal". The village is circular and is completely enclosed by a wooden palisade in three tiers like a pyramid. The top one is built crosswise, the middle one perpendicular and the lowest one of strips of wood placed lengthwise. The whole is well joined and lashed after their manner, and is some two lances in height. There is only one gate and entrance to this village, and that can be barred up. Over this gate and in many places about the enclosure are species of galleries with ladders for mounting to them, which galleries are provided with rocks and stones for the defence and protection of the place. There are some fifty houses in this village, each about fifty or more paces in length, and twelve or fifteen in width, built completely of wood and covered in and bordered up with large pieces of the bark and rind of trees, as broad as a table, which are well and cunningly lashed after their manner. And inside these houses are many rooms and chambers; and in the middle is a large space without a floor, where they light their fire and live together in common. Afterwards the men retire to the above-mentioned quarters with their wives and children. And furthermore there are lofts in the upper part of their houses, where they store the corn of which they make their bread. This they call *carraconny*, and they make it in the following manner. They have wooden mortars, like those used [in France] for braying hemp, and in these with wooden pestles they pound the corn into flour. This they knead into dough, of which they make small loaves, which they set on a broad hot stone and then cover them with hot pebbles. In this way they bake their bread for want of an oven. They make also many kinds of soup with this corn, as well as with beans and with pease, of which they have a considerable supply, and again with large cucumbers and other fruits. They have in their houses also large vessels like puncheons, in which they place their fish, such as eels and others, that are smoked during the summer, and on these they live during the winter. They make great store of these as we ourselves saw. All their food is eaten without salt. They sleep on the bark of trees, spread out upon the ground, with old furs of wild animals over them; and of these, to wit, otters, beavers, martens, foxes, wildcats, deer, stags and others, they make their clothing and blankets, but the greater portion of them go almost stark naked.

A SYMBIOTIC RELATIONSHIP

Joyce Marshall, trans. and ed., *Word from New France: The Selected Letters of Marie de l'Incarnation* (Toronto, Oxford University Press, 1967), pp. 315-16, 345-6.

I told you in another letter that part of the army has gone on ahead to get control of the river of the Iroquois [Richelieu] and build forts on its banks in the most advantageous places. To this I shall add that our Christian Algonkins have gone to camp with their families under protection of the forts and those that guard them. They are hunting where their enemies were accustomed to do so and obtain the greater part of their pelts. Their hunt is so bounteous that it is said they take more than a hundred beaver each day, not to speak of moose and other wild beasts.

In this the French and the Savages help one another. The French defend the Savages, and the Savages provide food for the French by the flesh of the beasts they kill, after they have removed the skins, which they take to the storehouses of the country. Monsieur de Tracy told me a few days ago that he had informed the King of all this and also the other advantages there are in making war upon the sworn enemy of our Faith.

Join your prayers to ours, that God may pour his benedictions upon an enterprise so advantageous to his glory. . . .

The esteem I have given you of late years for the squash of the Iroquois has given you an appetite for them. I am sending you some seed, which the Hurons brought us from the Iroquois country, but I do not know whether your soil will change the taste. They are prepared in divers manners—as a soup with milk, or fried. They are also cooked in the oven like apples or under the embers like pears, and it is true that, thus prepared, they have the taste of cooked rainette apples.

Melons grow in Montreal that are as good as those of France; they grow but rarely here because we are not as far to the south. There is also a certain species that is called watermelon that is shaped like squash and eaten like a melon. Some salt them, others sugar them; they are considered excellent and are not noxious. The other pot-herbs and vegetables are as in France. We harvest them like wheat for use all winter and till the end of May, while the gardens are covered with snow.

As for trees, we have plum-trees which, when well manured and culti-vated, give us fruit in abundance for three weeks. We do not cook the plums in the oven, for then only a pit covered with skin remains, but make marmalade out of them with sugar, which is excellent. We make ours with honey, and this is quite sweet enough for us and our children. We also make jam from gooseberries and from *piminan*, a wild fruit that sugar renders very pleasant. We are beginning to have rainette and cal-ville apples, which are very fine and good here, but the species are brought from France. Such are our husbandry and our delicacies, which would be counted as nothing in France but here are very much esteemed.

TRANSPORTATION, NATIVE STYLE

The Hargrave Correspondence, 1821-1843 (Toronto, The Champlain Society, 1938), pp. 144-5. Reprinted by permission.

After arriving at York, I was sent in a Boat to the Interior, and as you are not very well acquainted with the manner of travelling in this Country I will endeavour to give you a little information on the Subject, in the Summer we generally travel in Boats or Canoes, the Boats are about 36 feet long & Broad Flat bottomed, & have generally 6 men to pull with a Bowsman and Steersman the duty of the Bowsman is to watch in the bow of the boat, in order to push her from any rock or stone & to work like a common man when not in the Rapids, the other steers the Boat which is performed by a sweep or large Oar, as the rudder would have no effect in the Falls or Rapids, the Canoes are made of birch Bark are very long & about 5 ft. broad in the middle tapering towards the ends which are turned upwards, the bottom is round the bark is supported on the inside by timbers about 1½ in. broad & the thickness ¾ in. bent round so as to fit the shape of the Canoe, they have ten men who work with paddles, & it is surprising with what velocity they move, The hour for leaving the encampment (travelling with a Boat) is about 5 O'Clock, breakfast about nine & encamp about 7, the encamping is merely pitching the Gentlemens Sheeting Tents (the men sleep without any covering) procuring a suffi-ciency of dry wood for the fire in the night, In the Falls & bad Rapids we launch our boat up over land till we get into smooth water & carry the Cargo across, but in some rapids we only carry the cargo & haul the Boat up with the line, The manner of carrying is this every man has a leather strap, broad in the middle & getting narrow towards the ends, these are fastened to a piece & the strap is put over the head, the broad place is put upon the forehead (just tho for hodmen in Edin,) & another piece upon the top of the first, a piece is 90 lbs thus the men carry thence across the portages the whole weight rests upon the neck & puts the head backwards, The Winter voyaging is different & more interesting, transport in the winter is carried on by dogs yoked to a sledge upon which the things are put, a man drives them, & it is scarcely credible the load these dogs will draw, the encampment is made by clearing away the snow off a piece of ground, & laying pine brush taken from the trees neatly upon it building walls round it about 2 ft high also of brush, there is a large fire in the middle around it & when the storm rages The Thermomater is at 50 Below o. you will not perceive any one suffering from the inclemency of the weather altho' seated in the open air.

I once heard Mr. D. McTaggart hold forth in praise of walking in "the snow dry as sand" but if the Hon[ble] Gentl. had a trial of it he would find that aching toes & racked joints were no very enviable pleasures, & when every step you took your track was marked with Blood running from the foot cut by the snow shoes & it is impossible to walk without them; as to hunting it is no great pleasure to hunt for one's very subsistence.

DOMESTIC ARTS ON THE PACIFIC COAST

W. C. Hazlitt, *British Columbia and Vancouver Island* (London, 1858), pp. 91-3.

Their houses are constructed of wood, and vary in length from twenty to seventy feet, and in breadth from fifteen to twenty-five feet. Two or more posts of split timber, according to the number of partitions, are sunk firmly into the ground and rise upwards to the height of fifteen or eighteen feet. They are grooved at the top so as to receive the ends of a round beam or pole, stretching from one end to the other. On each side of this range is placed another row much lower, being about five feet high, which form the eaves of the house. But as the building is often sunk to the depth of four or five feet in the ground, the eaves come very near the surface of the earth. Smaller pieces of timber are then extended, by pairs, in the form of rafters from the lower to the higher beam, and are fastened at both ends by cords of cedar bark. On these rafters two or three ranges of small poles are placed horizontally, and in the same way fastened with similar cords. The sides are then made, with a range of wide boards sunk a small distance into the ground, with the upper ends projecting above the poles of the eaves, to which they are secured by a pole passing outside, parallel with the eave poles, and tied by cords of cedar bark passing through the holes made in the boards at certain distances. The gable ends and partitions are formed in the same way; being fastened by beams on the outside parallel with the rafters. The roof is then covered with a double range of thin boards, excepting a space of two or three feet in the centre, which serves for a chimney. The entrance is by a hole cut in the boards, and just large enough to admit the body.

The largest houses are divided by partitions, and three or four families may be found residing in a one-roomed house. In the centre of each room is a space, six or eight feet square, sunk to the depth of twelve inches below the rest of the floor, and enclosed by four pieces of square timber; here they make the fire, which is of wood and fine bark. The partitions in the houses are intended to separate different families. Around the fireplace mats are spread, and serve as seats by day, and frequently as beds at night; there is, however, a more permanent bed made, by fixing in two, or sometimes three sides of a room, posts reaching from the floor to the roof, and at the distance of four feet from the wall. From these posts to the wall one or two ranges of boards are placed so as to form shelves, on which they either sleep or stow their various articles of merchandise. In short, they are like berths in a ship. The uncured fish is hung in the smoke of their fires; as is also the flesh of the elk when they are fortunate enough to procure any.

Their culinary articles consist of a large square kettle, made of cedar wood, and a few platters and spoons made of ash. Their mode of cooking is expeditious. Having put a quantity of water into their kettle, they throw into it several hot stones, which quickly cause the water to boil; then the fish or flesh is put in; the steam is kept from evaporating by a small mat thrown over the kettle. By this method a large salmon would be boiled in twenty minutes, and meat in a proportionably short space of time. They occasionally roast their fish and flesh on small wooden skewers. There is generally a door, notes Mr. M'Lean, at each end, which is cut in the wall after the building is erected. These apertures are of a circular form, and about two and a half feet in diameter, so that a stranger finds it very awkward in passing through them. In effecting a passage you first introduce a leg, then bending low the body you press in head and shoulders: in this position you will have some difficulty in maintaining your equilibrium, for if you draw in the rest of the body too quickly, it is a chance but you will find yourself with your head undermost. The natives bolt through them with the agility of a weasel.

During the severity of winter, adds Mr. Cox, they make excavations in the ground sufficiently capacious to contain a number of persons, and here they burrow until warm weather. They preserve their dry salmon rolled up in baskets of birch bark, in holes of a similar description, but somewhat smaller. The smell from these subterraneous dwellings, while thus occupied, is horribly offensive, and no white man could stand within its influence.

THE TRANSFER OF TECHNOLOGY

A REPORT FROM NEW FRANCE ca. 1736

'Mémoire sur le Canada; D'après un Manuscrit aux Archives du Bureau de la Marine à Paris' (Library of the Public Archives of Canada), pp. 1-2, 5-9.

The Colony of New France might contain about forty thousand people of all ages and of all sexes, among whom are ten thousand men ready to bear arms.

The Canadians are naturally large, well made and of a vigorous temperament. As the arts in that region are in no way encumbered by masters, and because in the beginnings of the establishment of the Colony workers were rare, necessity has made the colonists industrious from generation to generation. The inhabitants of the country are all adroit users of the axe. They make themselves the greater part of their tools and utensils of agriculture. They build their houses and their barns; a number of them are weavers, making large sheets of cloth, and a material that they call *droguet*, which serves to clothe them and their family.

They appreciate polished manners and little attentions. They pride themselves on their bravery. They are extremely sensitive to scorn and resent the slightest punishment. They are selfish, vindictive, subject to drunkenness, they consume large quantities of liquor, and seem not to be truthful. This portrait suffices for the greater part of them, especially for the country folk. Those in the city are less refractory. All of them are religious. One sees few scoundrels. They are fickle, and have too good an opinion of themselves, which keeps them from succeeding as well as they might in the arts, agriculture, and commerce. Join to this the idleness that is occasioned by the length and rigour of the winter. They love hunting, sailing, travelling, and have not at all the coarse and homely air of our French peasants. They are usually compliant enough, when one appeals to their sense of honour, and if one governs with justice, but they are naturally stubborn. It is necessary to strengthen more and more the correct subordination that must exist in all the orders and among the country people. This part of the work has at all times been the most important and the most difficult to fulfill. One way of arriving at this is to choose the officers from the wisest proportion of inhabitants, those most capable of commanding, and to bring to bear on the part of the government all possible attention to keep them in their authority. One dares to say that the lack of firmness on the part of past governments has greatly harmed subordination. For several years crimes have been punished; disorders have been curbed with the appropriate punishments. The police have been better obeyed in relation to public roads, cabarets, &c., and, in general, the inhabitants have been more contained than they were before.

From the États du Commerce and from the censuses that have been sent, one knows the products of the colonies and their commerce. There will still be a few things concerning this to touch upon.

The principle crop is wheat. The country grows wheat not only as food for its inhabitants, but also for trade with Isle Royale and the islands. In good years, 80 thousand *minots* of wheat leave the colony in flour and biscuits. Less will leave in 1737: the harvest having been very bad last year. The lands are not all of the same goodness and of the same yield; those belonging to the government of Quebec are mixed between high land and low land and because of this situation the rainy years are more favourable to the first and the dry years to the others: it is not so for the lands belonging to the city of Montreal, which are flat and level.

Dry spring seasons are always to be feared for the produce of the land.

All the wheat that is sown is spring wheat. It is always desirous that the sowing take place in the first days of May each year, so that the wheat can profit by the rains of the season. When the winters are long, the sowing is too late. Ordinary land yields from eight to twelve or fifteen to one [measures of wheat to measures of wheat seed]. Better lands yield more.

Several years ago, an attempt was made to introduce the cultivation of fall wheat. Some thought that it would be dangerous to establish this practice as it would expose the Colony to famine, because it would find itself without means. In fact, autumn wheat is of a superior quality and of a better grade than spring wheat. Ordinarily it would succeed, but it was recognized in the trials that were made that if the snows were late, or if the thawing of the snow was followed by frosts, then the autumn wheat that was in leaf perished. This even happened to the field grasses which are tougher and less susceptible to cold.

The other species of grains that are cultivated are oats, peas, a little barley, and still less rye. The other crops consist of flax, hemp, and tobacco. There are few orchards.

It is proposed to perfect the growing of tobacco. The Farmers General estimate, on the basis of trials made on Canadian tobaccos that were sent to them, that they would be fit for consumption in France, if one undertook to follow the instructions they have sent for this crop. The inhabitants will not fail to apply themselves to this if they are given a little better price. It would not do if it were too much, for fear that this crop would only establish itself at the expense of wheat. This would accomplish nothing. It is thought that the price of from four *sols* six *deniers* to five *sols* per pound for this commodity sold in Quebec would be sufficient. But the Farmers General could not count on delivering more than two to three hundred thousand [pounds] in the next few years, until the inhabitants have cleared more land, and until this new product has rendered them more industrious. One cannot go wrong, in this conjecture.

There is no doubt that the exploration of the iron mines near Three Rivers will have the success that is hoped for; the works will be completed this year.

The copper mines of Lake Superior give very promising hopes. But up to the present, all the accounts pertaining to their discovery do not seem at all sufficient in detail to take costly measures for their exploration. Other accounts are promised on the discovery of an island in Lake Superior, which all the savages of this area unanimously maintain to be full of copper. This island is marked on the new map. If this fact is correct, one can dispense with the Temiscaming river and the Iron river, from which came the ingots or white iron pyrites of copper that were sent this year. De la Ronde, the son, should visit this island and give an account. There is nothing to be feared from the savages on the island in question, where one cannot go except with difficulty by canoe, and with many risks, to the place where the tribe of the Foxes and their allies live and hunt along the Tonnaganne river and thereabouts. All this part of America is full of copper mines; one can judge the situation a little from the attached account that describes the different areas where this metal is found.

It has been proposed to send to the Colony a man, who is not only an expert on metal, but is also a man of resources and practicality, for the purpose of visiting the mines, suggesting a plan for the exploration and the transport to Montreal. This man should be able to examine and resolve the difficulties present in such a plan. A man of this type is rare; the purpose merits the expense. If full assurance can be given that a project for the exploration of the mines will be carried out next year it would be well to fortify the posts along the passage, and meanwhile to bestow more than the usual favours on the savages, without their discovering our ideas. The posts to fortify are Michilimakinac, Detroit, Niagara, and even Fort Frontenac; otherwise, at the first outbreak, the jealousy of the English will bring them into the upper lands and chase the French out. It is estimated that Michilimakinac will need a garrison of 50 men; even though the country is barren they will find the means to subsist; 80 or 100 men at Detroit; 50 men at Niagara.

The building of ocean-going boats has found favour for several years. The contributions given by His Majesty for these constructions have helped greatly. The cultivation and export of tobacco will give rise to considerable building in the future. Cherry wood is recognized as being very good, at least for the bottoms of the ships. It is found in Canada abundantly in every size. Oak for planking will be available from around Lake Champlain, and from the lands above Montreal for a long time to come. Ship outfitters from Rouen and Bordeaux will have built this year two ships of from 2 to 300 tons at the embankment at the Palais de Quebec. In general, as soon as these new objects of commerce are introduced, construction will increase as well as other businesses.

Much of the land along the edges of Lake Champlain has been granted in the last few years; but it can only be settled gradually and in stages. It is thought that it would be appropriate to build a mill, either for wind or water, in a convenient place, near the Fort de la Pointe à la Chevelure, in order to speed the settlement of the land on that side. The King will find an extra advantage to this, in that it will reduce the cost of feeding the garrison when the neighbouring lands produce grain and the other necessities of life. This establishment, which is near the English, afterwards will generate a number of inhabitants, who will prevent our neighbours from penetrating into the centre of the colony.

THE IRONWORKS AT THREE RIVERS: A Report from the Government's Inspector, M. Franquet, in 1752

J. H. Bartlett, 'The Manufacture of Iron in Canada', *Transactions of the American Institute of Mining Engineers*, vol. XVI, (1885-6), pp. 513-14.

"M. Bigot, Intendant of New France, who resides at Quebec, had recommended me to visit the St. Maurice forges, as the establishment was extensive, and as he had no doubt that I would be pleased to be in a position to give an account of it. By stopping at Three Rivers, I could reach the forges in two hours, so having settled upon that course, I requested M. Rigaud, who was then in charge of that post, to accompany me. We left Three Rivers at 5 o'clock A.M., with M. Tonnancour and other friends, whom M. Rouville, director of the forges, had invited to accompany us. In leaving the town, we ascended a hill covered with sand, crossed a plain, and passed through a wood of stunted trees, on emerging from which we stood on a hill overlooking a valley, in which the said forges of the king are situated; we crossed a wooden bridge built over a small stream, and disembarked from our conveyance at the door of the Director's dwelling. After the first ceremony of reception by the Director, his wife, and the other employés, we proceeded to visit the works. The stream which drives the machinery is dammed up in three places; the first dam drives the wheel for the furnace, the second and third each a triphammer. Each dam has a water-pass to prevent overflow in high water; it is supposed that the stream or water-power is sufficiently strong to drive two other hammers. The buildings of the post are irregularly situated on the banks of a stream, and little or no taste seems to have been displayed in placing them. The principal building is the Director's residence, a very large establishment, but scarcely large enough for the number of employés who have to be accommodated.

"On entering the forge, I was received with a customary ceremony; the workmen moulded a pig of iron about 15 feet long, for my special benefit. The process is very simple, it is done by plunging a large ladle into the liquid boiling ore and emptying the material into a gutter made in the sand. After this ceremony I was shown the process of stove-moulding, which is a very simple affair, but rather an intricate operation; each stove is in six pieces, which are separately moulded, they are (afterwards) fitted into each other, and form a stove above three feet high. I then visited the shed where the workmen were moulding pots, kettles, and other hollow-ware. On leaving this part of the forge we were taken to the hammer forges, where bar iron of every kind is hammered out. In each department of the forges, the workmen observed the old ceremony of brushing a stranger's boots; in return they expect some money to buy liquor to drink to the visitor's health. This establishment is very extensive, employing upwards of 180 men. Nothing is consumed in the furnace but charcoal, which is made in the immediate vicinity of the post. The ore is rich, good, and tolerably clean; it formerly was found on the spot, now the Director has to send some distance for it. The management of these forges is economical. It must be readily understood, that owing to the numerous branches in which expenditure must be incurred, unless a competent man be at the head of affairs, many abuses would be the consequence. Among other employés, His Majesty the King supports a Recollet Father at this establishment, with the title of Aumonier. This iron is preferred to the Spanish iron, and is sold off at the King's stores in Quebec at the rate of from 25 to 30 castors (beaver skins) per hundred weight.

THE IRONWORKS AT THREE RIVERS: Peter Kalm
pays a Visit in 1749

Peter Kalm's Travels in North America (New York, Dover Publications, Inc., 1964), vol. II, pp. 420-1. Reprinted by permission of Dover Publications, Inc.

The *ironworks* which is the only one in this country, lies three miles to the west of Trois Rivières. Here are two great forges, besides two lesser ones under the same roof. The bellows were made of wood, and everything else is as in the Swedish forges. The melting furnaces stand close to the forges, and are the same as ours. The ore is gotten two French miles and a half from the ironworks, and is carried thither on sledges in the winter. It is a kind of moor ore, which lies in veins within six inches or a foot from the surface of the ground. Each vein is from six to eighteen inches deep, and below it is a white sand. The veins are surrounded with this sand on both sides and covered at the top with a thin earth. The ore is pretty rich and lies in the veins in loose lumps the size of two fists, though there are a few which are nearly eighteen inches thick. These lumps are full of holes, which are filled with ochre. The ore is so soft that it may be crushed betwixt the fingers. They make use of a gray limestone which is quarried in the neighborhood for promoting the smelting of the ore. To that purpose they likewise employ a clay marle, which is found near this place. Charcoal is to be had in great abundance here, because all the country round this place is covered with woods, which have never been disturbed except by storms and old age. The charcoal from evergreen trees, that is, from the fir, is best for the forge, but that of deciduous trees is best for the smelting oven. The iron which is here made was to me described as soft, pliable, and tough, and is said to have the quality of not being attacked by rust as easily as other iron. In this point there appears a great difference between the Spanish iron and this, in shipbuilding. This smeltery was first founded in 1737, by private persons, who afterwards ceded it to the king. They cast cannon and mortars here of different sizes, iron stoves which are in use all over Canada, kettles, etc. not to mention the bars which are made here. They have likewise tried to make steel here, but cannot bring it to any great perfection because they are unacquainted with the best manner of preparing it. Here are many officers and overseers who have very good houses, built on purpose for them. It is agreed on all sides that the revenues of the ironworks do not pay the expenses which the king must every year have for maintaining them. They lay the fault on the bad state of the population and say that the inhabitants in the country are few, and that these have enough to do in attending to their agriculture, and that it therefore costs large sums to get a sufficient number of workmen. But however plausible this may appear, yet it is surprising that the king should be a loser in carrying on this work, for the ore is easily broken, very near the furnaces, and it is very fusible. The iron is good, and can be very conveniently transported over the country. These are, moreover, the only ironworks in the country from which everybody must supply himself with iron tools and what other iron he wants. But the officers and workmen belonging to the smeltery appear to be in very affluent circumstances. A river runs down from the ironworks into the St. Lawrence River, by which all the iron can be sent in boats throughout the country at a low rate.—In the evening I returned again to Trois Rivières.

THE NEED FOR BRITISH AGRICULTURAL METHODS

John Robinson and Thomas Rispin, *A Journey through Nova Scotia* (York, 1774), pp. 14-15.

ANNAPOLIS ROYAL, adjoining the township of Granville, lies West from Halifax one hundred and thirty miles; and when in the possession of the French (who kept a garrison in it) was the capital of Nova-Scotia, and in a very flourishing condition; a great trade being carried on, and money and provisions were in great plenty. About seventy years ago it fell into the hands of the English. When Halifax was built, which is about twenty years ago, they removed the soldiers from the garrison at Annapolis, to the fort at that place: The trade went along with them, and has ever since been on the decline. The forts seem to be tumbling to ruins. This town is as finely situated for trade as any in the country: It stands at the head of a fine bason, six miles over; where ships of any burden may ride in the greatest safety: It runs for above fifteen miles through a narrow passage betwixt two mountains called Annapolis Gut, and empties itself into Fundy Bay, where it is about a mile wide; so that the township extends fifteen miles down the bason, four the bay, and upwards of twenty miles above the town, through which runs a fine navigable river, which comes upwards of seventy miles out of the country. On both sides of the river several families are settled, chiefly from New-England. They were sent by the government, most of them were soldiers and very poor. On their first settling they were supplied with a year's provisions. They were entire strangers to cultivation, and are very bad farmers. They plough here a little, and there a little, and sow it with the same grain, without ever a fallow, till it will grow nothing but twitch grass; then they cast it aside and go to a fresh place. The French, when in possession of this place, had their marshes diked in and ploughed, which grew wheat in such abundance that they sold it for one shilling a bushel; however, the present inhabitants do not grow so much as is sufficient for themselves, but are obliged to buy Indian corn at four and sixpence, rye at five, and wheat at six shillings a bushel; which they would have no occasion to do, would they but properly cultivate their own lands, leave off the use of rum, which they drink in common, even before breakfast; and to which, in a great measure they owe their poverty—By the growth of a sufficient quantity of barley, which by a little industry they might accomplish, and the brewing of malt liquor, the many fatal disorders which are the consequence of too liberal a use of rum would not be known amongst them, and the sums of money would be kept at home, to their very great advantage, which they now send out for the purchasing that liquor. If this river was settled by English farmers of substance, a very advantageous trade to the West-Indies might be carried on, by the exporting of horses, beef, butter, cheese, timber, deals, and corn; and in return, receive rum, rice, sugar, molasses, and other spices; which at present they have through so many hands, that they cost them more than one hundred and fifty per cent above prime cost. They likewise want a trade to England, for at present they have all their English goods from Boston, which comes at a very great disadvantage. If this could once be effected, the town would abound in plenty, and perhaps quickly regain more than its primitive lustre.

From the beginning, a flood of literature assured the prospective settler that Canada was a country of vast agricultural potential. Emigrants were urged to believe that almost any part of the country would readily yield bountiful harvests with the least application of agricultural technique. One of the reasons for painting such an unrealistic picture was that colonization schemes were so often tangled with motives unrelated to the settler's well-being. William Carson argued Newfoundland's case out of a desire to see civil government established there. Charles Barclay's plan to assist emigrants from the parish of Dorking aimed at a reduction of local poor rates, and was only one instance of the 'Canadian cure' for England's social and economic ills. It was also true that the authors of guidebooks realized that positive accounts of the country sold more copies. Anyone thinking of emigration wanted to believe that grass-hoppers would disappear in Manitoba.

Wringing a profit from the soil was a difficult business, as most settlers discovered when actually confronted with the job. The surprise is not that some gave up, but that so many stayed on. The literature that might have prepared the emigrant for his trials existed, too, if one wanted to read it. John Robinson and Thomas Rispin's *A Journey through Nova Scotia* presented an objective account of agricultural practices there, while Mac-Gregor's *Historical and Descriptive Sketches of the Maritime Colonies of British America* catches some of the anguish first settlers must have felt. To the Scottish civil engineer John Mactaggart, outspoken on most issues, deceptive accounts of agricultural ease were criminal.

The first and in some ways most onerous task was clearing the forest. That job gave the settler material for his housing. When burned, wood ashes could also be converted into potash, an ingredient of homemade soap, or a cash crop to be exported for use as an industrial alkali. But clearing the land was only the beginning. From then on, crop yields were largely a function of soil management. In the nineteenth century, fertilizers and proper drainage were advocated as the great panaceas. For the Canadian farmer, who used less intensive methods than his English counterpart, the problem was balancing capital investment against returns. The *Canadian Agriculturist* wrestled with that issue in its attempts to encourage drainage improvements. Jack Miner's poem puts the case less seriously, but with as much point.

Cultivation techniques varied considerably within Canada. Most observers pointed to the difference between the methods of French- and English-speaking farmers. Those who celebrated Ontario's agricultural progress usually contrasted it sharply with the traditional methods of Quebec farming. There were also differences between British and North American techniques, especially where capital and labour costs were important factors, and the agricultural problems of the West were often unlike those that faced eastern farmers. MacBeth's reminiscences of the Selkirk Colony reflected the western farmer's isolation and his orientation to the United States, especially for implements.

By the middle of the nineteenth century, Canadian farmers had worked out a varied set of cultivation techniques fitted to their environment and economic situation, and looked forward to years of increasing prosperity. Particularly in older settled areas, those with a sense of historical perspective felt considerable satisfaction. A well-established agricultural press and the existence of strong local and provincial agricultural societies suggested that future progress would depend on systematic research and experimentation. But in the early years agricultural success was the result of skillful adaptation, of fitting Old World techniques to New World conditions. That undramatic process usually receives less attention than original invention, but it was the primary force in the history of Canadian agricultural techniques.

A GARLAND OF PROMISES

THE PROSPECT FOR AGRICULTURE IN NEWFOUNDLAND

William Carson, *Reasons for Colonizing the Island of Newfoundland, in a Letter Addressed to the Inhabitants* (Greenock, 1813), pp. 13-15.

I shall as briefly as possible, endeavour to point out the advantages that would flow to this island, and the mother country, from the establishment of a civil Government, and from the appropriation and cultivation of the lands. In doing this I shall have to combat some prejudice, and some **error.** The island of Newfoundland has been represented as destitute of soil; the atmosphere as unfriendly to vegitation; agriculture as injurious to a fishery; and the country colonized as contrary to the interests of the British merchant, and incompatible with the policy of the mother country.

The surface of the island of Newfoundland, is upwards of 37,000 square miles, being 8000 square miles larger than Ireland. There are not more than ten square miles cultivated in the island. The interior is entirely unexplored. The only parts known are the barren ridges, extending along the sea coast, from one harbour to another. The low and fertile lands being covered with wood, and intersected with lakes and rivers, are avoided by the traveller. In the neighbourhood of St. John's there are about 1000 acres of land in cultivation; but, being the eastern extremity of the island, and the promontory of a Peninsula, it is much exposed to the bank fogs during summer, and during the spring months to the floating ice, which encircles two thirds of the promontory; refrigerating the atmosphere and blasting the tender plants; but this is only felt on the eastern shore, and only for a few miles into the country; yet the cultivated lands in the neighbourhood of St. John's, yield as plentiful a crop of hay, as the best cultivated grounds in the vicinity of London. Potatoes and turnips arrive at the greatest perfection, and in the sheltered spots oats and wheat ripen. Annually large flocks of lean cattle, from New England, Nova Scotia, &c. are fattened in the woods round St. John's. Deer, congregating to the number of many hundreds, have been seen in all the explored parts. These facts must be considered as sufficient proof of the capability of Newfoundland to become a pastoral and agricultural country. It lies in lat. 46, 40: to 51, 40, North. The northern extremity is nearly as far south as the southern extremity of England. The sun's power is sufficient to ripen all those grains, roots, and fruits, which arrive at perfection in Britain. The power of the summer sun is greater, and the winter's cold more severe, but, are mollified by similar causes in both countries, though not to the same extent. The severity and duration of the winters are not so great as on the continent of America, in latitudes much further to the south. Ploughing, and the other operations of the field, are seldom obstructed before Christmas, and the lands are open to receive the plough early in April.

In the neighbourhood of all the fishing harbours, a considerable quantity of excellent manure may be procured from the sea weed, cod's heads, and the refuse of the seal blubber. In a country so unexplored, it is impossible to say what are its stores of manure. The number of its rivers, and the general situation of its lakes, are favourable for the purposes of irrigation. The soil and climate of this island, are as well adapted for the purposes of agriculture, as the soil and climate of Nova Scotia, and part of the Canadas, from whence it is proposed to feed the inhabitants on reasonable terms. The present war has shown the fallacy of these pretensions, and exposed the delusion which prevailed upon this subject. The Canadas and Nova Scotia, are not much more than able to supply with their own growth, their internal demands. The inhabitants of these countries may carry on a lucrative commerce, between this and the States of America, in the articles of beef, bread, and flour; but the profits of our fisheries had much better be directed to the cultivation of the lands in this country, and thereby creating, and nourishing a numerous peasantry, than in purchasing the produce of agriculture at an enormous expense from our enemies.

LETTER OF REASSURANCE

Charles Barclay, *Letters from the Dorking Emigrants, Who Went to Upper Canada, in the Spring of 1832* (London, 1833), pp. 15-20.

ADDRESS
TO THE INHABITANTS OF DORKING.

Having introduced the plan for assisting persons from this parish to emigrate to Upper Canada, and having taken an active part in carrying it into effect, it gives me great gratification to publish the following letters, from some of the individuals who were sent out by your Association, during the last Spring. I have taken great pains to procure a sight of every letter which has been received from them, and I have met with no instance of complaint, nor expression of disappointment. The only case of failure which has come to my knowledge, is that of an individual, who narrowly escaped transportation for life at the Assizes for this County, in the Spring of 1832; who, upon his arrival in Upper Canada, broke open a store, and was committed to prison in the town of York, upon his liberation worked his passage home, and is now in confinement in Guilford Goal for disorderly conduct. The letters are literal copies of the originals, except the spelling and the omission of some repetitions.

The perusal of these letters will satisfy every unprejudiced mind that industrious persons, with or without small capitals, have a fair prospect of maintaining themselves and their families in comfort and independence by settling in Upper Canada. The idle and the dissolute will suffer the same privations and the same punishments there as in their own country. There is no provision for them. Every man must earn his subsistence by the labour of his hands.

I have no hesitation in giving the preference to this colony. The climate is very similar to our own, and the emigrant upon his arrival there will find himself surrounded by his fellow countrymen, engaged in similar objects, willing and able to give him both their advice and assistance. The expense of the passage is much lower than to any other Colony, and the voyage shorter and less harassing. As a national object it demands our preference, when we consider the importance of creating a strong and powerful barrier on this boundary of the United States, by the establishment of a numerous and thriving population. . . .

MY DEAR SISTER,   August 26, 1832.

No doubt you are very anxious to hear from us, I am thankful to say we all arrived safe in Upper Canada. We are 60 miles from York, 15 from Dundas, though we travelled all the way by water, except 20 miles by land. We are very near the back settlements of America. We are situated in a very pleasant spot, 12 acres cleared land, two houses, outbuilding, beautiful spring of water like your orchard water at Milton. Twelve shillings we give for a sow and 5 pigs, but we expect to have a cow, and there is about half-a-dozen here, and every thing are so much cheaper to what they are at England. The man that built this house lived here five years, he said he had not a penny, he was a shoemaker; he had 4 cows, 2 oxen, pigs, chicken, ducks, geese. There was'nt a tree cut down when he came, now there is a garden and 12 acres clear land and plenty of wood around us they are glad for us to burn. A plenty of maple tree that we make sugar of the sap; they get in March. We live under Capt. Roberts who has 200 acres of ground, and this spot he will let us have at 25 dollars a year which is £6 : 5s. English money.

My dear sister, I can assure you we live in a good friendly Christian country. There is a chapel about a mile from us and 20 houses. My father and Wm. has a dollar a day and their board. James has 1s. 3d. a week and his board. John and Charlotte is out. Dear sister I don't repent leaving England. The children are all very happy and well; David is very stout: they were at home a board of ship. I wish we had come years ago. Dear sister please give my kind love to my father, brothers and sisters and their family and all our friends, and wishes you were all here for you could never repent leaving England, for my brother Henry Willard has got a place and they wants to keep him till he is 21 years old, but we are not determined about it, and if Uncle James is in the same mind he was when we left England, I hope my dear sister you will not be backward in coming for we did not fear the water, you will not have half the care as I have had with the children, fearing that they will fall overboard, but you will not have that care on your mind, and I hope you will come next April if it is possible for you to come. Put forward for Sarah Britt, Tommy and Amey to come. We have great reason to thank God that we all got here safe, and there is the same Providence over you as there was over us. It was very hard parting with you thinking never to see you any more, but I hope you will try your best to get here, you will not have the care on your mind as we had, not knowing were to go to, or what we was going to do, for you know that we tried the road for you, and I hope you will follow us, and now shall tell you a few things about what I think you ought to bring. We was very sorry that we did not bring our grate, for it would have been very useful, and many other things would have been very useful. Get a good strong chest. Do not come away without things for your use, such as dishes, pots, embden grits, and now I am going to tell you what will be on board ship, bring a few onions, a little arrow-root, and a little vinegar, and plenty of bread baked hard, and I can tell you that we should have been very glad to had a morsel of bread before we got to Quebec. My dear sister we are very thankful that you did not come with us, for we had a very uncomfortable set to come with; there was not a day went over our heads but what there was a quarrelling or a fighting, with it, made it very uncomfortable, and for that reason I am very thankful that you did not come with us. On Tuesday the 22nd of May we saw land, on the 24th we came to the gulf, on Sunday the 27th of May we saw the snow on the hills, I was so cold, we could not stand upon deck, and there was such mountains as never was seen in England, the Pilot came on board the 28th, the Dorking fair day. It was just 8 weeks when we got to Quebec, on Saturday afternoon. Tell Mrs. Tocker of Albury, there was two gentlemen came on board Sunday morning, I shewed them the letter, and they knowed the gentleman well, and was with him the day before, and told me if I could get to go to shore that they would direct me were to find him, but our Captain would not suffer one to go ashore, except the Doctor and himself, and I ask the Doctor to take the letter to the gentleman, and the Doctor left it but never see the gentleman himself, and so I heard no more about that. We have nobody to thank for but the Captain. They had plenty of every thing in the cabin, we had nothing but musty biscuit and salt beef, I mention this because you should not come away without necessaries. We arrived at Montreal, Wednesday morning, and Saturday morning we went out of ship, and then we went into the stores, and we stop there till Monday, and then we got into the boat, we was a week going up the river to Prescot. We was one night there. We went into a very fine steam boat, Great Britain. The last voyage it carried 700 people. There was 500 when we was in, and we arrived at York Friday morning, and it is a very beautiful place, and if we had stop there we could have got work, but lodging was so dear. Mr. Harper and John Worsfold we understood went to Hambleton by land. We arrived at Hambleton on Monday morning. We have heard no more about them, and we are very anxious to find them, and they have wrote home to England, I will thank you to give the directions. Give our kind love to John Wolgar and Mary, and tell them that it is the best thing as ever they did to come to America, they will never wish to go back again. They dont put up dinners in this Country, but they dine along with the masters and mistresses as you call them in England, but they will not be called so here, they are equals-like and if hired to anybody they call them their employers. John Wolgar is to bring a good long rifle gun, for the Bears comes round us, I expect we shall get some in the fall, and there is pigeons, and pheasants, partridges, quails and rabbits. Dear sister you know that we could hardly get a taste of meat in England, but now we can roast a quarter of meat. Mutton is 2½d. per lb., pork 3½d., veal the same, butter 7½d., sugar is the same as it is in England, and we are in hopes of making some sugar next season. One 100 weight of flour for 12s. 6d. They do not reap their wheat in this country, but they cradle it here, and it is worth anybodys while to lease here, for one good leaser could get a bushel of wheat a day, for they rake it in this country. There is no leasers in this country, they let the hogs eat it. I hope we shall be able to get a good grist this harvest. You must not be afraid to come acrost the water, I have been upon deck when the moon and stars shone beautiful, and have said that we must put our trust in God, for he is our only refuge, for I have thought of it a great many times, that Providence have been on our sides, and we have great reason to thank God for his kindness that we all got here safe, I should think it a great mercy that near 400 people came over in one ship and only one little infant died of them, and there was four births before we got there. Give our best respects to all kind friends at Dorking, London, Broadmore, and all that enquires after us. Tell James Willard that we wishes that he would bring a pitsaw with him for there is plenty of timber here, we may have it for cutting. There is two families arrived here this spring from London, one family's name was Heath, brother to Counsellor Heath below Cold-harbour, and Maria have got a situation and gone with them to the gulf, about 20 miles from us, she is to have a pound a month, she would have got plenty of places coming up the country, but would not leave us till we got a little settled. We are very anxious to know where Harper is. We shall not take any land till we find out them.

We conclude, so no more from your affectionate brother,

WILLIAM and CHARLOTTE WILLARD.

MAKING LIGHT OF LOCUSTS

Alexander Begg, *Practical Hand-Book and Guide to Manitoba and the North-West* (Toronto, 1877), pp. 48-51.

The grasshoppers first appeared in this country in the year 1818, six years after the commencement of the Red River settlement.

They did not do much harm in that year, but in 1819 they destroyed the crops, and for three successive years the hopes of the husbandman. They did not, however, appear again for thirty-six years until 1864, but did no great harm till 1868, when they swept the entire crop of the settlement. We cannot deny that this country has been severely scourged by these pests, of late years; but it is the opinion of many of the oldest settlers that we will not be again visited by them to any great extent for a period of years, and by that time, the advance of settlements will have a tendency to restrict their ravages.

It is not our desire to hide defects, and while we admit the grasshoppers to be a great scourge, at the same time their visits are only occasional, and there is every reason to believe, that since they have visited this country so much of late years, we will be freed from their ravages for some time. One fact is worthy of mention, that a total destruction of crops has only taken place six times within fifty-nine years, which, it must be admitted, is a small average, and not sufficient to deter any one from settling in the country on that account. Honourable Mr. Sutherland, in his testimony before a Select Committee of the House of Commons at Ottawa, gives the following statement on the 3rd of April, 1876:—

"I think (he says) that extensive settlement will prevent the ravages of the grasshoppers, and we have good reason to believe that we will be exempt from them during the coming season, as there were no deposits of eggs in the Province last year (a prediction verified by fact afterwards, as there were no grasshoppers last summer), and in all probability we will be relieved from that plague for many years to come. To my own knowledge, the Province was not affected by grasshoppers for twenty years previous to 1867, since which date we have had them off and on about every two years, or each alternate year."

The fall of snow on the prairie is on an average from twenty to twenty-four inches, and as there are no thaws in the winter, it does not pack, but is dry and light and disappears very quickly, allowing the husbandman to commence his labours at an early date.

The causes of prairie fires are numerous—Indians probably most frequently set fire to them in order the more easily to find out their game. Haymakers do the same for the sake of clearing the ground of old grass, and camp fires and numerous smokers do the rest. These fires happen only in the spring and fall in old grass, and it must be remembered they only occur on the open prairie. Crops are seldom, if ever, injured by them, and where fields are cultivated and fenced, the fires do not reach. Settlers when making hay, however, if they build their stacks out in the prairie should plough several furrows round them, so as to stop the flames from reaching them. It is always better, however, to remove the hay when made as soon as possible to your farm yard, so as to make sure of your crop and prevent any possibility of its destruction by fire. As the country opens up these fires will become less frequent.

THORNS AMONG THE ROSES

THE ANGUISH OF FIRST SETTLEMENT

John MacGregor, *Historical and Descriptive Sketches of the Maritime Colonies of British America* (London, 1828), p. 261.

There are, in the very face of a wood-farm, a thousand seeming, and it must be confessed, many real difficulties, sufficient at first to stagger people of more than ordinary firmness; but particularly an English farmer who has all his life been accustomed to cultivate land subjected for centuries to the plough. It is not to be wondered at, that he feels discouraged at the sight of wilderness land covered with heavy forest trees, which he must cut down and destroy. He is not acquainted with the use of the axe; and if he were, the very piling and burning of the wood, after the trees are felled, is a most disagreeable piece of labour. He has, besides, to make a fence of the logs, to keep off the cattle and sheep, which are allowed to range at large; and then he must not only submit to the hard toil of *hoeing* in potatoes or grain, but often to coarse diet. Were it not for the example which he has before him of others, who had to undergo similar hardships before they attained the means which yield them independence and comfort, he might, indeed, give up in despair and be forgiven for doing so.

A CONTRARY VIEW OF EMIGRATION

John Mactaggart, *Three Years in Canada: An Account of the Actual State of the Country in 1826-7-8* (London, 1829), vol. II, pp. 254-6.

Letters from settlers to their friends in Britain are not to be entirely depended upon; few of them are exactly true, and for these reasons: They wish as many of their friends to follow them as possible, for it is natural in man to have his friends about him; and to do this he must paint the beauties of Canada in glowing colours; he must dwell upon the fertility of the soil, the cheapness of farms. If they cause them to forsake a *comfortable* home, and come out to Canada, they commit no small crime. By remaining as they are, they benefit their own country, according to their station; by leaving it, they in some degree do it an injury; and after being *deceived* in going abroad, they blame their friends, themselves, and the country they are brought to adopt. They may, it is true, *return home again*, if they are able; but this by a family of spirit will not be thought of,—they will wear away life with vexation, and in this state they are too frequently met with. There is nothing like travellers telling the honest truth, and letting people judge for themselves. There are certain classes of emigrants that might do well, but these must not be poor, nor yet very rich: such as have been in the school of adversity, and are no strangers to difficulties. Such letters do much injury; they not only bring out people to be deceived, and so become *discontented*, but from being friends at *home*, they are foes ever afterwards. All the noise about cheap provisions, plenty to eat and drink, and but little to do, is nonsense; and, indeed, if any one out of the country would consider it, they might see it at once. I can only say, that I have seen *more* distress in Canada than ever I saw *out* of it; and if we used as much exertion to live at home, as we are obliged to do when there, few of us would go there. But we are slow of belief, and probably it is as well; the truth is generally disbelieved. Any thing that gratifies the imagination is easily imposed on us, while that which de-tracts from the ideal is abhorred, and will not be received.

They who invite their friends extol the *absence of taxes*, the salubrity of the climate, the pleasures, amusements, pastimes, &c. They must not say a word about the *difficulty of clearing the woods*, the toils of the hatchet, the heavy lifts, rheumatic complaints, &c.; they must not say that only a mere speck of the country is yet cleared, and that they may get *land almost for nothing*; for what is its value, remote from towns and places, where it may be brought to some account? Not one of the *logs* that are seen landed on our shores is cut on the farm of any settler; there is no cleared land within 300 miles of where they are obtained. There are no taxes of any extent, because there are very few who could pay them were they imposed. Where there is little taxation in a country, there is often little wealth.

BAD MANAGERS IN NOVA SCOTIA

John Robinson and Thomas Rispin, *A Journey through Nova Scotia* (York, 1774), pp. 31-3.

It is, indeed, surprising what chemerical notions many persons enter-tained of Nova-Scotia, previous to their leaving this country, with a view of settling at that place. They imagined that they should find lands culti-vated, fields sown, and houses built ready to their hands; and that they would have nothing to do, but to take possession, and reap. Not finding things in quite so favourable a situation as they foolishly expected, and having no inclination, by diligence and industry, to render them so, they return, and, by way of excuse for themselves, represent it as a miserable country, and the inhabitants in a starving condition. However, the truth is, it is a very extensive country, abounding with fine navigable rivers, and is as well situated for trade as any place in the world. . . .

The greatest disadvantage this country at present labours under is, that its inhabitants are few; and those in general, ignorant, indolent, bad managers, and what is the natural consequence of such qualities, the greatest part of them are poor: They have neither inclination nor industry to make great improvements. Can it then be wondered at, that a country so poorly, so thinly, and so lately inhabited, should have rather an unfavourable appearance, especially to those who have lived in the finest and best cultivated counties in England, where neither pains nor expense has been spared to improve their lands to the utmost advantage? Besides, where there is a want of proper management, have we not seen, even in our own country, men that occupied estates of their own, and could not make a living of them; but when the same farm has fallen into the hands of a skilful, industrious farmer, he has both paid the rent, and lived better on it than the owner could.

CULTIVATION AND LAND MANAGEMENT

AN APPEAL FOR IMPROVEMENT

Papers and Letters on Agriculture, Recommended to the Attention of the Canadian Farmers, by the Agricultural Society in Canada (Quebec, 1790), p. 28.

[Circular letter to the Curates of the Country Parishes]

SIR,

As the ease and comfort of the people, especially the poorer class, depend greatly on the state of Agriculture in the country where they live, it is with confidence we apply to you to aid the Agriculture Society in promoting the general good; for we conceive that the surest means to convey instruction to those who till the ground will be through their Pastors. We have therefore, Sir, troubled you with communication of several experiments already made in this Province, in consequence of instructions from the Society, particularly respecting the preparation of feed corn—the efficacy of some of the receipts sent you have been proved by repeated trials.

We entreat you, Sir, to endeavour to persuade your parishioners to practise the modes pointed out for preparing their wheat before they sow it. We have taken measures to furnish regularly, and without expence to such of the Clergy as do not take in the Quebec Gazette, with communication of all such improvements in husbandry as may hereafter be discovered and easily followed by the practical farmer.

We have further to request that you may communicate to us your thoughts on the best means of improving the Agriculture of the country, together with the result of your own experiments, those of your Parishioners, and others that may come to your knowledge.

I have the honour to be,

    SIR,

        Your most obedient humble servant,

                        (For the DIRECTORS of the Ag. Soc.)

                        HUGH FINLAY, Secretary

Quebec,
January, 1790

A NOVEL PROPOSAL FOR CLEARING THE LAND

John Mactaggart, *Three Years in Canada: An Account of the Actual State of the Country in 1826-7-8* (London, 1829), vol. I, pp. 112-13.

Millers, and others, when they raise the small rivers with dams, often flood extensive swamps, thickly growing with all kinds of timber. The waters thus raised on the roots and trunks of the trees, beyond the natural level, tend to destroy them; the sun and air are withheld from the soil on which they grow, so they gradually continue to wither away. When first we meet with large tracts of swamp forest thus running to decay, we are greatly at a loss to account for the cause of this melancholy phenomenon. We observe hundreds of acres of woods withering away, while at the same time they seem growing in three or four feet of water. The neighbouring forests are all, perhaps, in full bud and bloom; but the others remain, as in winter, without a leaf, without the slightest show of vegetation. In this state they will remain for ten or twelve years, in some instances less, according to the nature of the waters of the rivers which have flooded them. Afterwards they fall, as if cut away, or rather eaten through at that place said to be between wind and water; but, more strictly speaking, that place between the various levels of floods. Here an action takes place that shaves them down, as it were, by the surface of the water. I have often thought that *dams*, in Canada, might be applied with more effect than axes to get rid of the trees of the forest, so expensive and troublesome to settlers. I am aware of many places in the wilderness where a small dam, perhaps one hundred feet long, and twenty feet high, would destroy, in eight years, the whole timber off 50,000 acres of fertile land. Surely this is much preferable to *girdling*, that barbarous method of slaying the trees by cutting girdles round them with the hatchet, and so leaving them to perish where they stand, withering for many years, and at last blown down by the wind—falling, perhaps, on some of the cattle grazing amongst them. By dams, land may be cleared for almost nothing; whereas at present it costs 4*l.* an acre.

DRAINING THE LAND

'Land Drainage', *The Canadian Agriculturist, and Journal of the Board of Agriculture of Upper Canada*, vol. xII (March 1, 1860), pp. 93-6.

We are glad to see that this important means of agricultural improvement is beginning to occupy public attention, and that our city press has taken up the subject in an earnest and patriotic spirit. . . .

Of the importance and benefits of underdraining, in all countries of the northern temperate zone, where usually the rain-fall is more or less considerable, we do not here intend to speak. Suffice it to say that in Canada there are good data for concluding that if draining were generally introduced, not only would our soils be rendered drier, warmer, and more easily and cheaply worked, but the seasons for sowing and reaping would be earlier, the crops of all kinds more abundant; and with a judicious course of rotation, combined with more thorough culture, those dreaded enemies—the rust and midge—whose devastations have of late years become so alarmingly great, would be comparatively eradicated. We hold, therefore, the objects contemplated by the more extended application of draining to be of primary national importance, demanding the earnest co-operation of the Legislature, and municipal bodies generally, with our more intelligent and enterprising farmers. . . .

Our main object in the present article is to call the attention of farmers in general to the ruder and less perfect means of ridding the land of much of its wetness that are at all times more or less within their reach. There is some risk amidst what is now being said and written on the subject of thorough drainage and the means of accomplishing it, that a large number of farmers, especially in the more remote districts, will conclude that the performance of this important operation is wholly beyond their reach and means. If the purchase of pipes or tiles, and conveying them to considerable distances; the laying out and executing of drains on a uniform scale, in accordance with modern European practice, be absolutely essential requisites, why it is plain that by far the larger portion of Canadian farmers must abandon the idea, for the present at least, as impracticable and hopeless. . . . But upon nine-tenths of Canadian farms there are certain preliminary operations to be performed before underdraining can be extensively, and, as we believe, profitably carried into effect.

In making a farm out of the forest, and for many years after the trees have disappeared, the first and most necessary operations are unquestionably not underdraining, but the extracting of stumps, the levelling of the surface, and the cutting of open ditches, for the exit of stagnant surface water, into which covered drains can be subsequently made to empty. The first thing to be done in most instances is to improve the natural or arterial drainage of a farm or a district, which will often give great relief. The next step is surface or furrow draining, which if properly executed will be found tolerably effacacious. Wherever the first condition has been obtained the second can in general be readily effected. These primitive operations, which were as well known to and practised by the ancient Romans as ourselves, will in general be found as much as the settler for many years will be able to accomplish; and, which indeed, but comparatively few do in fact effectually perform. A farm well ditched along the fences, enclosing conveniently laid out fields,—with a constantly improving surface, and well constructed water furrows, will be found upon the whole tolerably dry; at all events it will be relieved of any very injurious amount of surface water. When the natural outfall is insufficient, and cannot be improved without the co-operation of neighboring farmers; it will be seen to be the duty and interest of all parties concerned to unite, each doing his fair share in rendering the natural outfall sufficient. In case parties refuse to do what is reasonable in such a case, there is a law, we believe, that will compel them to do their part of the work; or the agrieved party can do it and charge the others with the cost. Until such preliminary operations as these be completed; the more refined and effective systems of draining, and indeed all other means of territorial improvement cannot be with any chance of success even begun.

Let no farmer conclude then, however distant his location or scanty his means, that because he cannot carry out underdraining according to the modern practices of older and wealthier countries, that he is altogether impotent regarding this essential means of improvement. He can do something every year in the way suggested, and which will in a short time produce the most beneficial results. . . .

When a farm has got its natural drainage improved by deepening and straightening the water courses where needed, with open ditches and furrows through the lowest and wettest portions, and the surface sufficiently levelled and inclined to allow the surface water to escape freely into the natural or artificial channels thus provided, its owner may begin to think seriously of underdraining. . . .

. . . Much may be done towards relieving the land of superfluous water, by making here and there a drain, at the right places, with a view of cutting off the supply from the higher to the lower levels, and conducting the water to the nearest outlet. A single drain, cut to a proper depth in the right direction, will sometimes divert the water of a permanent spring, and thus cut off the cause of wetness from an acre or two of ground, that was before comparatively worthless.

As to the *materials* for making drains, where stones cannot be conveniently procured, and pipes or tiles are too expensive on account of distance of carriage, or otherwise, the farmer need not give up the idea of commencing the needful operation in despair. A trench dug out, gradually narrowing to the bottom, and filled ten or twelve inches with old rails, under-brush, &c., will generally prove effectual for several years. . . .

In case of water being so abundant that a conduit is necessary, a few boards can be nailed together, so as to form an efficient and enduring drain. We have seen hundreds of miles of drains in the old country, before the introduction of tiles, made from 30 to 36 inches deep in stiff clays, and filled at the bottom with heath or brush, and even with twisted ropes of straw, that have been in effectual operation, even on arable lands, after 15 or 20 years. In such cases the drain was dug with sides at a uniform angle, having a breadth at the bottom of only 2 or 3 inches, and the clay rammed closely down on the material at the bottom. The brushwood in a few years would rot and disappear, but the aperture would remain, the clay arch gradually attaining sufficient strength to support itself. This method is only adapted to stiff clays. And in this country such drains must be sufficiently deep to be beyond the reach of frost, (say 3 feet) and their mouths should be formed for a few feet with stone or other enduring material, to prevent injury from frost.

We wish to be distinctly understood in the preceding remarks as having no wish or inclination to slight or undervalue the benefits of a thorough system of underdraining, carried out in a permanent manner. Much land in the neighbourhood of large populations, where pipes of 2 inches diameter can be obtained for six or eight dollars a thousand, might be profitably drained, after the methods now pursued in Europe. But even on such lands we should always bear in mind that it is only the better class of soils, such as are naturally rich, and only require to be laid dry, that will yield to any system of draining the largest amount of profit. In carrying out the English practice of draining in Canada, we must take special care so to modify it as to suit the particular wants and means of the great body of our farmers, and also the climate and soils of this country. Our opinion is that in general we require deeper drains and at greater and not uniform distances, than they do on the stiff English clays. If the preceding remarks should afford any useful suggestions, particularly to our remote and more needy farmers, and in any degree prevent them from neglecting draining altogether, because they are incapable, from want of means and the unsuitable state of their lands, of carrying out a more complete and expensive system, which can only be adapted to more favorable situations and circumstances, our object will have been accomplished.

TILE

Jack Miner, 'Tile', in R. W. Irwin, *A Review of Land Drainage in Ontario. Engineering Technical Publication 7*, Ontario Agricultural College, University of Guelph, 1961. p. 20. Reprinted by permission.

> I am only a hole in a humble vocation,
>   Yet I greatly control your civilization;
> I am very tenacious and hard as stone,
>   And am like old Horatius in holding my own.
> So lay me down, keep me straight in the ditch,
>   And while you are sleeping I'll be making you rich.
>
> Every farmer of pride dearly loves to provide
>   For the future, the son and the daughter;
> So give me the chance and I'll greatly enhance
>   Every acre I drain of its water.
>
> And here's my great beauty — I'm always on duty,
>   Out of reach of the bulls and the bears;
> And when you're in your grave I'll continue to slave
>   For the children — their children — and theirs.
>
> My habits are good, I require no food,
>   (My joints are all made without mortar)
> And I always abstain, when deep in the drain
>   From everything stronger than water.
>
> If your land is too wet and you're burdened with debt,
>   And encumbrance begins to accrue,
> Obey Nature's laws, by removing the cause,
>   Drain your farm or it will drain you.
>
> 'Tis so foolish to plant where the Goose and Brant
>   Might paddle from March to September,

You might as well sow on a November snow,
    And expect seed to grow — in December.

Some farmers are failing, and weeping and wailing
    And blame the Good Lord without reason,
When if they would stop sowing seed in the slop
    They might raise a good crop every season.

Most farmers lament the money they've spent
    For things only made to beguile;
But never as yet did a farmer regret
    The money expended for tile.

THE COMFORTS OF ACCOMPLISHMENT

FARM LIFE IN THE SELKIRK COLONY

R. G. MacBeth, *Farm Life in the Selkirk Colony* (Winnipeg, 1897), pp. 1-4.

The colonists brought out from Scotland by Lord Selkirk chose to settle along the banks of the Red River on narrow farms (the general width being ten chains frontage on the river) running back at right angles from it on the prairie. These farms extended back two miles as a freehold with an additional two miles as a hay privilege. Ultimately these outer two miles were given in fee simple to the owner of the frontage except in cases where others by actual occupation had secured possession of them in part, in which case the frontage owner got an equivalent elsewhere. These ten chain lots owned by the head of the family were frequently subdivided amongst the sons, so that when the Ontario people, accustomed to square farms, began to come amongst us, they were greatly amused at "our farming on lanes," and pointed out the disadvantages of having to go a distance of two miles or more to the cultivated plots at the outlying ends of these river strips. But there was much method in the madness of long, narrow farms; or, to be plainer, there were many good reasons to justify that plan of settlement. To begin with, the settlers built along the river banks for convenience in obtaining water. Outside the swamps and sloughs, the river was practically the only source of water supply. Wells were little known, suction pumps were unheard of, and I remember that a "chain and wheel" pump which my father imported from "the States" was looked upon as one of the seven wonders of the time. Then again settlement by the river bank had food as well as water supply in view, for fish, from "gold eyes" to sturgeon, were then plentiful in the un-polluted stream, and afforded a provision by no means to be despised. As to the narrow lots, it can be readily seen that the colonists settled together for mutual defence and the advantages of social life as well as for church and school facilities, and if the sons, settling on subdivisions, seem lacking in ambition, it must be remembered that to go outside the settlement in the early days was to go beyond the pale of defence, with such possibilities of social life and of church and school facilities as were in view.

From the beginning of actual settlement farming was the principal occupation of the colonists. The facilities for farming were not of the best. The implements (the spade and hoe for planting and sowing) were as primitive as well could be; but with these, by dint of great exertion, the settlers soon managed to make a livelihood. The reaping was done with the sickle and later on with the cradle. Then the age of machinery came in, and the hoe gave place to the old wooden plough whose oaken mould-board was pointed with a rudely made iron share. The sickle and cradle gave way to the first cumbrous reaper, behind whose platform a stand was placed for the able bodied man who forked off the grain in sheaves as it fell, and to do this with regularity and neatness in heavy crops tested even the brawniest Highlander of them all. However the cutting of the wheat was only the first of a series of difficult processes through which finally bread was reached. The threshing was carried on first with flails and the use of great "fans" and winnowing riddles to separate the wheat from the chaff, a process that enables us to understand many scriptural figures. Shortly after this era of flails the two horse tread-mill was intro-duced, by which threshing became a comparatively easy, if somewhat slow process, varied only by the occasional fall backwards of a lazy horse or the flying off of the main band from the fly wheel. To get the wheat into flour was the next problem. First of all the "quern" was used, two flat round stones (the upper and the nether), the upper one, having a handle, turned the stone upon the wheat and brought it into some sem-blance of flour, not over white but in the best degree a health-producing substance. Oriental customs may not have prevailed in the colony, but it was in view of such a scene as might be seen at these "querns" that our Lord spoke of identity in occupation and diversity of character in the swift separation "two women shall be grinding at the mill—the one shall be taken and the other left." In time the Hudson's Bay sent out an expert and built a mill near Fort Douglas, and one of the settlers who was em-ployed upon it took such careful observation of the process and such measurements that he was able to build one later on for himself and several at different points in the settlement. These did fair work, but in seasons of protracted calm flour famines had to be staved off by a general sharing up amongst neighbors. Next in order came water-mills, only partially successful, and finally the era of steam revolutionized old methods and gave the settlers the somewhat doubtful boon of flour excelling the old commodity in whiteness but not in wholesomeness.

Besides the raising of grain and root crops the settlers, as the years advanced, went into stock raising, and had horses, cattle, sheep and swine on their farms. In the days before the incoming of machinery they raised horses principally for the buffalo hunters from famous running stock imported originally from England. The "plain hunters" came in at certain seasons around Fort Garry, when the settlers would take to them such horses as they had to sell. Trials of speed followed, and the winning horses brought good prices in cash from the hunters who had just disposed of their buffalo meat, robes and furs to the Hudson's Bay Company. Oxen were used by the settlers very generally in the operations of the farm, and for the purposes of hay and wood hauling were hitched single in the Red River cart or sled, both of which in their primitive state were made entirely of wood. Sheep were useful in the extreme as affording clothing in "hodden grey." The processes from sheep shearing to the home-made suit were slow and primitive enough in the light of to-day's machinery, but the article was good, as we can testify from personal experience. The spinning wheel, the weaver's loom, the "fulling" of the cloth by the kicking of it by bare-footed boys all stand out in the memory with many an incident grave and gay interwoven.

In the summer time the live stock of which we have spoken ran wild upon the prairie, horses especially being out of sight and sound for months, and we recall as a great constitution builder, days spent in the saddle in search of the wandering stock. In the long winter of course they must be housed, and so making hay while the sun shone was a great reality to us all. Hay cutting began on a certain day in July, and, except for the "outer two miles" above referred to (and on them only for a period), was done upon prairie that was free as air to everybody. The best hay meadows were located in good time before the date of commencement and on the night previous people were camped all round them. Each one knew pretty well the spot he was going to strike the next morning, and if more than one had their eyes on the same spot, it became the property of the one who got there first and made a "circle" by cutting around the field he wished to claim. When hay was scarce there was considerable rivalry, but there was a code of unwritten camp law that prevented difficulties, and mutual helpfulness rather than opposition was the rule. Occasionally prairie fires swept athwart the haystack of some unfortunate settler, but in such a case all the rest turned in and helped him out, and I recall how, when this happened in the case of an uncle of mine, the neighbors rallied around and put a hundred cart loads of hay into his barn next day. The camp life during the time of hay making was a pleasant experience, with the tents grouped like a village and the huge camp-fires the centres of the social circles in the gathering night. On Saturday evenings the way homeward was taken with the younger men like a troop of cavalry and indulging in many a race by the way. Hay was never placed under cover but in long stacks in the hay-yard, and from these stacks we pulled the hay in the winter time with wooden hooks and carried it within the stables in our arms. By degrees implements and instruments of various kinds were imported from "the States" and elsewhere and were handed round from one to the other amongst the neighbors as if they were common property.

STAGNATION IN LOWER CANADA

H. Y. Hind, *et al.*, *Eighty Years' Progress in British North America* (Toronto, 1863), pp. 33-5.

There can be no doubt that the wretched mode of subdividing land and laying out farms which formerly prevailed in Lower Canada, has been instrumental in retarding the progress of husbandry in that part of the province. Very generally the farms in the old settled parts originally consisted of narrow strips whose lengths and breadths were in the ratio of ten to one; three arpents wide by thirty arpents in depth being the form of the long rectangle exhibited by a French Canadian farm when first surveyed. This is the same as if the farms were 200 yards broad by 2,000 yards long, a form inconvenient for practical agriculture, involving a yearly increasing expenditure of time and labor in its cultivation as the cleared portions become more remote from the homestead, for which no advantages of river or road frontage could compensate as the country became cleared. But when the seigneuries were surveyed, steamboats, railroads, and even macadamized roads were not thought of, and people did not then indulge in the habit of looking far into the future, or those of later date care to contemplate the condition to which they were drifting by continuing the mode of subdividing the soil which their fathers had inaugurated. With the increase of population, and the love for the paternal roof, which distinguishes the *habitans* of Lower Canada, their farms have been again subdivided longitudinally, sometimes into three parts, or one arpent in breadth by thirty in depth, or in the proportion of 66⅔ yards broad to 2,000 long; and in the older seigneuries the ratio of breadth to length is not unfrequently as one is to sixty or 33⅓ yards broad to 2,000 yards long. These are some of the heirlooms of that old feudal system which sat like a huge incubus on Lower Canada, and whose depressing influence will long leave its mark on the energies and character of its people.

FARM PRACTICE.

We do not require to go far back into the history of that part of the province to find husbandry in all its branches in a very primitive condition. Thirty years ago, rotation of crops was wholly unknown, and no rules of art were practiced by the happy, light-hearted French Canadian, who with rigid steps pursued the systems handed down to him by his ancestors, and strictly adhered to usages which generations had sanctioned. In addition to the entire absence of rotation of crops, the practice of carting manure on to the ice of a neighboring river, in order that it might be washed away in the spring, was generally practiced, and even now prevails to a considerable extent. Barns were removed when the accumulations before the door impeded entrance or exit, and the old primitive forms of plows, harrows and all other farming implements and vehicles, were retained, with a wholesome horror of innovation in form or material. Nor need we travel far to find them still flourishing in all their original imperfections and want of adaptation to the end in view.

The narrowness of the French Canadian farms has led to those seemingly interminable lines of neat whitewashed cottages which border the main roads, or fringe the river St. Lawrence, wearing the aspect of a continuous village. A stranger, steaming down the noble river, sees with admiration and delight an uninterrupted thread of white cottages, fronting the water, with here and there the broad, glittering tinned roof of the parish church, and in the background the primeval forest; he gazes upon a beautiful picture, suggesting pleasing associations, and thoughts of rural contentment and prosperity, susceptible of increase as elsewhere in the world. Such is the outward show, but let him take a nearer view and examine in detail. He will find little or no change save in increase of numbers, between what he now surveys and what he might have seen one generation or even two generations ago. Improvement is progressing, but with snail-like progress, where ancient habits and customs are preserved, and where families cling to the soil on which they were born, and divide and subdivide their farms until they become narrow strips not much wider than a modern highway, with the house fronting the river, and "the land all longitude."

PROGRESS IN UPPER CANADA

H. Y. Hind, *et al.*, *Eighty Years' Progress in British North America* (Toronto, 1863), pp. 42-8.

GOVERNMENT AND LEGISLATIVE ENCOURAGEMENT.

The first public Act for the encouragement of Agriculture in Canada, which came into operation in 1830, authorized the governor to pay one hundred pounds to any District Agricultural Society which raised the sum of £50 by subscription, for the purpose of importing valuable live stock, grain, useful implements, &c.

Several acts were passed in subsequent years, being modifications of that of 1830, all of them having for their object the encouragement of Agricultural Societies and Agriculture. In 1847 an additional step was taken, fraught with very important consequences to the interests of husbandry in Canada. An Act for the incorporation of the Provincial Agricultural Associations came into operation; and in 1850, Boards of Agriculture for Upper and Lower Canada were established by law. In 1851, an Act was passed to provide for the better organization of Agricultural Societies, and finally, in 1852, the most important step of all was taken, and "An Act to provide for the establishment of a Bureau of Agriculture, and to amend and consolidate the laws relating to Agriculture," came into operation.

The District Societies, which, in 1830, drew their annual pittance from Government, and represented the agricultural interests of the country, have thus grown, in twenty-two years, to a comprehensive and centralized organization, consisting of, 1st, the Bureau; 2d, the Boards of Agriculture for Upper and Lower Canada; 3d, the Agricultural Associations for Upper and Lower Canada; 4th, County Societies; 5th, Township Societies.

In 1857, another change took place, being also a step in advance; an Act was passed "to take better provision for the encouragement of Agriculture, and also to provide for the promotion of Mechanical Science." The head of the Bureau of Agriculture received the title of 'Minister of Agriculture,' with very extensive powers for obtaining and distributing information respecting the condition of Husbandry and the Progress of Arts and Manufactures in the Province. By this act Boards of Arts and Manufactures were created, and Horticultural Societies incorporated.

With the means at the disposal of the County Societies, a valuable impulse has no doubt been given to agriculture in all its branches; chiefly by encouraging the introduction of a superior breed of animals and of improved implements. Several societies have devoted a considerable portion of their funds to the importation of improved breeds of cattle and horses. The awarding of premiums for stock, implements and farm productions generally, has encouraged private enterprise and awakened a spirit of emulation which has been most successful in promoting progress and improvement, and the rank which Upper Canada now occupies as an agricultural country is mainly due to the excellent organization and energetic spirit which has always distinguished the county societies since their first establishment.

THE PROVINCIAL AGRICULTURAL ASSOCIATION.

As a necessary result of the successful working of the county and township Agricultural Societies, a growing desire began to be felt, now nearly twenty years ago, for the organization of a Provincial Society which would bring the farmers and manufacturers from all parts of the Province together, and, by friendly rivalry and competition at an annual exhibition, present at one view the best results of the agricultural and mechanical industry of the country. After several ineffectual attempts to obtain general and united action, a meeting of delegates from county societies was held at Hamilton in August, 1846, and an Association formed, entitled the "Provincial Agricultural Association and Board of Agriculture for Canada West."

The first Exhibition of the Association was held at Toronto in October, 1846. The amount of prizes offered in money reached $1,112, besides books, making the total prize list to have a money value of about $1,600. The result of the Exhibition surpassed the most sanguine anticipations of its promotors, and excited the astonishment of many who were not familiar with the progress already made by the County Societies, at the display of stock, implements, grain, fruit, and vegetables. . . .

Such is the progress which has been made during fifteen years, in bringing together the different industries of Upper Canada, and teaching her people those lessons which can only be learned by friendly competition in an arena open to all, without distinction, prejudice, or favor. The cause of this rapid improvement is no doubt in great part due to the immigration of scientific agriculturists, as well as practical farmers, who have learned and studied husbandry in all its branches in the best districts of England and Scotland. Any improvement which takes place, either in stock, implements, or farming practice, either in Europe or the United States, is immediately imported, and, if satisfactory, adopted in Upper Canada. By means of the different agricultural societies, all needful information respecting the results attained are speedily made known, and there is now no lack of enterprising and energetic men who gladly embrace every opportunity of improving the farming practice. The financial condition of the Association and the Board of Agriculture, afford incontestible proof of the deep root which these institutions have taken in Canada. It will be remembered that in 1846 they commenced their operations without funds, relying solely on subscriptions. In 1859, the large sum of $110,908.78 passed through the hands of the treasurer. Out of the surplus funds a handsome and commodious brick building has been erected in Toronto for the purposes of the Board, amply provided with space for museum, library, reading-room, large hall for public meetings, and a capacious seed-store.

3 | The Conquest of Space and Time

Transportation and communication have been central ingredients in Canada's history. The country's economic development, for instance, hinged on transportation. Harold Innis made it one of the main themes of his staple theory. To begin with, the newly planted colonies could only survive by contact with the homeland. The culture shock of transplantation to a wilderness stimulated a powerful demand for European communities to recreate the society that had been left behind. To satisfy these needs there was a demand for cheap ocean shipping, and also for inexpensive transport into the interior so that saleable commodities could be collected for exchange. The urban centres that grew up along the St Lawrence in the eighteenth and nineteenth centuries therefore encouraged a dual transportation system: one led into the continent and the other stretched across the Atlantic.

Of all inland transportation facilities, none was more thoroughly detested than the Canadian road. Apart from a few military routes, each lake and river port tended to generate roads to its own hinterland. Whether humble wagon roads or bone-rattling corduroy surfaces, they reached into those areas not accessible by other means of transport. Canada depended on the established usage of statute labour to build and maintain roads, but the practice did not lead either to a continuous or well maintained highway system. There were spokesmen for better roads who recognized that inanimate power might someday be used to propel vehicles, but until that became a practical matter, winter provided Canadians with the most successful highway materials.

Every change in the technique of transportation was bound to have important repercussions throughout the economy. Water transport dominated the early history of Canada. The first settlers were quick to grasp the significance of the St Lawrence, the country's grand highway, as the best means of moving people and goods in and out of North America. That elementary historical fact shaped economic visions as surely as it did subsequent shifts in technique. The idea that the St Lawrence route must someday draw the commerce of the entire continent died hard. When the railroads came they were harnessed to the old dream, and the first lines were built to by-pass difficult portages along the St Lawrence, just as canals had earlier served the same purpose. Even with the completion of the Grand Trunk, when railways were made relatively independent of the water system, they were meant to fulfill the same vision.

Railroads, like canals, were usually conceived in terms of the transportation of agricultural surpluses. But, as in the east, they also stimulated western ideas of industrial development. In fact, railways came to be seen as the key to exploiting all the country's natural resources for the benefit of the French- as well as English-speaking Canadians. Even those who worked on labour gangs felt a sense of the drama. As the opening of the Victoria Bridge had suggested, iron rails led to Canada's future.

The construction of canals and railroads raised important questions about finance and technique. Large-scale engineering endeavours called for substantial capital, and their projectors looked to stock sales in the U.S. and Great Britain for the money they needed. Ogden Creighton's *General View of the Welland Canal*, for instance, was published in London to stimulate British capitalists. Englishmen were often encouraged to invest in Canadian transportation systems because these ventures had proved profitable at home. But canals and railroads in this country were not so much designed to serve an existing market as they were to create one. They were developmental in nature, a factor that baffled foreign investors as much as it influenced construction techniques.

Where investors imagined profits, British engineers saw significant differences in technology. John Mactaggart perceived the Rideau Canal's masonry dams and lock chambers, built by Royal Engineers, as an example of 'British substantiality'. The widespread use of wood in building the Welland Canal seemed to him simply another instance of North American shoddiness. Railway construction also involved serious differences of technical opinion. The question of a proper gauge for Canadian rails, for instance, pitted British tradition against North American experience. And because English capital was a critical source of funding, the gauge question became a political as well as a technical issue, not finally settled until the whole country shifted to the four foot, eight-and-one-half inch standard. Since railroad building was an important ingredient in the civil engineer's career, claims of priority in design were also matters of dispute.

Improvements in transportation and communication held a symbolic value for nineteenth-century Canadians. Thomas C. Keefer's wonderfully evocative picture of the railroad's civilizing influence on a typical country village catches some of the cultural implications. Even the sardonic Mactaggart could rhapsodize on the potential of a great Canadian canal from sea to sea. The railway and telegraph, particularly, seemed to presage man's conquest over great natural forces. Unlike any previous system, the telegraph offered all-weather, year-round, practically instantaneous communications over great distances. It was as if one spoke in 'a flash of lightning'. Steam power gave Canadians a sense of control over the expanse of their territory; the telegraph suggested a command of time.

By the end of the nineteenth century, when electricity became available as a source of motive power, transportation was an obvious field for its application. It is somehow fitting that Keefer, who had begun his engineering career as an advocate for the canal development of the St Lawrence route, should see in electric trains the hope for the final realization of his dreams.

ROAD BUILDING

A GOVERNOR'S PROCLAMATION

Proclamation of Guy Carleton, Concerning Winter Roads (Quebec, 1776).

Sir GUY CARLETON, *Knight of the Bath, Captain-General and Governor in Chief of the Province of* Quebec, *and dependent territories in* America, *Vice Admiral thereof,* &c., &c., &c.
General and Commander in Chief of the troops of his Majesty in the said province and the frontiers thereof, &c., &c., &c.

As it is indispensably necessary for the service of the King and the convenience of the public that all the Royal roads as well as those connecting with them be stamped and maintained during the winter of double width or wide enough that two vehicles could easily pass side by side without any inconvenience, I order all the Captains and other officers of the militia throughout the extent of this province to oblige and constrain the inhabitants and owners of the lands and buildings of their different parishes, each to build without delay a road eight feet in width on the frontage of their lands and to maintain it in good order during the winter, and to lay brushwood of the tops of pine or cedar seven or eight feet high placed at a distance of twenty-four feet on both sides of the said road. And in order that the winter roads might be stamped evenly across their entire width, travelers are required to always stay to the right, either going to the villages or returning. I also enjoin and rigorously command each and all inhabitants and owners of land or buildings in the said province, to carry out the orders given to them in this regard by the Captains and other officers of the militia of their different parishes under pain of being disobedient.
Given under my signature and the seal of my arms, at the Chateau St. Louis, *in the city of* Quebec, *this twelfth day of* December, *in the*

seventeenth year of the reign of our sovereign King GEORGE III, *by the grace of* God *King of* Great Britain, *of* France *and of* Ireland, *defender of the faith*, &c. &c. &c. *and in the year of our Lord* 1776.

CORDUROY ROADS

John Mactaggart, *Three Years in Canada: An Account of the Actual State of the Country in 1826-7-8* (London, 1829), vol. II, pp. 110-12.

In too many places in Canada the roads are carried over broad swamps and wide gullies, on round logs of wood, or rather trees, averaging a foot diameter, each laid close by one another's side, and no attempt made to fill up the spaces between them. These turnpikes are fancied to resemble that famous King's cloth, called *Corduroy*—hence their name. When Dante wrote his celebrated poem the "Inferno," the critics blamed his muse for not selecting a proper highway to Pandemonium; but had she been aware of the nature of the Corduroy species, there is no doubt but that would have been chosen, as certainly none can be more decidedly infernal. In passing over them in a lumbering waggon, the poor human frame is jolted to pieces. But out of evil there always comes good; for were the country people to take too much care of their roads, so that passengers would have no reason to complain of them, then they would receive no aid from the Colonial funds towards the trouble bestowed. As they are then, they will continue gradually to improve; for when the officers of State take a drive, or when the members of Parliament travel to their public business, the *Road Bill* and *Turnpike Act* are strongly forced upon their recollections; the Corduroy roads send in their own petitions in earnest. But not to joke too much on this important subject, as surely nothing can be more beneficial to any country than good roads and canals: if these roads and bridges were covered with boughs of trees, and these again with more tender branches, the *tenderest uppermost*, and these again covered with earth or clay, dug out of the *watertables* or *ditches* alongside, (and the more earth, or clay dug out of the side ditches the better,) a good road would be the consequence. Canada not being a damp moist country, there is less need of Macadam here to chip the whitstone or crack the flints. In the spring and fall, the best of roads would be bad; but in summer, the dry weather makes them delightful, and the frost and snow of winter much more so. There is a great complaint, however, made of running the greater part of the roads *straight lines*. Confound straight lines!—confound that unscientific system of *setting the compass*, and running to that set, or rhomb, smack over hill and dale, river and swamp, without paying the least attention to declivities or acclivities, dangers and difficulties. Look at Nature; see how she makes her rivers meander and wimple, and at every bend doing good to some creature, or to some portion of the country; yet we will not follow her in our road-making business; we will hurry on with it in a direct course, as if it were a matter of immense moment, the delivery of a letter or a newspaper at Montreal, Sorrel, or elsewhere, while the broad extent of the flourishing country is neglected and disregarded.

THE WANT OF GOOD ROADS

Thomas Roy, *Remarks on the Principles and Practice of Road-Making, as Applicable to Canada* (Toronto, 1841), pp. 5-9.

One of the first objects which occupies the attention of an energetic people, when they are striving to advance in the march of improvement, and to take a higher standing amongst the nations of the earth, is the forming and establishing of roads and other mediums of communication, in order to promote the development of the resources of their own country, and to enable them to maintain a commercial and social intercourse with foreign nations.

Just as these mediums of communication are perfected, and in a direct ratio to the degree of perfection to which they are brought, is the advancement of comfort and opulence, and the diffusion of the refinements and elegancies of life amongst any people. We might prove this position by reference to the histories of all countries, in all ages, from the eras when the roads of ancient Egypt, Mexico, and Rome, were constructed, down to our own times, wherein the far more useful, and all but perfect roads, canals, and railroads of England afford full proof of our statement. But, however interesting and instructive such a discussion might be, it is not necessary to enter upon it, for we believe our position will not be disputed.

In the Province of Canada, our circumstances are fraught with many peculiarities, and in nothing more than in those matters which concern our roads and lines of communication. Almost the whole of our population, at least in the upper portion, are natives, or descendants from natives of countries where such lines of communication are established in a greater or lesser degree of perfection, and no circumstance tends so much to paralyze the exertions of our settlers from the old country as the want of good roads.

Upon the first laying out of the Townships in the Upper Province, even a superabundance of reserves was left for roads; but these concession lines and side-lines run straight on, across ravines and rivers, over hills, through swamps, lakes, and other hindrances, and could never have been intended to serve as leading lines of communication when the Province became settled, and good roads became necessary for the conveyance of produce and goods to and from distant markets. Their intention is to serve the same purpose as the parish roads in England, or to connect the various parts of the Townships with leading roads, to be constructed upon proper locations, and in proper directions, as circumstances may require.

It is not the improvement of these concession and side-lines which we propose to discuss; this ought to be done in the best manner that circumstances will permit, by the statute labour, the commuted statute labour of each Township. But it is to draw attention to the best and most economical methods of constructing leading lines of road throughout the Province, in such locations as shall most effectively open up every portion of it, and progressively develop its vast resources. One objection to forming a general system of common roads in this Province may as well be met here. It is often said, why lay out large sums upon common roads; they will soon be superseded by railways? Those who raise this objection, do not appear to have taken a very accurate view of the subject. Railways are of great and paramount advantage to densely populated countries, where there is great travel, and a constant transit of goods; especially between shipping ports and manufacturing towns, or, in mining districts, from the mines to the works, or to the shipping ports; but it is doubtful if there are more than three or four locations in the Province of Canada where railways are really required, and where the returns would pay a dividend upon the cost of construction, for at least twenty years to come. In support of this position, let us advert to the geographical situation of this Province. For, when investigating this subject, we ought to keep out of sight advantages, real or imaginary, which it is said may be derived from United States intercourse. These may be fit subjects for Joint Stock Companies to speculate upon, but ought not to bias the Legislature of the Province.

In Lower Canada, that portion of the country which is most fit for settlement extends a few miles back from the sides of the St Lawrence River. Even where the distance is greatest, produce would be brought down to the shipping ports on the river by the farmers' waggons, if good roads were formed, in preference to sending it by railways. Above Montreal, the Ottawa River will (when locks are constructed at the rapids) afford four hundred miles of inland navigation. These locks, common roads, and a few branch canals to the small lakes, would most entirely open up the Ottawa valley to the ocean. Again, were common roads constructed, the whole of the country between Montreal and Kingston would be rendered accessible to the ocean by the St Lawrence River and the

Rideau Canal. The numerous ports on Lakes Ontario, Erie, St Clair, and Huron, afford an access to the ocean from the countries adjacent to their shores, provided common roads were constructed from the interior to these ports. But there is a large extent of country, chiefly in the London and Brock Districts, which is too remote from the Lakes to be fully benefitted by their navigation, unless some more effectual medium of communication than common roads is provided.— Two methods present themselves: a railway from London to Hamilton, and a boat canal from the Rondeau, on Lake Erie, through the valley of the Thames to Woodstock. As the chief article of transport would be the agricultural produce, it is needless to say that the last would be the most useful and effective; but common roads, even in these Districts, will not be the less necessary to lead to these main arteries. The remaining portions of the Province are that extensive, rich, and fertile, but yet unsettled country, on the south shore of Lake Huron, and the Lake Simcoe, and the Balsam Lake countries. The first of these possesses the fine harbour of Owen's Sound, but the two latter, although they possess the navigation of their respective lakes, have no outlet to the ocean for their productions. These parts appear to be the only portions of Canada where the construction of railways is all but indispensable. But it is not our object to speculate upon these matters.

From the above sketch of the situation of the Province, and assuming, that if good roads were constructed, every farmer who resides within twenty-five miles of a shipping port, would prefer carting his produce with his own teams to paying the fare for it upon a railway, we can see no reason to apprehend that common roads will be superseded in Canada by railways.

But there is another aspect, equally important, in which the subject ought to be viewed, that is, the probability that railways may be rivalled by steam-carriages upon common roads. This is no chimerical idea. Great exertions are making at the present time to bring these carriages into use, and every season produces some further improvement. The chief hindrance has been the steep acclivities still to be found on many of the old roads in England. It is however allowed, by the ablest Engineers who have studied the subject, that steam-carriages could work well upon common roads, provided there were no acclivities exceeding one in thirty, and that there were no sharp turns upon the roads. Upon such roads they grant that steam-carriages could convey goods and passengers at a velocity of sixteen miles an hour. This fact ought not to be lost sight of when laying out new lines of road in Canada, for, owing to the general levelness of the country, there are few situations where a skilful Engineer would fail in obtaining lines of road, with acclivities even less than one in thirty, without materially increasing the expense provided he had full liberty to choose the location.

THE GREAT DEMOCRATIC HIGHWAY

H. Y. Hind, *et al.*, *Eighty Years' Progress in British North America* (Toronto, 1863), pp. 116-19.

Before the era of wheeled vehicles, communication between back settlements, save in winter, is restricted to "bridle roads," by which men and women on horseback may assemble for worship, visit their neighbors, and attend upon all those occasions of births, marriages, and deaths so much noticed in the forest and so little in town. On pack-horses, also, grain is taken to and from the mill, and other movables transported. These roads are formed simply by clearing away the branches and logs, so that a man on horseback may ride, and are most frequently old lumbermen's roads, which have become impassable from fallen timber, and the growth of underbrush. In winter, however, the snow and ice, the great democratic elements in the physical constitution of Canada, make all roads alike, and the humblest settler in the most remote back-township has not only an excellent road, but can make himself a vehicle capable of transporting the largest loads; and, sheltered by the forest, the once broken track is protected from those drifts which are the only drawbacks to the snow-roads in the clearings.

It is impossible to over-estimate the importance of the frost and snow to the people of Canada, or to place any money value upon them. That which most Europeans have deplored as the only drawback to this country is in truth the source of its rapid prosperity. The operations of agriculture and commerce do not necessarily require perennial communication with a market. As there is but one crop of grain and lumber in the year, it is sufficient if once in the year an opportunity is afforded to transport it, and this Canada possesses in a higher degree than any other "more favored clime." In the dead of winter, when all agricultural out-door operations have ceased, the farmer, after having threshed his grain, can sally forth to any market he may select, even if distant one hundred miles or more, and combine other business or pleasure in the town with that of the sale of his products. He can go any where while the snow lasts, for all roads are alike; and he can take as large a load as can be transported by the same power on the best wheel roads in Europe. For domestic purposes the ice and snow are equally valuable to him; for, while unable to cultivate the fields, he can make the forest resound with his axe, and every swamp is accessible to his horses and his sledges; thus securing his annual supply of fuel without the necessity of money or barter. If he has a family of grown-up sons, he may cut the timber and fuel and transport it to the market, because there is not a week in the whole winter in which out-door work is unpleasant; and there is, therefore, less loss of time than in milder and more rainy climates. The presence of the ice and snow at the season when horses and cattle and their owners can not be employed in field operations, and its certain continuance over the greater part of the country for several months, define the mode of conducting the business without inconvenience and to the best advantage. Whatever is intended for export is, where good summer roads are wanting, hauled down to the shipping ports while the snow lasts; and if a house is to be built, the stone is quarried and hauled when little else can be done, and all preparations are made before the season for building commences. The statistics of shipments show that only about one-third of the crop is sent forward in the year in which it is grown; and although in many instances the produce can not be brought out until the snow falls, it is evident that from choice the greater part will be held back until that season. The autumnal plowing and sowing after harvest, ditching, fencing, and other duties, often make it inconvenient to commence threshing before the winter: moreover, there is also the hope that better prices, when western exports are suspended, and cheaper transportation on the snow, will more than compensate for any loss of interest.

The frost which bridges every river and makes a hard and level causeway of every swamp, with the snow, which fills every rut and cavity and buries boulders, logs, and stumps, enable the lumberman to send supplies for a whole year to his shanties; and, in like manner, the pioneer settler takes advantage of this season, to prepare for his summer's work of establishing a home in the heart of the forest. It is only by contrasting this state of things with India, the Turkish Empire, or other snowless and roadless countries of the world, that we can determine what it is worth to have, as Canada has for months in every year, the best possible road, not only on all main lines, but to every man's door and to every corner of his property.

CANALS

A TIDY PLAN

Sketches of Plans for Settling in Upper Canada, a Portion of the Unemployed Labourers of Great Britain and Ireland (London, 1822), pp. 28-35.

It will doubtless be in the remembrance of many persons in the province, that a plan was agitated in 1820, relative to making a canal, from the Rice Lake to the head of the Bay of Quinte, by the means of a subscription of

LA CHINE RAPIDS

the *produce* of the country to defray the expense, and that subscription, entitling the contributors to proportionate shares in the canal: it may also be well remembered, how readily the views of the proposer were entered into by the richer and poorer classes of the district of Newcastle, the district in which the then proposed canal was to have been cut, as well as by many of the inhabitants higher up the country; let us then see how we can connect this plan of opening a canal by the above means of defraying the expense with that of settling 6000 men, women, and children, in comfort, in the neighbouring country.

We will divide the party into three divisions of 2000 each, to be sent out to the river Trent, which connects the Rice Lake with the Bay of Quinte, in three successive springs. On the arrival of the first 2000, let those who are capable of labour, immediately be put to fitting work, at the proposed canal, instead of proceeding forthwith to their location. Provisions, clothing, lodging, medical assistance, and certain instruction for the children, will be provided by preliminary arrangements, to be hereafter noticed. The second spring, will bring the next division, and the course of the ensuing year, will be as the former; the arrival of the third 2000, will be the commencement of new and pleasant scenes to the first division, *they* will now be permitted to have so much time to visit the lands appointed during which they will be allowed provision, &c. for location, in order to fix upon a lot, to put up their "tshantees," as also afterwards to put up their houses, to clear five acres of land, for a spring crop, together with the use of a pair of oxen, for a given time to perform the "logging;" again, they must have partial allowances whilst preparing for the autumn season, and finishing the settlement duties, together with some assistance during the following winter. On the opening of the fourth spring, perfect freedom begins to dawn; we must now (for the last time) supply our friends (according to the number of their *helpless* children) with a few other necessaries, the deeds of their land free of any expense, and then leave them to the protection of their Maker, the laws of their adopted country, and their own industry. Should the patrons of a system for colonising upon the above principles, perceive, at, or before this period, that the result may be convenience to the mother country, advantage to the province, and happiness to the settlers, it can be continued to many succeeding bodies of 2000 persons, inasmuch as after the completion of the work from the Bay of Quinte to the Rice Lake, there will be no obstacle to proceeding thence to the carrying place in the township of Smith, and forward through the shallow Lakes to the boundaries of the Canadas.

The fourth year will also witness the approach of the second body to freedom from their contract, and to independence; and again their quitting for ever their temporary houses at the canal will be the harbinger of the third body, *selecting* their new abode in the *wild* lands. . . .

With respect to the supply of provisions, &c. to meet the wants of our emigrants on their arrival, nothing can be more simple than the mode contemplated in 1820, viz, that every old resident should, according to his means, subscribe his quota of the required produce. Some would subscribe wheat, others oats, barley, peas, beans and hops; others whiskey and maple sugar; others cattle, horses, sheep and hogs; barrelled pork and beef, and salt from the home pits; others again hay and straw, lumber, scantling, &c. Our friend, the enterprising supporter of the new Iron works on the Trent, would experience the pleasure of contributing, for his shares, the iron implements that will be wanted; and the home manufacturers, the spinners, the possessors of wool, &c. will not be found backward in their supplies: in short, for such an object there can be no doubt of abundant contributors coming forward with whatever the province produces. The distribution may either be under the general management, or various bodies or gangs may be apportioned to the care of various individuals, sharers in the canal.

It will not be a work of charity, as the word is generally understood; the present inhabitants of Canada will not be gratuitously giving away so much of their staple commodities; inasmuch as they will have their shares in the canal for remuneration, according to their subscriptions; and then the acquisition of the improved water-course, and of an industrious body of settlers in the heart of the province will not be disregarded. And how well do these settlers merit their title to these supplies, as well as ultimately to their allotment of land? There is obligation on neither side, although the foundation will be laid for the intercommunication of the most friendly sentiments. The settlers are taken to their new homes; they are maintained for three years; and they will go to their cleared land free of expense. In return they give to their old country, their absence, and to Canada the accomplishment of works desired by all who have thought upon the subject, and the acquisition of some thousands of valuable members.

AN APPEAL TO BRITISH CAPITALISTS

Ogden Creighton, *General View of the Welland Canal* (London, 1830), pp. 1-5.

THE WELLAND CANAL COMPANY, in the province of Upper Canada, was incorporated in 1824, for the purpose of constructing a Canal for boat navigation around the natural barrier caused by the Falls of Niagara. In 1825, on petition of the Stockholders, the amount of capital was increased to £200,000 Canada currency, or £180,000 sterling, divided into 16,000 shares of £12:10s. Canada currency, or £11:5s. sterling each, in order to enable the Company to construct a Canal sufficiently large to pass the vessels used in navigating the Lakes from 50 to 100 tons burden, without the necessity of transhipment.

This important work is now completed so far that the navigation is open from Lake Erie to Lake Ontario, by way of the Niagara river; and will in another year be open to Lake Erie, by the western route. The advantages presented by the two routes may be seen by a reference to the map of the Isthmus, formed by the Niagara River and Lakes Erie and Ontario, which accompanies this description.

The original design of the Company, was to feed the lower section of the Canal from the waters of the Welland River, by cutting through a ridge of about fifty-six feet high. The attempt proved very expensive, and was ultimately abandoned in consequence of the quick-sands near the bottom. The canal has, however, been completed on the same route, but somewhat altered in the manner. Instead of excavating to the bottom at the place of deep cutting, the level has been raised, a dam thrown across the Grand river, about six miles from its mouth, and a feeder, sufficient for navigation, made to the deep cutting, a distance of twenty-seven miles. Thus a Canal has been made, in reality more advantageous than it ever could have been by persisting in the original plan of using the waters of the Welland River. The amount of cost altogether, will be about £270,000 sterling, of which about £250,000 sterling have been expended.

For this sum a most important commercial avenue is opened, which cannot fail to add much to the wealth and prosperity of his Majesty's subjects in Canada, as well as increase the trade and promote the interest of the United Kingdom.

There are thirty seven locks to ascend to the summit level from Lake Ontario, a height of 330 feet. The Canal is fifty-six feet wide on the surface of the water, and eight-and-an-half in depth. The chambers of the locks are twenty-two feet wide and one hundred long; a size abundantly sufficient for vessels of one hundred and twenty-five tons burthen. The natural situation of the ground is such, that in the arrangement of the locks an unusual facility has been afforded in ascending and descending. There are no two locks so near together that vessels meeting shall be detained; the space between the locks being sufficient to admit of their passing with ease. The supply of water is abundant for any extent of hydraulic machinery the Company may permit to be placed on the line of the Canal, without the remotest danger of impairing the navigation. The improvements now in progress to connect the waters of Lake Ontario, with the St. Lawrence at Montreal, by a Canal navigable for the vessels of the lakes, will increase the value of the Welland Canal, and give to the interior of an immense and fertile country, the advantage of a sea coast. There is indeed no improvement that can be made on any avenue from the lakes to the sea coast, either by our American neighbours in the state of New York, or his Majesty's government and enterprising individuals in Canada, along the St. Lawrence and Ottawa Rivers, which will not materially aid the Welland Canal. The ease and safety with which the Atlantic Ocean is now crossed, has brought the Canadas so much nearer to us in effect for commercial operations, than they formerly appeared to be, that by the continued and quick returns, they seem to form almost a part of the Home British Empire.

THE WELLAND CANAL
A Report from its Directors

Welland Canal Company. Director's Report [1825] in William Hamilton Merritt, *Brief Review of the Origin, Progress, Present State, and Future Prospects of the Welland Canal* (St Catharines, 1852), pp. 42-3.

Improvements suggest and assist each other, and tend to the nourishment and development of that vivifying principle which exalts one nation above another, and which connects the distant branches of one parent stem to each other, by the ties of common origin, of mutual attachment, and of reciprocal advantage: that principle which has enabled Great Britain to maintain the character of being at the same time the first nation in war, the first in manufactures, the first in public improvement: that principle which enabled the small and scattered population of this young Province successfully to resist the repeated inroads of their powerful invaders, in war, and which, it is hoped, may, in *peace*, enable them to follow the great example of the Mother Country, in the career of improvement, and like her, derive wealth and power from the honorable exertion of individual enterprise.

In the progress of improvements, and amongst those *public works* which bestow wealth and power on nations, and which confer permanent distinction on individuals, there are none of equal importance or celebrity with the construction of Canals. The conquests of Louis xiv. are forgotten, or remembered only to be held up to execration; but the Canal of Languedoc remains a blessing to France, and to *his* name a monument of imperishable renown. The Duke of Bridgewater's rank and wealth would not have preserved his name from oblivion; but he will always be remembered, as the man who embarked his fortune in constructing the first Canal in Great Britain, regardless alike of popular prejudices, of friendly remonstrances, and of prophetic threats of ruin. And in our times, and in our immediate neighborhood, it is probable that the name of Dewitt Clinton will always remain associated with the grand Erie Canal of the State of New-York, when the names and the measures of other contemporary Chief Magistrates of States and of Nations, will be consigned to the same forgetfulness which has already swallowed up so many of their predecessors.

The Directors of the Welland Canal Company profess not to be insensible to the honor conferred upon them, in being chosen to begin so noble a work as a Canal for Ship Navigation around the Cataract of Niagara; and as their services are gratuitous, the honor of conducting the undertaking is their only reward. It is one of those rare measures which, though of immense magnitude, is of comparatively easy and absolutely certain accomplishment. The natural advantages of the ground, combined with the inexhaustible supply of water, are such as no other Canal ever had, and such as can be found for no other Canal; and when finished on the intended scale, it will be one of the grandest works ever effected by any country or by any nation. No work in Europe, or in Asia, ancient or modern, will bear a comparison with it, in usefulness, to an equal extent of territory: and it will yield only to the Canal which may hereafter unite the Pacific with the Atlantic Ocean, through the Isthmus of Darien.

But each undertaking has its own peculiar advantages, and the Welland Canal will possess some advantages even over the projected Canal of Darien. The Pacific is already accessible by navigation around the Cape of Good Hope, or Cape Horn; but the interior Seas of North America, which contain more than half of the fresh water in this Planet, and the fertile and extensive shores of which are destined to be peopled by an active, an intelligent, and an enterprising race—boasting their descent from England, and preserving and perpetuating her language and her institutions— these interior Seas can be approached in Ships only through the Welland Canal.

Such is the importance, and such will be the splendid and immense results, of the work now offered to the notice of those enterprising and enlightened capitalists who may be disposed to contribute to its completion; at the same time that they secure for themselves a participation in its advantages, and a share of the liberal profits which it may reasonably and speedily be expected to produce.

THE WELLAND CANAL
A Dissenting View

John Mactaggart, *Three Years in Canada: An Account of the Actual State of the Country in 1826-7-8* (London, 1829), vol. II, pp. 153-63.

"As the work, therefore, stands in the Twelve-mile Creek, it seems to me not to be substantial enough even for a boat canal of locks twenty feet wide, five deep, and 100 feet long; whereas the locks are thirty-two feet wide, eight deep, and 125 long, intended for schooners and steam-boats. The wooden lock of ten-feet lift has about 2000 tons of water pressing on the bottom of it when full, which bottom ought to be strongly piled and planked, and somewhat inverted; then, as the pressure on the sides of the lock increases according to the squares of the depths, on the first foot down sides there will be 3½ tons pressing on the whole length, and at the bottoms of the sides 324 tons, viz. on the bottom foot—making about 2100 pressure on each side. Then the lock-walls, being fifteen feet wide of framework, filled with clay puddle, and having fifteen feet width of clay backing, bring 2600 tons of matter to resist the water in the lock when full. Taking the water at 60 pounds per cubic foot, which it is nearly, and the clay at 100 pounds, which I believe is rather too much, we thus have 500 tons to keep down the side from blowing—that is, floating up—from the waters forcing their way beneath it, which is sufficient would things remain in equilibrium; but this they do not, for when the lock is empty, or rather when the lift-waters are out of it, which are ten feet deep, there only remain eight feet water in the lock, or 960 tons to oppose 2600 tons. If then a freshet comes down the creek, when this water is in the lock, the pressure will increase behind the sides enormously, and may be apt to crush them together; or if the lift-waters be in the lock, and any accident take place in the waste weirs, such as choking up, then the sides of the lock are in danger of spreading, from the waters rushing over the lock. In the creek I examined a waste weir which had been driven away by a freshet, and found that no piles had been driven about it, and that the clay put in as backing had been frozen lumps, which dissolved with the first thaw, and left the weir to destruction; but had it been backed up with unfrozen lumps, it would have given way, if wanting piles. In such a place as the Twelve-mile Creek, formed of such a fine tough clay, piles and sheeting piles must ever be used to give stability to the works therein.

"After passing the village of St. Catherine, the locks are diminished in dimensions to those for a boat canal. The reasons for this alteration do not seem very obvious. Why not continue it a ship canal throughout, of the dimensions commenced with? which dimensions are proportionable and good. There must be some private interests of individuals at work with this erroneous alteration, which I have no business to inquire into; but, as an artist, I must say, that the canal of itself will suffer by the alteration, and the public feel the injury for many years to come. About 3000l. will set the matter right and make the locks as they should be; while about 18,600l. will build the whole of the locks, over and above what is allowed to build the small locks; or, in other words, there will only be about 20,000l. saved, as it were, by building the small locks instead of the large, which saving will yet turn out to be a lamentable loss.

"In the locks now excavating up the mountain, seven of them will have rock foundations. These seven ought to be built with stone, and not wood; and they may be built at as little expense with stone as with wood, and certainly when built will be far superior. Good quarries may be opened beside them, and the porous sand-stone now excavating out of the mountain, will answer well for backing up behind the puddle.—The bottoms of these locks, being full of fissures, will therefore require puddling and flagging with plank or stone. The gates of the locks are not of proper construction, the upper and lower being both alike in dimensions—this they should not be. The upper gate should not have the lift of the lock added to it: that is to say, there are ten, eight, and seven feet, as the lifts may be, extending in depth of workmanship more than there is any occasion for. The penstock lifted by rack and pinion should be adopted, and not the paddle-gate to be wrenched open by lever, as this strains both spindle and paddle, and damages the gates. The paddle-gate may do for the sluices of a boat-canal, but not for a ship-canal. . . .

"Mr. Barret, the resident Engineer on the works, was kind enough to conduct me through the whole, and afforded whatever information was in his power. I think him a young man extremely anxious to do justice to the Works; and it is not his fault, in my opinion, if these are not properly executed. He has been blamed for making some things too strong; but these very works must be made *stronger* still, else they will not answer. I think him honest, and an advocate for substantial superstructure.

"In conclusion, you may probably consider this report severe; nevertheless, I feel it my duty to lay before you the Welland Canal as I have found it, and humbly to offer my ideas respecting its improvement and future construction, conceiving that the truth thus told cannot disgrace any one, and may in the end be the best means of promoting the welfare of Canada.

"I have the honour to be, &c."

This Report was not very well received by the Shareholders, but they were quite unable to deny any of its statements; they would work away as they had done, regardless of my remarks, and had the *felicity* of observing some of the *wooden locks* float down before the *freshets*, like *large bird-cages*, into Lake Ontario. The frosts and thaws filled up the deep cut, with the summer excavations, and all their *berms* or benches of earth slid in.

I then proposed to the Company, to excavate the whole of this *cut* at *sixpence* sterling per cubic yard, which would save them about four shillings on every cubic yard they were then getting out. This saving I proposed to expend on their *wooden locks*, and make them more secure: but this they would not listen to. Yet, it will take nearly *three* times the money to construct it on the present system. A canal, however, will certainly be made of it by and by, in spite of *private interest*, obstinate *management*, and *perversion* of the laws of nature: but *when*, I will not take upon myself to say.

OLD AND NEW WORLD ENGINEERING PRACTICES

David Stevenson, *Sketch of the Civil Engineering of North America* (London, 1838), pp. 192-3.

English and American engineers are guided by the same principles in designing their works; but the different nature of the materials employed in their construction, and the climates and circumstances of the two countries, naturally produce a considerable dissimilarity in the practice of civil-engineers in England and America. At the first view, one is struck with the temporary and apparently unfinished state of many of the American works, and is very apt, before inquiring into the subject, to impute to want of ability what turns out, on investigation, to be a judicious and ingenious arrangement to suit the circumstances of a new country, of which the climate is severe,—a country where stone is scarce and wood is plentiful, and where manual labour is very expensive. It is vain to look to the American works for the finish that characterises those of France, or the stability for which those of Britain are famed. Undressed slopes of cuttings and embankments, roughly built rubble arches, stone parapet-walls coped with timber, and canal-locks wholly constructed of that material, every where offend the eye accustomed to view European workmanship. But it must not be supposed that this arises from want of knowledge of the principles of engineering, or of skill to do them justice in the execution. The use of wood, for example, which may be considered by many as inapplicable to the construction of canal-locks, where it must not only encounter the tear and wear occasioned by the lockage of vessels, but must be subject to the destructive consequences of alternate immersion in water and exposure to the atmosphere, is yet the result of deliberate judgment. The Americans have, in many cases, been induced to use the material of the country, ill adapted though it be in some respects to the purposes to which it is applied, in order to meet the wants of a rising community, by speedily and perhaps superficially completing a work of importance, which would otherwise be delayed, from a want of the means to execute it in a more substantial manner; and although the works are wanting in finish, and even in solidity, they do not fail for many years to serve the purposes for which they were constructed, as efficiently as works of a more lasting description.

When the wooden locks on any of the canals begin to shew symptoms of decay, stone structures are generally substituted, and materials suitable for their erection are with ease and expedition conveyed from the part of the country where they are most abundant, by means of the canal itself to which they are to be applied; and thus the less substantial work ultimately becomes the means of facilitating its own improvement, by affording a more easy, cheap, and speedy transport of those durable and expensive materials, without the use of which, perfection is unattainable.

AN AMERICAN VIEW OF THE CANADIAN THREAT

'Report of the Select Committee of the Legislature of New York, on the Petition of the Inhabitants of the County of Oswego', published in 'Report on the Canal Navigation of the Canadas', *Papers on Subjects Connected with the Duties of the Corps of Royal Engineers*, vol. v, (1842), pp. 189-90.

"The lethargy under which the people of Canada have slumbered for the last century has been thrown off, and they are now fully awake to the importance of internal improvements. They are beginning to appreciate the *natural water communications with which nature has so bountifully supplied them.* They have entered the lists, and are nobly contending for a participation in, *if not a monopoly of*, the rich dowry of the western trade. Their enterprise has caused a communication to be opened around the Falls of Niagara, a distance of forty-one miles, by which vessels carrying 1000 barrels of flour can go through, without being lightened, at an expense of one cent per barrel, exclusive of tolls. The amount of business done upon this canal will be seen by a reference to the fact, that 50,000 barrels of salt passed through it during the last season; and had the requisite repairs been made so as to have opened the canal with the commencement of lake navigation, the revenue would have amounted to more than $50,000.

"The evil which the Canal Commissioners *feared in 1812 now really exists.* The produce designed for transportation upon the Upper Lakes is now let down to Lake Ontario by means of this canal with facility and for a trifling expense. The prediction of the Canal Commissioners, *'that articles for exportation when once afloat on Lake Ontario would, generally speaking, go to Montreal, unless our British neighbours were blind to their own interests,'* is now fully verified. By a reference to the parliamentary proceedings of the Canadas during the last winter, it will appear obvious that they are not thus blind; that, on the contrary, they duly appreciate the importance of this trade, and that the greatest industry, activity, and talent are employed in the attainment of further

THE BAY AND RIVER STEAMER 'CHARLOTTE' BUILT AT ERNEST TOWN, U.C., 1818

improvements on the most magnificent scale. Appropriations have already been made for the improvement of the St. Lawrence, by which it is intended to connect the Atlantic with the lakes by ship and steam-boat navigation. Let them make the Welland Canal and the St. Lawrence navigable as they purpose to do, and which they will do, for steam-boats, *and Cleveland will be within sixty hours' ride of Montreal.* When these improvements are completed, *vessels of 300 tons can load at Chicago, at Cleveland, at Detroit, at Oswego, and other ports on the lakes, and deliver their cargoes at foreign ports.* When direct exportation has once succeeded, *direct importation will follow as a matter of course.* When the Welland Canal shall be completed, *and the St. Lawrence improved, as designed, goods may be delivered at Cleveland, from London, for less than one half of what it now costs by the way of New York and the Erie Canal.* Make the Erie Canal a public highway, *and the Canadian route will be preferable by one quarter in point of expense.* The vast superiority in the great point of economy in transportation effected upon *natural water communication, admitting of navigation by large vessels or steam-boats, above transportation upon canals and railroads, has been satisfactorily proved by experience on the Hudson, the lakes, and the great rivers of the West.*

TOWARDS THE 'GRAND CANADIAN CANAL'

John Mactaggart, *Three Years in Canada: An Account of the Actual State of the Country in 1826-7-8* (London, 1829), vol. I, pp. 165-9.

The Grand Canadian Canal is not the Rideau Canal, nor the Welland Canal. These are only mere sections of it, which are to be met with on the grand line between Quebec and the noble summit-level of Lake Superior. This famous Canal will be finished in a few years as far as the summit-level. Steam-boats may go up from Quebec to Lake Superior ere three years from this time; from thence with little trouble, they will pass through the *notch* of the rocky mountains and be locked down the Columbia to the Pacific ocean. The route, however, will be better to be kept off the American frontier, which is Columbia, and to go down Cook's river, or the large Salmon river at Nootka Sound. The town of Nootka is likely yet to be as large as London, and ought to be laid out on an extensive plan, as the trade between it and the Oriental world may become wonderfully great, in a short time. Then when the steam-packet line is established between Quebec and London, as it soon will be, we may come and go between China and Britain in about two months. The names of the stages will be London, Cove of Cork, the Azores, Newfoundland

Quebec, Montreal, Kingston, Port Dalhousie, Port Maitland, Erie, Huron, Superior, Rocky Mountains, Athabaska, Nootka and Canton. Can this be called a foolish prophecy, or an idle dream?—By no means; it is perfectly practicable. The magnitude of the whole may probably be too much for the minds of the generality of mankind to grasp; but what signifies that? Were the work absolutely finished, millions would not believe it! Pagans consider the sun in a different light from Astronomers. The eyes of both are dazzled by his beams, while his real nature is unknown,— as far beyond the understanding of man, as he is in miles from the earth, and probably much farther.

THE RAILROAD

THE AGENT OF CIVILIZATION

Thomas C. Keefer, *Philosophy of Railroads* (Montreal, 1850), pp. 6-9.

Let us take a case of which Canada (we are proud and sad to say) presents more than one instance. A well cultivated district, in which all the lands are occupied (perhaps by the second generation) with or without water power, but situated twenty to fifty miles from the chief towns upon our great highway, the St. Lawrence, and without navigable water communication with it. The occupants are all thriving and independent farmers, the water power is employed only to an extent to meet their local wants, and the village is limited to the few mechanics, and the one store required for this rural district. The barter of the shopkeeper is restricted by the consumption of his customers, and he becomes the sole forwarder of the surplus product of the district. There is no stimulus for increased production—there are less facilities for it: the redundant population have all been accustomed to agriculture, and as the field for this is unrestricted, they move Westward to prevent a subdivision of the homesteads, and to become greater landowners than their fathers. There exists the well known scarcity of labourers for the harvest, because there is no employment for them during the remainder of the year; and they have not yet been led by necessity to that subdivision of labour and that variety of employment which are the results of an increasing and more confined population. Each farmer has his comfortable house, his well stored barn, variety of stock, his meadows and his woodland; he cultivates just so much as he finds convenient, and his slight surplus is exchanged for his modest wants. Distance, the expense of transportation, and the absence of that energy which debt or contact with busier men should produce, have prevented any efforts to supply the commercial towns on the part of the contented denizens of our "Sleepy Hollow." To themselves, to the superficial observer, their district has attained the limit of improvement. If they have no water power, or one limited to the supply of the needful grist or saw mill, it is clear to their minds that they were never destined for a manufacturing people; and if they have abundant water power, their local market would not support one manufactory, while land carriage, want of people, money, and more than all, *information*, precludes the idea of their manufacturing for a distant market. It is still more evident, from their position, they are not to become a commercial people and build up large cities; they, therefore, jog along with evident self-satisfaction—the venerable churchyard is slowly filling up with tombstones—and the quiet residents arrive at the conclusion that they are a peculiarly favoured people, in having escaped the rage for improvement. They are grateful that their farms have not been disfigured by canals or railroads, or the spirits of their sires troubled by the hideous screech of the steam-whistle.

We will now suppose, (we would we could more than suppose), that two of our cities should be moved to unite by the iron bond of a Railway, which, in its course, will traverse the district just described. Excitement prevails in the "Hollow;"—sleep has deserted her peculiar people— the livelong night is passed in mutual contemplation of farms "cut up" or covered over, visions of bloody skirmishes between "Far downs" and Corkonians, of rifled gardens and orchards, of plundered poultry yards and abducted pigs. The probable mother of a possible child bewails her future offspring "drawn and quartered" on the rail by the terrible locomotive, and a whole hecatomb of cattle, pigs and sheep, are devoted, by imagination, to this insatiate Juggernaut. The Engineers who come to spy out the land are met with curses both loud and deep, the laws of property are discussed, the delinquent Member for the County denounced,—until a handsome Rodman, by well-timed admiration of Eliza Ann, the rural spokesman's daughter, succeeds in obtaining comfortable quarters for his party, with board, lodging, and washing, at 12s. 6d. per week. The work has commenced; the farmer is offered better prices for his hay and grain than he ever before received:—even milk and vegetables,—things he never dreamed of selling,—are now sought for; his teams, instead of eating up his substance as formerly in winter, are constantly employed, and his sons are profitably engaged in "getting out timber" for the contractors; he grows a much larger quantity of oats and potatoes than before,—and when the workmen have left, he finds to his astonishment that his old friend the storekeeper is prepared to take all he can spare, to send by the Railroad "down to town."

And now some of the "city folks" come out and take up a water privilege, or erect steam power, and commence manufacturing. Iron is bought, cut into nails, screws and hinges. Cotton is spun and wove, and all the variety of manufactures introduced, because here motive power, rents and foods are cheaper, and labour more easily controlled, than in the cities, while transportation and distance have by the Railroad been reduced to a minimum. A town has been built, and peopled by the operatives—land rises rapidly in value—the neglected swamp is cleared and the timber is converted into all sorts of wooden "notions"—tons of vegetables, grains, or grasses, are grown where none grew before—the patient click of the loom, the rushing of the shuttle, the busy hum of the spindle, the thundering of the trip-hammer, and the roaring of steam, are mingled in one continuous sound of active industry. While the physical features of our little hamlet are undergoing such a wonderful transformation, the moral influence of the iron civilizer upon the old inhabitants is bringing a rapid "change over the spirit of their dreams." The young men and the maidens, the old men and the matrons, daily collect around the cars: they wonder where so many well-dressed and rich-looking people come from and are going to, &c.,—what queer machines those are which they see passing backwards and forwards. They have perhaps an old neighbour, whose son had long since wandered off, and now they see him returned, a first class passenger, with all the prestige of broadcloth, gold chains, rings, gloves, and a travelled reputation: the damsels rapidly impress upon "the mind's eye" the shapes of the bonnets, visites, &c., of that superior class of beings who are flying (like angels) over the country, and *drink in*, with wide-mouthed admiration, the transcendent splendour and indescribable beauty of "that 'ere shawl." All are interested, all are benefited, *cuique suum*. Is he a farmer? he has a practical illustration of the superior cheapness of transportation by increasing the load—the cart is abandoned for the waggon—for he sees the Railroad, notwithstanding the great cost of the cuttings, embankments, tunnels, bridges, engines, cars, and stations, carrying his produce for a less sum than his personal expenses and the feeding of his horses would amount to. Is he a blacksmith? he determines his son shall no longer shoe horses, but build engines. Is he a carpenter? he is proud of his occupation as he surveys the new bridge over the old creek. Even the village tailor gathers "a wrinkle," as he criticises the latest effort of Buckmaster or Gibb, whilst the unconscious advertiser is swallowing his coffee. Thus curiosity and emulation are excited, and the results are discernible in a general predilection for improved "modes." A spirit is engendered which is not confined to dress or equipage, but is rapidly extended to agriculture, roads, and instructive societies, and finally exerts its most powerful influence where it is most needed,—in the improved character it gives to the exercise of the franchise. This right is now enjoyed by too large a class, whose chief contact with public affairs has been limited to an occasional chat with ambitious retailers of dry goods, groceries, hardware, and political mysteries—or to a semi-annual sitting in a jury-box, unconsciously absorbing all the virtuous indignation of some *nisi prius* wrangler, whose "familiar face" is shortly after presented to them at the hustings, generously proffering to defend or advocate anything for four dollars per diem and a prospective Judgeship. He is opposed, perhaps, by the public-spirited shopkeeper, who, with mortgages, long credits, tea and tobacco,—aided by a "last call" to all doubtful supporters,—incites the noble yeomanry to assert their rights as "free and independent electors." If the "natives" can overcome these prejudices of local associations, or if the lawyer's "collections" and "notes" are sufficiently diffuse, ten chances to one the greatest talker is elected, and an improved judicature, instead of an improved country, is the result.

Nothing would be a more powerful antidote to this state of primitive, but not innocuous simplicity, than the transit of Railways through our agricultural districts. The civilizing tendency of the locomotive is one of the modern anomalies, which, however inexplicable it may appear to some, is yet so fortunately patent to all, that it is admitted as readily as the action of steam, though the substance be invisible and its secret ways unknown to man. Poverty, indifference, the bigotry or jealousy of religious denominations, local dissensions or political demagogueism, may stifle or neutralize the influence of the best intended efforts of an educational system; but that invisible power which has waged successful war with the material elements, will assuredly overcome the prejudices of mental weakness or the designs of mental tyrants. It calls for no cooperation, it waits for no convenient season, but with a restless, rushing roaring assiduity, it keeps up a constant and unavoidable spirit of enquiry or comparison; and while ministering to the material wants, and appealing to the covetousness of the multitude, it unconsciously, irresistibly, impels them to a more intimate union with their fellow men.

A RAILROAD PROPOSAL, 1847

Engineer's Report, and Statistical Information Relative to the Proposed Railway from Port Hope to Peterboro (Port Hope, C.W., 1847), pp. 8-1?

The President and Directors of the Peterboro and Port Hope Railway, be to lay before the Stockholders and the Public, information which ha been elicited by the survey of the proposed line, relative to the situatio products, and business of that part of the country between the Town this Railway is intended to connect.

It is now evident from careful investigation, that the proposed line Railway, will not only be especially beneficial to the Landowner, Farme

Merchant, Storekeeper, Tradesman, Mechanic and the travelling community, but that all who do or may hold Shares in the Capital Stock of the Company will find their investment productive of a large return.

The State of the Stock Book may show to those at a distance from this locality the confidence the people of Peterboro and Port Hope have in the undertaking; about £20,000 has been taken up principally by them, being about one third the estimated cost of the line.

The Route as surveyed, and which commends itself to the Board of Directors is the product of careful examination and diligent perseverance in the Engineer, who has studiously observed and attended to the instructions he received "to find the nearest and best line consistent with expense."

It passes through a highly fertile, well cultivated and thickly populated country, in the neighbourhood of valuable Grist and Saw Mills, and Mill Sites, and of Villages which with its aid must rapidly grow into importance.

After taking a course 3¼ miles westward from the harbour of Port Hope, it is carried northward through the Township of Hope, till it attains the 8th Concession line, thence eastward to the village of Bewdly at the head of Rice Lake where has lately been erected a Steam Saw Mill capable of cutting 12,000 feet of lumber daily, 2 taverns, several dwelling houses, blacksmith's shop &c. there is also a wharf & storehouses at which the Steamer Forester touches. Timber of every description and in every character may be brought up Rice Lake to this point by rafts at a small cost and by the proposed railway the great difficulty and expense of transporting it to Lake Ontario will be removed.

From Bewdley, it is proposed (to avoid the high hills north of Black's Swamp,) to carry the Railway through a part of the Township of Monaghan, and again to join the Peterboro' Road at the commencement of a village called Centreville.

The high road from Millbrook in Cavan, to the Peterboro and Port Hope road leads to this place, from which it is distant only four miles, this must eventually become an excellent business situation and probably a Station. The produce of the Township of Cavan, Emily Ops, Manvers and South Monaghan, could be collected here, and when the Railway is completed would find transport by it to Port Hope, both on account of the great saving of time and expense.

The Marmora Iron Works, are situated in the Township of Marmora about 7 miles from the eastern end of Rice Lake.

We understand that these works are about to be put into full operation by parties who have ample means and ability to carry them on. The Iron is of the first quality and most abundant. In this neighborhood is also found Red Ochre, excellent Lithographic Stone and Marble.

From Centreville the line takes the course of the Peterboro' road and may be made upon it for six miles, until it reaches Palmer's Inn, which is also a good situation for the collection of traffic for the Railway. This place according to the present travelled road is 7 miles distant from Peterboro', but a considerable saving of distance, will be effected by the line passing about N. E. to Peterboro.

PETERBORO', the County Town of the Colborne District, containing a population of about 3000 inhabitants, possesses natural advantages, equal perhaps, to any locality in Canada, and needs only the cheap and ready means of transport which a Railway will afford, to make it rise in importance both in size and wealth.

Its situation is beautiful, and is most advantageous for business, being built on the River Otonabee, and has never failed to call forth the admiration of its visitors,—but that which most astonishes the traveller is its almost boundless water power: a fall of 160 feet is found between Buckhorn Lake, and the Bridge of Peterboro. The Mill privileges found within a short distance can scarcely be estimated. The regular quantity of water passing per minute, is equal to 86,400 Cubic feet, or, 691,200 Gallons. This is nearly the minimum quantity for this River at Peterboro, throughout the year.

Two excellent Flouring Mills, each furnished with four run of stones, are now in operation, which are found to be quite inadequate for the Manufactory of Flour, two more are about to be erected by Z. Burnham, and E. Perry, Esquires: and within a short distance of the Town there are several others.

Saw Mills to the number of 13 send their Lumber to this Town, these mills are capable of cutting 60,000 feet of lumber in 24 hours, but some of them for want of a good market are comparatively idle; 20s, per 1000 feet has lately been paid for carriage of Lumber to Lake Ontario, a distance of 30 miles, which almost prohibits its transportation.

The supply of timber for Saw Mills can scarcely be calculated, as it can be easily Rafted from a distance of upwards of 100 miles, by means of the chain of Lakes lying to the northward.

STONE suitable for building purposes is also abundant, one kind found in this neighbourhood, is capable of bearing a high polish.

By Railway the frontier Towns could be supplied with this material at a much lower price than is now paid, viz: £1 17s 6d. per Toise. Lime also, at 5d, per bushel, can be obtained here, whereas 10d per bushel is commonly paid at the Front.

There are 3 Foundries, in this Town capable of making the heaviest mill castings. There are 2 Cloth Factories, one intended for 28 Looms; machine and Axe Factories; a Mill for sawing Lath; a Turning and Furniture Factory &c.

There is nothing remarkable in the existence of such establishments in a North American Town; but when we know the disadvantages under which the Inhabitants of Peterboro labour, paying for freight upon their imports, 30s, per ton from Lake Ontario, we see in this beginning of machinery and business, and in the enterprise which they have awakened to, together with the advantages of the beautiful River Otonabee, the assurance of a good maintenance of the Railway. . . .

The proposed Railway will afford an uninterrupted trade at all seasons of the year, and enable the Merchants and Storekeepers of Peterboro' to keep their stock replenished and have a continual variety of Goods.

The Railway united with the boundless water power of the Otonabee, for Mills, and the great variety and quantity of timber in the Colborne District must suggest to the minds of thinking, calculating men, the great advantages held out for ship building at Port Hope.

As a natural Harbour it is acknowledged by the most respectable and talented Captains, navigating Lake Ontario, not to have its equal between Toronto and Kingston. Its capabilities as a harbour of refuge have been highly commended to the British and Colonial Governments, and *it may be added*, its desirable advantages for the construction of building Docks.

It is proposed to allow interest upon all instalments on Stock, from the date of Payment, as in all those cases where this has been done in England, the works have advanced to completion, at least one or two years beyond those lines that have not done so, and from the quick return of a large percentage, after the road is completed, the pre-payment of Interest is reduced to almost nothing to the shareholders, besides the inducement that is held out to money holders, possessing moderate means, of immediate investment, and return for the same.

The profitableness of such an investment must be most apparent to a discerning public, by comparing the Engineer's estimates of the cost of the proposed Railway, with the confidently anticipated return. Contractors are already proposing to complete and furnish it at these estimates.

UTILITY *vs* APPEARANCE

Walter Shanley, *Reports on the Preliminary and Locating Surveys of the Bytown and Prescott Railway* (Toronto, 1853), pp. 23-4.

I trust that I have succeeded in showing that in an *Engineering point of view* everything, save distance, is in favor of the lower location, the point I selected when making a general examination of the ground last winter;—because, even at that unfavorable season of the year, any one practiced in such matters could see, 'with half an eye,' that no spot within the limits of the Town (East of the Canal) is so cheaply accessible or, when reached, so well adapted for the Terminus of your Railway as Lot Letter 'O,' and I was then of opinion—as I still am—that economy, both as regards *time* and *money*, is an element which, to ensure the success of the undertaking, must enter largely into the construction of the Bytown and Prescott Railway,—an opinion in which I am gratified to find I have the support of many who differ from me entirely on the question of 'location'—for in the Proceedings of a partial meeting of Stockholders held some short time since in this Town, for the purpose of bringing before the Public the alleged advantages of the Basin Terminus, I find a Resolution, unanimously concurred in, to the effect, that in constructing this Road "Economy is of all things desirable"—a cardinal maxim— which all true friends of the enterprise should unite with them in inculcating. . . .

Before dismissing this subject of the Terminus, I would beg leave to place it before you in one other point of view,—that of *Appearance*— which, however minor a consideration when placed in the scale against *Utility*, should not be wholly disregarded, where both attributes can be made to harmonize, in legislating in the premises for the future *City of the Ottawa*.

Immediately before reaching the Canal Basin the Track, for upwards of half a mile, would lie in the bottom of a deep, unsightly cut, much resembling the "Deep Cut" of the Canal,—close by. Through this Trains would skulk into the Town, to reach a Terminus which would, inevitably, be soon built round on all sides—giving it a confined and hampered appearance, and limiting the prospect to an occasional view of the Basin, when it did not happen to be obscured from sight by the presence of a small number of diminutive craft.

On the other hand, the approach to Lot Letter "O" would be, for several miles, on the surface of a fine open country, where Trains would show to advantage—reaching their destination on a fair and level plane, fronting on, and in full view, of the noble Ottawa—*a view which can never be obstructed*, and the effect of which upon the stranger visiting Bytown would be to create a lively and enduring impression of the beauty of its situation.

TRACK AND GAUGE

Walter Shanley, *Reports on the Preliminary and Locating Surveys of the Bytown and Prescott Railway* (Toronto, 1853), pp. 37-8.

The Rail is to be of the "inverted T" pattern and to weigh sixty pounds to the yard. It is to rest on, and be firmly spiked to, cross-ties—which are to be laid thirty one inches apart from centre to centre. The ties to be of Tamarac or Cedar, seven by nine inches and seven and a half feet long. Wherever the road-bed can be ballasted previous to the Track being laid the ties will simply be bedded in the ballast—which will be of coarse sand or gravel—two feet in depth; but where, from the absence of such material, the Track will have to be laid at "Sub-grade" the ties will lie on two sills of Hemlock plank—ten by three inches. The position of these "subsills" beneath the tie corresponding to that of the rails above it. The Rails are to be secured, where they join, by cast Iron chairs, of about twenty pounds weight.

The width of Track for which my Estimates are intended is that known as the "Narrow Gauge,"—4 feet 8½ inches between the Rails.

The Subject of the Gauge,—one which has given rise to much discussion both on this continent and in Great Britain—is at present, I believe, engaging the attention of the Railway Committee of the House of Assembly.

The Commercial advantages to which the narrow gauge, especially as regards Canada, can lay just claim, so far out-weigh, in my judgment, the alleged—but not yet proven—mechanical superiority of a wider track, that I feel satisfied it will be adopted as the gauge for this Province—and certainly nothing short of Legislative enactment to the contrary could induce me to recommend any other for your Road.

THE CANADIAN GAUGE

H.Y. Hind, et al., *Eighty Years' Progress in British North America* (Toronto, 1863), pp. 253-5.

The gauge of the Canadian railways is five feet six inches, although this is not the exclusive one in use. The St. Lawrence and Champlain; Stanstead, Shefford, and Chambly; the Prescott and Ottawa; and the St. Lawrence and Industry roads, in all 147 miles, are of the American gauge of four feet eight and one-half inches.

Some energetic gentlemen in the city of Portland, ambitious of obtaining something of that railway aid which had contributed so much to the success of Boston, conceived the bold idea of tapping the St. Lawrence at Montreal by a railway over the route of the White Mountains, through the vast forests of Maine, New Hampshire, Vermont, and Canada. The distance is nearly three hundred miles, with an intervening summit of about one-third of a mile in height above the termini, the line having besides the frequent and severe curves and gradients usual to such a route. Having enlisted Montreal in the project, they took the precaution to bind the Canadians, under seals and penalties, to adopt the peculiar and exceptional gauge of five feet six inches; and an elaborate and sententious report was prepared, which proved to the unsophisticated Canadians, that by the simple adoption of this great improvement in gauge, Boston and New York would be distanced. When the Grand Trunk bill was passed, Lower Canada being in the ascendant, the Portland gauge was forced upon the province, the Lower Canadians being unanimous in its favor, because they had been led to believe that it would divert western trade from the New York route and send it down to Montreal.

The Great Western Railway, which was not restricted to a particular gauge by its charter, had decided on the American one, but was compelled to change it by threats from the government, both to withhold the guarantee, and also to charter a continuation of the Grand Trunk, on the Canadian gauge, from Toronto to Sarnia. To the latter intimation the company yielded, vainly supposing that they thereby acquired a right of protection from a competing line, especially as they formed a portion of the Trunk railway. But as soon as Grand Trunk became supreme in the provincial cabinet, the unfortunate Great Western had the disagreeable alternative of amalgamation or competition presented to them, and of the two evils they naturally chose the least. The Grand Trunk went to Sarnia, the guarantee following it, to the great benefit of the intervening counties, and of the contractors; and as it went to Sarnia, so it must also go to Rivière du Loup, in order that there might not be an undue preponderance of mileage in Upper Canada; and this is where the contractors and the counties got the better of the shareholders. The latter have, however, no cause of complaint against the province on this score, for, by their prospectus, they undertook to go to Sarnia, and not only to Rivière du Loup, but thirty-five miles beyond, besides constructing the Grand Junction, a work which has not been, and is not likely to be, commenced.

It has long since been demonstrated, that what is called the narrow or Stephenson gauge, of four feet eight and one-half inches, is wide enough for all practical purposes; and that any increased width is an unnecessary expense in first cost, and an increase of dead weight, and of resistance at curves in working.

In case of invasion, however, there would be this advantage in the Canadian gauge, that on all approaches—excepting that from Portland—the enemy must relay to his own gauge nearly the whole of our railways, before his own rolling stock could be used—unless indeed we should so blunder as to let ours fall into his hands.

CREDIT WHERE CREDIT IS DUE

The Canadian Engineer of the Victoria Bridge, by a Montrealer (Montreal, 1860), pp. 7-8.

PROVINCIAL PARLIAMENT
Legislative Council
Reported for the Montreal Gazette
MR. KEEFER AND THE VICTORIA BRIDGE

Quebec, May 4th, 1860

HON. MR. ALLAN said that before the orders of the day were called, there was a subject to which he desired to call the attention of the House and which he desired the Government to hear. The subject was one connected with the expected visit of His Royal Highness the Prince of Wales to this Province. There were peculiar circumstances connected with the claims which he was about to mention, which rendered the present an appropriate time to draw attention to them. The Railroads, Canals, and Bridges of the Province could compare favourably with those of any other part of the world. Among our Railroads stood prominent that noble road stretching from one end of the Province to the other, the Grand Trunk. This great road however would not be what it is were it not for the connecting link of the Victoria Bridge, the opening of which was the principal object of the approaching Royal visit. Many persons eminent in the sciences, among others of rank and wealth, would accompany His Royal Highness on that occasion. It was true that for many of our public works, the Province was indebted to British capitalists—and especially was the Victoria Bridge so indebted for their timely aid. It was also true that one of England's greatest engineers had given the sanction of his name to the Victoria Bridge. But it was also true that that great work was indebted in the first place for its conception to Canadian skill. To a Canadian engineer was due the first enunciation of the scheme of laying down the present bridge in the place where it now stands. In 1847, Hon. Mr. Young of Montreal and the Finance Minister obtained a survey of the St. Lawrence in order to see if it were possible to erect the bridge. The survey was carried on by an engineer of experience, but this gentleman reported that the scheme of bridging at Point St. Charles was impracticable. At the same time he reported the feasibility of building a bridge over Nun's Island. In 1851, Hon. Mr. Young obtained another survey of the St. Lawrence for the same purpose conducted by Mr. Thos. C. Keefer, an engineer whose talents were well known in the Province. The result of this survey was given in a report published immediately afterwards. In this report Mr. Keefer demonstrated the practicability of erecting the bridge in the place where it now stands. The plans on which the bridge should be constructed were also laid down. It was recommended that it should be a solid railroad bridge, that it should be erected high over navigation, instead of having draw-bridges in it. A certain distance was to intervene between the piers. It was to be for railroad traffic alone, and lastly, and what was of greatest importance, solid approaches should be constructed to diminish the waterway, instead of enlarging it as might have been proposed, and to guard against the crush of ice. It was worthy of remark that the present bridge was constructed precisely as this report recommended. (Hear.) In consequence of the changes which afterwards took place in the management of the G.T.R. the undertaking was transferred to English hands, and the work in question was constructed by other persons. The Bridge, however, was built in accordance with Mr. Keefer's report. (Hear.) All the leading principles set forth in his report were adopted by the English Engineers. This being the case, he (Mr. Allan) claimed that Mr. Keefer should not be overlooked; that the English Engineer should not receive the whole of that credit, an equal portion of which was due to the Canadian. He claimed for Mr. Keefer that his name should be engraved on the Victoria Bridge beside the names of Stephenson, Ross and the other engineers connected with that work, whose names were already cut upon it. He made this proposition with the greater confidence, because on many occasions the celebrated Stephenson had acknowledged Mr. Keefer's claims with regard to the originating of the work. (Hear.) The Grand Trunk Railroad Company had also acknowledged Mr. Keefer's claims, for they had been compelled to pay him a certain sum for his report, and also for his services; and not only had justice been done to Mr. Keefer by Stephenson and the Grand Trunk Company, but even in the American Railroad Journals credit was given to him—not once but on several occasions. (Hear.) Now in view of all this, Canada ought not to be backward in acknowledging the merits of one of her sons. He (Mr. Allan) laid these facts before the House in order that not only might honorable gentlemen be aware of the true features of the case, but also that they might go forth to the country. There was no doubt that anything that might come from the Government on the subject would have great weight; and he appealed to his Hon. friend the Commissioner of Crown Lands to lend his valuable aid to see justice done in the premises. He believed that it was just one of those subjects which he might venture to bring before the House—especially in view of the event which was soon to take place—the opening of the Bridge; and it was therefore that he ventured to trespass on the time of honorable gentlemen. (Hear.)

BUILDING THE VICTORIA BRIDGE: MACHINE FOR DREDGING PUDDLE CHAMBERS

THE RAILWAY AND WESTERN INDUSTRIAL DEVELOPMENT

'Preface', *Manufacturing and Business Opportunities in Western Canada along the Lines of the Canadian Pacific Railway* (Winnipeg, 1911).

The Industrial Department of the Canadian Pacific Railway, Western Lines, offers every facility at its command in the locating of Settlers, development of enterprises and manufactories at all points, and desiring to increase the industries along its lines invites particular attention to the superior advantages offered at numerous stations for additional manufacturing plants and to the many desirable business openings in this territory, as indicated in the following detailed information, showing population, industries located in each town, manufacturing and business opportunities, and such other information as would be of value to the prospective settler, manufacturer, or business man looking for a new location.

It will be of interest to note a few figures, which will show some of the enormous wealth producing powers of the Great Canadian West. For instance the Grain Crop of the four Western Provinces, according to the Official Return for the Fiscal Year ending 31st March, 1909, was 355,042,449 bushels, which included, wheat 144,700,231 bushels, oats 178,610,406 bushels, barley 28,841,108 bushels, flax 4,784,786 bushels, rye 68,891 bushels, peas 37,027 bushels. The wheat crop of the three Prairie Provinces in 1909 produced 119,744,655 bushels, from which it is estimated the Producer received from actual sales over $118,000,000, and still retained seed and feed requirements.

In addition to the grain crop, it was estimated at the end of 1909 that the potato crop would yield $3,831,000, turnips and other roots $800,000, hay and clover $2,377,000, cattle $7,277,000, hogs $1,784,000, sheep $167,851.53. The live stock values are at Winnipeg and do not include consumption at local points, which would necessarily very much increase the above figures. Dairying, creameries and poultry farming yield large revenues.

It is estimated by the Geological Survey Department of Canada that the total coal content of the three Provinces of Manitoba, Saskatchewan and Alberta, together with Eastern British Columbia, is 143,490,000,000 tons covering an approximate area of 22,506 square miles. In the above total it is estimated that the various classes of coal occur in the following proportions:

Anthracite - - - - - - - -	400,000,000 tons
Anthracite and semi-anthracite - -	860,000,000 "
Bituminous and semi-anthracite -	43,070,000,000 "

Coal and Lignite Coal - - - -	21,000,000,000	"
Lignite - - - - - - - - -	78,160,000,000	"
	143,490,000,000	tons

The total coal production of the Province of British Columbia for the year 1909 was 2,406,600 tons; Alberta 2,174,329 tons and Saskatchewan 208,902 tons.

In 1909 British Columbia produced in minerals alone $24,443,025, of which coal yielded $7,022,666, copper $5,918,522, gold $5,401,000, silver $1,239,270, lead $1,709,259, coke $1,552,218, and other materials such as marble, granite, etc., $1,600,000.

Lumber produced $12,000,000 in B.C., and this is an industry which is carried on extensively in the northern parts of the Provinces of Alberta, Saskatchewan and Manitoba as well as in Western Ontario. In the latter province, west of the Great Lakes, the development of iron and other minerals is now in active operation.

The fisheries of the Pacific Coast alone produce something like $8,000,000 annually and employ 12,000 men. In addition to this there is the celebrated White Fish, a product of the inland lakes.

There are many important industries awaiting increased development and amongst others may be mentioned the canning of fruit and vegetables. The production of all fruits and vegetables is growing rapidly, and there is already a large field for the establishment of fruit canneries.

The live stock industry lends itself to much greater development than is at present the case, and in this relation there is a wide field for meat packing and refrigeration.

One of the causes for the slow development of the silver-lead mining industry in the Kootenays, has been the difficulty in treating the zinc product of these ores; but a process of treatment has now been perfected, and it has been demonstrated that ore carrying large values in zinc can be treated so as to save all values and produce a handsome profit on the spelter. When a sufficient tonnage of this ore is produced (and large bodies of ore are known to exist) there will be opportunities for the construction of smelters for the treatment of zinc, which, being done in Canada, will ensure the entire Canadian market in spelter and its by-products, with equality in the export market with the zinc producers of the United States.

Natural gas, which is found in large quantities along the South Saskatchewan River, in Alberta and adjoining territories, is being used in the manufacture of common, pressed and fire brick, tiling, sewer pipe and other clay products, suitable clay being found in close proximity to the natural-gas fields. The great demand in the West for all clay products justifies increased development of this industry. Tests are now being made for the manufacture of gasoline from natural gas, which, if successful, will open up a new and profitable industry in the Province of Alberta and elsewhere.

Attention is directed to the unlimited supply of pulp wood, which exists in many parts of the Western Provinces. Large mills for manufacture of pulp paper are at present under construction on the Powell River, 75 miles from Vancouver on the Main Land, and other mills are already in existence, but this is a field which capital can extend almost without limit.

The water powers of the West (a very inadequate synopsis of which is printed at the end of this book) are enormous. Some of these powers are now in course of development and manufacturing of every description can be carried on here as economically (if not more so) as in any other part of the world.

The flax industry is only yet in its infancy, the production as shown above for the fiscal year 1909 being 4,784,786 bushels. There are several large linseed oil mills in the West at the present time, but additional mills will be necessary to keep pace with the increased demand for this product. No use is at present made of the flax straw, which is all destroyed. There is a large field for allied products such as flax tow (for upholstery purposes), linen wool from flax fibre, etc.

The resources of this Western Country are so immense, and at the present time have been developed to such a small extent, that it is impossible to more than touch the fringe of what can be understood to be a large and important subject. However, what has been said may be sufficient to further direct the attention of capital to the West, where a profitable undertaking can always be accomplished, when worked on an equitably economical basis.

Attention is directed to the new towns which will be opened up next spring and summer on the new branch lines running from Regina to Bulyea; Craven to Colonsay; Outlook to Kerrobert and Macklin; Carmangay to Aldersyde; Weyburn West and Irricana East as shown on pages 74, 88, 91, 92, 93, 100, 112.

The rapid expansion of our lines of railway and the new towns which are constantly being opened up naturally tends to increase the number of business openings that are available, and at the same time it may be that there are many opportunities shown in this book, which will be filled before it is in the hands of the public. Great care has been taken in compiling the information contained herein, the data having been collected from reliable sources.

The Industrial Department will at any time be glad to receive advice of errors which may have crept in, and at the same time, will gladly welcome suggestions which will tend to the increased usefulness of this publication.

We are in close touch with conditions throughout this immense territory and desire to do everything possible to aid in its development and growth, and will consider it a favor if you will write to the undersigned for any information you desire regarding the resources of this great and growing country. JOHN F. SWEETING,

Winnipeg, Manitoba. Industrial Agent.

CONTRACTS AND CONSTRUCTION ON THE TRANSCONTINENTAL

Edmund W. Bradwin, *The Bunkhouse Man: A Study of Work and Play in the Camps of Canada*, 1903-1914 (New York, Columbia University Press, 1928), pp. 41-7. Reprinted by permission.

The letting of a railway contract for the building of several hundred miles of grade on a new transcontinental is a matter of some import. In the case of the National Transcontinental Railway such matters were handled from Ottawa, the several contracts being let by the National Transcontinental Commission, representing the Dominion Government. As each section of the new road was ready for a start on construction, a call for tenders was published broadcast throughout the country, and the contract, ostensibly, was let in open competition. That, however, may often be a mere formality. It is obvious that only certain firms will engage in railway construction and the competition lies wholly within well-known groups. Between the dates of calling for tenders and the final letting of the work there is much struggle and stress, or plain wire-pulling, on the part of the men contending for the contract. The co-operation of interested firms is sought—steel plants, bridge works, and machinery outfitters of different kinds—for each of these have usually a favourite in the matter of the contract. Business directorates not uncommonly inter-lock in such allied industries. Every influence, political and otherwise, is used to secure the contract for a favourite commercial protegé.

The successful bidder, the company receiving the contract, is known on the line as the 'head-contractor.' It may represent a group of men, but usually such companies imply the dominant purpose of one man, and the contract throughout its length is designated locally by the name of the head-contractor.

Once obtained, a railway contract is, in many ways, a sinecure. There are big chances of very material profits during the probable six years of tenure. Indeed, when the contract thus secured extends for hundreds of miles through the hinterland, away from regularly organized districts, the head-contractor has in his new field something of the power of a satrap. He exercises much influence and authority in his demesne. In fact the letting of one of the larger contracts on the National Transcontinental Railway may not unreasonably have been compared to the appointment of a governor, in the historic days, to one of the lesser provinces of Imperial Rome. Some phases of tax farming when the Empire laid tribute, whether in the cities of Numidia or in the villages of Pannonia, were not wholly dissociated from the exactions in pay that foreign-born workers encountered, in a later time, on isolated railway contracts in Canada.

There is an idea prevalent among nine lay persons out of ten that the large railway contractor is at an immense outlay; that the immediate plant which he puts on a work costs huge amounts; that there are always attendant risks of grave losses, and that in the face of all these, he should be amply rewarded for his pluck and business enterprise. This supposition is sometimes right, but it may, also, be far astray. While a contractor has often started work with a valuable plant, yet quite as frequently he has begun work with a very indifferent outfit. It is not uncommon on railway construction for the contract to make the man and his plant too.

Most railway contractors have the faculty of getting loyal service from their immediate assistants. The right men are well paid. From the juniors, among the well-housed clerical staff, to the capable managers and super-intendents, the head-contractor has, at his service, a splendid body of trained men. Many of these have followed his fortunes for years, and their ability insures the efficient conduct of his affairs during his continued absence from the line.

The head-contractor, once the contract is secured, hastens to sub-let the different works on the first eighty or one hundred miles, which, so far, only stretches on paper along the location-line already run by the engineers. The cutting of the right-of-way is first sub-let. This means cutting, clearing, and sometimes burning a swath sixty-six feet wide through the woods following the staked centre posts of the engineers. The pile-driving, the trestle work, and some rock cuts will then be let, and a few large buildings erected which later serve as the warehouses and offices of the headquarters camp.

There are numerous contracts let for particular works; one man con-tracts to do the concrete work called for in the specifications; another will take the contract of cutting railway ties; the medical system and the mail route will, also, be allotted. Finally, ten or more sub-contractors will receive sections of the road which they undertake to complete up to grade level. All these different works are sub-let on a good margin from the price originally granted the head-contractor, whose skill in sub-letting should net him substantial gains on his contract.

The secondary stage of construction includes the laying of steel, bal-lasting with lifts of gravel and bringing the grade to a finished condition. This is a slow and expensive process, calling for considerable capital ex-penditure to provide the necessary machine equipment and rolling stock.

Work in this stage of construction is not sub-let, being usually performed by the head-contractor himself.

The awarding of a railway contract presupposes, of course, that the preliminary work has already been completed by the engineers. These men, working in groups, and often under primitive conditions, run the try-lines and procure the needed information that determines the final location of the road. It is from the blueprints, supplied originally from engineers in the field, that a work is divided into sections, and then publicly let for contract.

Along the Transcontinental the engineers were the outposts of the Railway Commission. Scattered in residencies at ten-mile intervals, they checked up the contractors, according to required specifications, as the work progressed. They were the local observers for the Government, as well as technical advisers to the Commission, and communications pertaining to the conduct of the work passed weekly between the district engineers and the authorities at Ottawa.

How does the sub-contractor form a basis for the minimum price he will accept for his services? The sub-contractor has access, at the office of the head-contractor, to blueprints of the line which have been supplied in duplicate by the engineers. These show in detail the profile of the road, the mud cuts, the fills, the trestles, the rock work, the ditching, and all other extras required on the whole contract. From these he selects the ten-mile section which appeals most to one of his experience, taking into consideration as well the equipment he has at his disposal. The sub-contractor is further required to sign contracts for the work he undertakes; his plant and equipment, as well as his supplies, are all under lien to the head-contractor for the due performance of the work. He undertakes, also, to finish his contract in a specified time.

From the details supplied at the office of the head-contractor the sub-contractor has a good idea of the number of yards of work to be done on this ten-mile stretch—the extent of the clay excavation and the fills and the total amount of rock to be moved. From these figures he can estimate fairly well the number of men he will need, and he knows, too, quite accurately what supplies to store in his warehouse sufficient to complete his work.

All supplies for each of the sub-contractors are furnished at the headquarters camp. Thus, when outfitted, the sub-contractor is often under obligations to the head-contractor for many thousands of dollars; his van goods, his cookery supplies, his feed, his machine parts, have all been advanced him from the huge stores at headquarters camp. Even the freighting may be handled by the head-contractor and a further indebtedness be thus incurred.

Having arranged for a piece of new work the sub-contractor proceeds at once to erect camp buildings at a suitable point on his location somewhere ahead of the steel. The winter months are largely spent in preparation of the work on his contract which will commence in the spring break-up. The sub-contractor will usually have a small plant, including steel rails of light weight, a donkey engine or two, several horses, some carts, a blacksmith outfit, and considerable lesser equipment, probably, from a former work.

To tote supplies is a serious task. If the camp of the sub-contractor is thirty miles ahead of the steel it will mean sometimes a two or three-day trip, for rough roads have to be hastily constructed, the hills avoided and the swamps and muskegs edged with corduroy. The frequent detours and the many sudden twists add greatly to the length of the haul, for mud at times half envelopes the heavy wheels. Not five hundred pounds can be toted under such conditions, even with a four-horse team. What wonder that sharp frosts, with plenty of snow and ice, are welcomed? With sleigh and team a two-ton load may be taken fifteen miles in a day, but once the break-up is at hand trouble again besets the teamster on every side.

Few scenes in camps surpass in interest the busy hauling of supplies necessary for construction. Various kinds are forwarded—pork, smoked meats, flour, canned goods of all descriptions, dried fruits, raisins, prunes, apricots, and beans for the cookery; hay in bales and oats for the stables; dynamite for the powder cellar; mackinaws, boots, rubbers, socks, shirts, shoepacks, stationery, painkiller, mosquito-oil, snuff and tobacco for the van or office store. The blacksmith shop, too, will early be requisitioned for service, so it is rigged with anvil, sledges, big link chains, steel rods for drills, dump carts in parts, and spares of many kinds. Stores of whatever sort are the sinews for the construction season, and their due selection is a matter of deep concern to any sub-contractor.

Transport must usually be performed during weeks in the depths of winter, and weather then in northern parts must be wooed in its variable moods. Distance, too, and the uncertainty of the roads tend toward irregularity that disrupts the best-laid plans. So, while the sleighing is good, the tote-teams are hustled. The shouts of the teamsters are heard late and early throughout the short winter days, and the frosted snow crunches with the heavy hoof as loaded teams on the sleigh-haul travel with an early start, while yet Arcturus hangs big in the eastern sky.

True, these be but routine tasks, yet in them lies the tinge of romance. We are prone in Canada to ignore the heroism of men such as these in obscure places. The youth of the Dominion know more of the storied march of Hannibal or the Crossing of the Alps than of the accomplishments of men on frontier works.

The written pages of textbooks much in use cease not to depict how men of another land and in a former time, upon conquest bent, encountered in their onward march the ice of the steeps and snows of the mountain passes. Combated by inclement weather, they are urged ever into sustained effort by the vision of fertile valleys beyond, and loot in recompence from opulent towns on the rich plains of Piedmont. But during long weeks of the winter months amid scenes of rocks and wooded isolation, where temperatures are lower than soldiers would endure, men of the camps in lightsome mood go daily forth in the performance of their wonted tasks, turning out often long before daylight with the thermometer registering 40° below zero.

Here in passing let me acknowledge the tangible accomplishments of the railway contractor himself. Plans and schemes first visualized by engineers, have been made real by his practical force and genius. In a land such as Canada, with its great natural obstacles, and in many portions still a wilderness but scantily peopled, these men of action, undaunted by barriers, have tackled undertakings the performance of which in an earlier age would have been deemed heroic. Canada can well honour the vision and daring of her railway builders. Their acts and deeds, often pursued with audacity and purpose and in the face of great difficulties, would not demean the campaign of a marshal.

A BRIDGE TO THE FUTURE

Charles Legge, *A Glance at the Victoria Bridge and the Men Who Built It* (Montreal, 1860), pp. 152-3.

ON Saturday, the 17th day of December [1859], invitations were issued by Mr. Hodges to a large number of citizens of Montreal to attend an informal opening of the bridge for general traffic, to which about one thousand ladies and gentlemen responded.

The excursion train containing this great number of people, was drawn by two engines and occupied 7½ minutes in passing through the tubes; high speed under the circumstances not being necessary. After proceeding six or seven miles down the line, the train returned, and, on emerging from the bridge on the Montreal end, the excursionists left the cars and partook of a champagne dejeuner on the north abutment, provided by the host; when the usual amount of speechifying took place.

On the following Monday the bridge was handed over to the Company, and has ever since been in use.

We have now completed a very imperfect sketch of this great undertaking, from the time the project was first launched into existence, by the Hon. John Young, up to the period when the embodiment of the idea in stone and iron enabled a thousand souls to be wafted with the speed of the wind across the great river, high above its conflicting and angry ele-

ments, at a time also when all communication for freight purposes with the south side of the river was interrupted, and even for passengers to cross in canoes during the day was a work of danger and extreme suffering from exposure and cold, when, by the means now in use, during the silent watches of the night when the citizens of Montreal were buried in repose, thousands of tons of freight glided swiftly and silently over the running ice, and, by the great connecting link brought into use, caused a pulsation to be felt in all the veins and arteries of commerce throughout the land.

In speaking of its future success, who can estimate it, being intimately connected with the prosperity of Canada! We have endeavoured to sketch this, in dwelling on the country's rapid progress in material wealth, during the past few years, and may well form sanguine anticipations of its future; indeed, but few minds are capable of estimating the enormous increase of population and wealth yet to be in our Western World, when Canada will extend to the confines of the Pacific Ocean and be covered with a net work of railways all converging to this point of crossing the St Lawrence. Then, and not till then, must be left—to the yet unborn millions,—the rendering of the verdicts as to the full measure of success which will attend the Victoria Bridge.

A few months more and the Prince of Wales will behold for the first time, our noble Province, the brightest jewel in his future diadem; and as he gazes on the wondrous structure which is destined to carry the name of his revered parent and sovereign down to the latest time, may we not anticipate a thrill of pride and joy in the contemplation of the splendid future yet in store for his Western Empire; and will not thousands unite with him in wishing God-speed to the march of this young Northern Giant in the van of enterprise, liberty and happiness on the western continent, emulating the noble example of its mother in the eastern world!

ELECTRIC COMMUNICATION

A PROPOSED TELEGRAPH SYSTEM IN NEW BRUNSWICK

Report and Estimate Concerning an Electro-Magnetic Telegraph Between Fredericton and St John (Fredericton, 1847), pp. 1-3.

Fredericton, 25th January, 1847.

Sir,—At the desire of Your Excellency we have prepared a short Report upon a line of Telegraphic communication between Fredericton and St. John.

It has been drawn up with as much care as the novelty of the subject, and the means of judging at our command have allowed, and, in submitting it, we desire to say that it will always be our anxious wish to assist Your Excellency in forwarding this most important and laudable undertaking.

A revolution in the Telegraphic system has been recently effected by the aid of a force called Electro-Magnetism, and this application of the force in question, seems to be fraught with consequences not less important to mankind than those which have resulted from the application of steam to the purposes of locomotion.

The Electro-Magnetic Telegraph can be made to convey intelligence in few or in many words, on matters of trivial or of vital importance, openly or with secrecy, for one or for one thousand miles, by night or by day, in winter or summer, at a cost not greater than is incurred by the present Post Office system, and with a velocity which is only comparable to that of a thought or a sensation, or to a ray of light, or a flash of lightning.

Not only are all these marvellous effects asserted to be possible, but they have been demonstrated, and are capable of being realized wherever it is thought worth while to try.

The value of such a mode of transmitting intelligence cannot be overestimated, and we feel confident that, within a very few years, the adoption of this system will become general in all civilized countries. The thoughts, the feelings, and the wishes of one man will be conveyed to another, one hundred miles off, as fast as they can be uttered or intelligibly expressed to himself, or to his nearest neighbour, and we will at length have acquired a power over time and space as great as that which we have already acquired over matter.

As these remarks are based upon a consideration of what has been already achieved and done by means of the Electro-Magnetic Telegraph, it remains still to determine whether the importance of the communications between any two given places is sufficient to justify the outlay required to secure the advantages of such rapid transmission.

Although we do not feel that it is our province to decide upon the importance of the communications now going on between the Seat of Government and the chief seat of Commerce in New Brunswick, yet we cannot refrain from stating our decided conviction that, if the present communications are not of sufficient importance, the mere fact of the establishment of an Electro-Magnetic Telegraph would soon make them so.

These considerations are entirely apart from any that might attach to a line of Railway from St. John to Fredericton, or to the connection of our Telegraphic Circuit with others from Quebec to Fredericton, or from St.

John to Halifax; we speak at present in favor of a line between this place and St. John, and of that line as being worthy of immediate adoption.

By the estimate which we have attempted to make, the cost of construction and maintenance for the first year would not much exceed five thousand pounds currency, and the permanent charges would not exceed one thousand pounds a-year, so that we may be justified in saying that the outlay is not great in comparison of the public advantages which would result from its establishment.

But it is not all expenditure: there is a certainty of considerable returns, at both termini, in the course of every year. If these exceeded the interest on the money expended, it might fairly be asked whether, in view of the responsibility connected therewith, the Government was not entitled to secure and maintain the Telegraph as a source of Provincial Revenue; or, supposing that the returns did not cover the interest on the investment, whether the Government ought not to assume the loss, in consideration of the public benefit derived therefrom. It is to be doubted, after all, whether private parties would be likely to take up an enterprise of so novel a character; whether they could give it the same title to public confidence; or whether they could, so efficiently as the Government, protect it against wanton or malicious injury.

There has been considerable difficulty in preparing the estimate herewith annexed, and there are several of the rates which we state with great diffidence; yet, on the whole, we apprehend that the general charge will be found adequate to meet the several heads of expenditure.

It will be necessary to make some further explanatory remarks upon the various charges, which, it will be seen, refer—1st, to the apparatus and the wires; 2nd, to the posts which sustain the wires; and, lastly, to the salaries and office expenditure.

The system which we advise for adoption in New Brunswick is that of Professor Morse, of New York. His method is not only cheaper than all the others, but likewise excels them in the important peculiarity which it offers of *registering upon paper* all Telegraphic communications.

It would be only fair to Professor Morse to ascertain how far the adoption of his system in this country, without reference to him, would prejudice his rights. At all events, we are not now prepared to recommend any system which does not *register upon paper* the Telegraphic dispatch.

We suggest that a double circuit should be established in the first instance, and that this be attempted with two wires only, the earth being, by a peculiar arrangement, rendered available in both circuits. If a third wire, or other circuits, were found to be necessary, they could be added at any time, and at an outlay for the wire only.

The estimate has been made out for a line of 65 miles, which, we believe, is the length of the route to St. John, by the valley of the Nerepis River; and we have preferred the present highway to any other line, because it is already well cleared of trees, and, therefore, less likely to endanger the wires and posts by "windfalls," &c. A shorter line through the woods might, no doubt, be found; but, in such a rough country, and in such a tempestuous climate, it would be liable to accidents which would be always difficult to detect, and almost impossible speedily to repair. On the present highway the wires would always be under inspection, and there would be no difficulty in proceeding with any occasional repairs.

By the route proposed, the wires would keep the right bank of the River St. John as far as the Falls, where nature has very greatly favoured their transmission across the River to the City of St. John.

We suggest that posts, eight inches square below, six inches square above, and about twenty feet long, with a board capping (to prevent the lodgment of water or ice about the wires) and strongly braced, and loaded with two or three tons of stone, should be set upon the ground, at distances not exceeding 200 feet apart, where the ground is favorable for sinking. The posts might be set in the ground, but it would be necessary to enter them to the depth of five or six feet, a cross sill having been previously fixed at their lower extremity, to prevent the disturbing action of the frozen soil upon them.

Where the posts are thus sunk, we conceive that a considerable saving might be effected in the estimated charges for scantling, for framing, and for loading with stones.

Whatever method of securing the posts is adopted, it must never be forgotten that their stability and sufficiency are of paramount importance.

It would seem, at first sight, that metallic tubes placed under ground would be safer and better conductors of the wires; but the expense of trenching, and the difficulty of seeing and remedying defects, forbid their adoption in the present case.

If the Telegraph was adopted by Government, and put under the control of the Post Office authorities, we imagine that the requisite accommodation for the apparatus might readily be found in their offices, at the respective termini; and the charges for transmission of correspondence and intelligence need not exceed the average rate under the present method.

The salary of the Chief Superintendent of construction ought not to be less than £500.

His familiarity with all the chemical and mechanical details must be undoubted; while his personal presence on the line would be continually required, and no portion of the work could be completed without his most thorough supervision and warranty. The above charge need not, however, become a permanent one, although those for the Clerks and Messengers undoubtedly would remain. The Clerks would have to acquire a familiarity not only with the Telegraphic characters, but also with the details of the galvanic battery and register.

The estimated average cost per mile of this line is considerably greater than that which has been adopted as the ground of action elsewhere; but it does not at present seem possible to establish a double circuit in this Province at any thing so low as £41 per mile.

All which is most respectfully submitted by Your Excellency's most obedient and humble servants,

J. ROBB, M.D.,

J. B. TOLDERVY, M.D.

To His Excellency Sir Wm. M. G. Colebrooke, K.H.,
    Lieutenant Governor, &c., &c.

MAINTAINING A WESTERN TELEGRAPH

J.S. Macdonald, 'The Dominion Telegraph', *Canadian North West Historical Publications*, vol. 1 (Saskatchewan, 1930), pp. 24-5, 42-3.

During the years 1879-80 very few settlers came into the country, and but little telegraph business was transacted, the uncertainty of communication and the high tariff being added deterrents. The writer arrived in Battleford in October, 1880 and at once took charge of the Battleford office as chief operator. . . .

From the beginning much trouble was experienced in the attempt to maintain the line in a working condition, especially on the eastern section. The poles were poplar, a wood altogether unsuitable; the wire was much heavier than that ordinarily used for telegraph purposes. On the plains, buffalo, using the poles as scratching posts, overturned numbers of them, while the wire running through uncut, leafy groves lost so much current in wet weather that at such times it was impossible to telegraph any considerable distance. With linemen 100 miles or further apart, their only conveyance a buckboard with a single horse over a trail without bridges and at times impassable, it was practically impossible to maintain continuous operation. In Spring and Autumn, prairie fires were the chief source of trouble. A fire starting in the southern portion of the country met no barrier until it reached the South Saskatchewan River and unless extinguished by rain, might burn over a vast area destroying great numbers of poles as it progressed. Then, as later, the wire worked well and without interruption from the first frosts of Autumn until the coming of Spring. The position of lineman during these years was a particularly trying one. Far from trading posts or any source of supply, there was but little variety of food, and strangely enough few of the men had shotguns despite the abundance of game. A few cases of scurvy developed, the victims coming to Battleford in the Spring for treatment. Often, too, provisions would give out or be spoiled because of rain coming through tent or shack while the occupant was absent repairing the line. . . .

During the years 1878 to 1884 numerous parties of surveyors were engaged in running meridian, base and township lines, preparatory to dividing the land into sections and quarter sections. Being the capital and possessing a telegraph office, Battleford was a gathering point for the heads of these parties when it became necessary for them to communicate with their Department at Ottawa. With a mail but once in three weeks, communication by letter was out of the question. On one occasion, in 1879, while waiting for the line to be repaired, Mr. Wilkins, c.e., erected a sun dial in front of the telegraph office. It was a most ingenious affair consisting of four arms so graduated that each threw a shadow on the other, showing the time at intervals of five minutes. It remained in working order for several seasons during which it was the standard for time the country over, Battleford office giving the time over the wire to the various points on the line. The first meteorological reports were telegraphed from Battleford in the Summer of 1879. . . .

Late one evening [during the Second Riel Rebellion] a courier brought from headquarters a number of important telegraphs, most of which contained instructions to various Commanding Officers regarding the movement of troops. I had barely started sending these when the wire ceased working. From the fact that a slight current came through, I knew that the wire was on the ground. By five o'clock the following morning, the lineman and I were on our way eastward, taking the despatches with us. After some 20 miles we came upon the wire lying on the ground for a distance of about 100 yards. To effect a circuit, it was necessary to find a moist place in which to ground the wire, but although we dug some distance we could obtain no sign of dampness. In this dilemma I, being bookish, remembered Gulliver's action at a critical time, and repeating the incident to Joe, suggested that he follow Gulliver's example. But Joe's sense of decorum was outraged, and he vehemently protested that he had not come from Montreal and risked his life a hundred times among savages to undertake tasks such as this. Then I told him that I would return in five minutes and if when I returned the wire was not working, he should consider himself discharged, and that he would have to get back to Montreal as best he could—which, of course, was sheer bluff. But, on my return, the wire was working clearly, and the "ground" held long enough for me to get the despatches through to their destinations.

RAILROADS AND NORTHERN EXPLOITATION

C. Baillargé, *La Baie d'Hudson. Exploitation proposée de ses ressources de terre et de mer. Nouvelle Colonie. Chemin de fer pour s'y rendre* (Jolliette, P.Q., 1895), pp. 18-19, 41-2.

Let us then no longer let the inhabitants of the United States steal the march on us, after they have left us behind in the exploitation of the resources of an interior sea lying entirely within Canada, and which is at least as much within the jurisdiction of the province of Quebec as it is in that of Ontario, for the boundary line between the two provinces bifurcates the bay, and whose exploitation should belong more to Quebec than to Ontario, which is much richer than Quebec in all respects and has no need of this additional source of profits while Quebec has great need of them.

The first step to be taken will be for the local government, through the intermediary of the Federal government, to put an end to the exploitation of the fisheries and other resources of Hudson Bay by our neighbours the Americans who do not pay and who have never paid a single penny to Canada for almost fifty years during which they have sailed in our waters without any right.

Let it be remembered that, a few years ago, the whale fishery was a very important industry in the Gulf of St. Lawrence, where not less than ten ships were employed. But after the Americans acquired the right to fish in these waters, in a short time they completely destroyed the fishing, chasing the fish from the gulf by the same means that they employed to catch them: explosive bombs and other disreputable means.

Lieutenant Gordon says: "In spite of the fact that this industry (the whale fishery in Hudson Bay) is still of comparatively little importance, I am persuaded that, given the considerable profits that have been realized by those who have been engaged in it, the facilities of its extension, and the constantly increasing attention that is now being given to the resources of the region of Hudson Bay, there is no doubt that a greater number of vessels will be drawn there before long. I am certain," he continues, "that there are a large number of whales in these waters, because of the fact that they were constantly seen during the voyage of the *Neptune* in the bay, and because, so far as I know, none of those engaged in the fishing have returned without a good cargo." The barque *George and Mary*, Capt. Fisher, of Connecticut, wintered on Marble Island during the last season, was free of the ice on the seventh of June last and succeeded in taking three whales in Hudson Bay even before reaching the *Welcome*; and if one considers that from five to six of these mammals would complete its cargo, it is easy to see that this fishery is far from declining. For the Hudson Bay Company it is the dolphin fishery that is the most extensive. The blubber of these mammals weighs from 250 to 400 pounds and produces an abundance of the best quality oil. . . .

The French, gentlemen, did not know anything about their country, and the Prussian taught them. We do not know anything about ours. Let us not wait until the enemy comes to confront us with our ignorance. Let us recall that Sir Edmund Head has called us "the inferior race." It is time to see if we will confirm or give the lie to his words. Let us make haste, I have told you; already Upper Canada, Ontario, has begun a railway which, by way of Lake Nipissing and Parry Sound reaches from Georgian Bay to Lake Huron, through Temiscaming and Abittibi, must reach James Bay at Moose Factory in 1894, in route for the fisheries of Hudson's Bay.

It is no further for us to get there than for them, or a few more miles via Lake St. Jean, to touch in passing Mistassini and from there to the south-east angle of Rupert's House Bay where the river of the same name discharges its waters and which is 120 miles from the south-west angle of the same bay where the other route of our Ontario brothers will end.

A little effort, gentlemen, the people are sovereign, it is they who must impose their wills upon their deputies in parliament who are there to make them known. Concessions have already been granted, several years ago, to the promoters of two railroads which, from Winnipeg and Nipissing must reach James Bay, and this on behalf of the two governments, federal and local, and as much in money as in land.

I have already said that Ontario is richer than we are, more prosperous and has less need than we to seek its fortune elsewhere. It is up to you to say if we are any longer to continue to expatriate ourselves like this every year and as thousands have already permanently done, to go work the mud of our neighbors to make bricks for them, to carry them on our shoulders, to scrub their boots, in a word, to serve them as domestics while they, proud enough of their intelligence to put it to better use, brush past us to fish in our waters and steal our patrimony from us.

Let us work, gentlemen. God has said to pray, that is true, but not at all that kind of contemplative prayer which, like faith, amounts to nothing without works. God has said: take care of yourself and I will help you; therefore, what he wants is the prayer of work, the most effective of all. At a university meeting of the Académie St-Denis, the other day, Monseigneur Paquet said: work does not leave any time for disreputable things. Yes, God has said: "you will win your life by the sweat of your brow." My own prayer is an eighteen-hour a day one. I give fourteen hours a day to my civic duties, the other four make up for it if I can spend them writing these things to you, and at coming to tell them to you.

ELECTRICITY FOR TRANSPORTATION

T. C. Keefer, 'Presidential Address', *Transactions of the Royal Society of Canada*, vol. II, (1899), 14-15.

The substitution of electricity for steam, as the motive power for railways, is regarded as inevitable sooner or later on many roads. It has already taken place as regards suburban railways, notably in the case of the Charlevoix road and Hull and Alymer railway, where water is doing the work which has heretofore been done by coal. The chief obstacles to an early change on the larger roads are the hundreds of millions invested in locomotives, and the very large outlay required to equip existing steam roads with the electric system. The principal inducement would be the passenger service, owing to the increased speed possible,—it being confidently stated that, with electricity, a speed considerably over one hundred miles per hour could be attained. Moreover there would be entire abolition of the poisonous smoke which drops upon the Pullman in preference to any coach ahead of it.

While the conversion of trunk lines would be attended with a cost which is for the present prohibitory, this objection does not apply to new lines which may be worked independently, or in connection with electric ones. When the time arrives for such railways, water power will have a field of usefulness of which we can at present form little conception. Water wheels and wires would displace the coal docks, the coal laden vessels, the huge coal yards, and the trains required for distributing their contents over hundreds of miles of lines.

An interior line connecting Lake St. John, on the Saguenay, with Lake Temiscamingue, on the Ottawa, which could ultimately be extended, via Missanabi, Nepigon, and Lac Seul to the Saskatchewan, would be a colonization road—removed from the frontier—one which could be worked possibly altogether by water power, and would open a virgin tract in which electro-chemical and electro-metallurgical industries might arise, as well as those connected with the products of the forests and the mine.

Transportation, next to production, is the most important commercial question to a country of vast distances, and low priced products affording great tonnage such as we produce, and for which we have expended hundreds of millions in canals and railways, harbours, lighthouses and steamers,—a sum disproportioned to our realized wealth, as it certainly is to our population. But, *noblesse oblige*, we possess a vast estate, are compelled to develop it—and await results.

4 | The Victorian Dream: Technology and Progress

Canadians in the Victorian era were convinced they lived in an age of unparalleled progress. The past was a long and dark chapter of bloodshed, ignorance, superstition, and poverty. But science, and especially science applied to benefit the human condition, had transformed the world. When they talked of science, the Victorians metaphorically employed a biographical amalgam of Galileo, Bacon, Newton, Watt, and sometimes Benjamin Franklin—mixing science and technology with little concern for any distinctions between the two. In the popular mind there was none; Newton's laws and Liebig's scientific agriculture were equally the triumphs of rationality.

It was a matter of some embarrassment for nineteenth-century Canadians that the country had not yet produced in the arts or sciences any figures of distinction comparable to those mentioned above. According to John B. Robinson, the lack was explainable in terms of the compelling needs of a frontier society, but it still indicated an intellectual poverty that called for correction. The most obvious solution was to create institutions and publications for the diffusion of knowledge, particularly in science and its applications.

The mechanics' institute, a type of organization begun in Great Britain to provide useful knowledge for working men, lent itself easily to Canadian needs, and a great many were established throughout the country. Mechanics' institutes argued for the pursuit of science from several positions: the study of nature led to a better appreciation of God's work; knowledge was profitable; the improvement of the lower ranks improved the rest of society. New publications had similarly to justify themselves and, like the *Canadian Journal*, they often did so in terms of 'those scientific changes and discoveries which are in progress throughout the world'.

Founders of societies and of periodicals shared the sense that the advanced nations of the world were engaged in a race. The agricultural and industrial exhibitions of the nineteenth century were organized with the same idea in mind. As Charles Day claimed in his address at the Montreal industrial exhibition in 1850, the occasion reflected a new level in the advancement of civilization. Instead of the bloody competitions of the past, exhibitions were designed to stimulate a friendly rivalry. After England's 1851 Crystal Palace Exhibition, all industrial fairs served as international yardsticks against which national progress could be gauged. The Crystal Palace also made people aware of national 'styles' in industry, and incidentally gave Canada a somewhat picturesque reputation that subsequent displays tried hard to live down. Whether or not to spend the effort and money to send a national display was sometimes debated, as in the case of the American Centennial Exhibition. But afterwards even awkward compliments were welcome.

Progress was moral as well as material. Railroads had a civilizing influence. They brought people into better communication with each other and increased toleration. Science and industry were the arts of peace. That theme was echoed at industrial exhibitions throughout the country. The factory demonstrated the conquest of poverty. Steam power and the mechanization of productive processes suggested that for the first time in history, the mass of people would also have leisure to enjoy their new wealth.

Inevitably, notions of progress stimulated nationalism. To share in an age of advancement required self-awareness. The initial issue of *Canada Farmer*, for instance, argued the importance of scientific agriculture in terms of patriotism and the ability to compete in an unprotected international marketplace. For French-speaking Canadians, too, technical progress was closely connected with ideas of cultural identity, although not necessarily in a positive way. To some, mechanization and materialism threatened traditional values, and they framed new catechisms to teach the old virtues. But Arthur Buies, a journalist who had studied abroad and marched with Garibaldi in 1860, returned home with different ideas. He argued that survival in an industrial age demanded a renovation of Quebec's educational system.

For Canadians, the dream of progress was an especially powerful image. They could see the changes of a single generation. For them, the juxtaposition of savage and civilized, a popular Victorian contrast, was more than drawing-room conversation. Even devices as simple as a cream separator were singled out to illustrate the march of advancement. Technical accomplishment became a symbol of Canadian progress toward economic prosperity, political freedom, and social well-being.

INSTITUTIONS FOR ADVANCEMENT

A RATIONALE FOR THE PAST

'The President's Address', *The Canadian Journal*, vol. II, (1853-4), 143-4.

Two generations have passed away since a civilized people began to occupy Upper Canada;—our own Journal, in a late article full of interesting matter, informs us that for twenty years of that time we have had a population over 300,000—for ten years exceeding 500,000, and we may be certain that at present our numbers are beyond a million.—Upon the first impression it would seem, on a comparison with other countries, that, under such circumstances and in all this time, some native Canadian might have been expected to start from the canvas more distinctly than any has done;—that some one gifted with peculiar powers would have gained for himself a name likely to endure, and would have conferred celebrity upon the country of his birth, by some striking discovery in art or science, or at least by a proficiency in some liberal pursuit, that would have attracted general attention, and established even abroad a deference to his name as an authority.

We might refer to some other countries, particularly in the North of Europe, where, in communities not so populous, there have, from time to time, arisen men so distinguished by the gifts of genius, and by the use they made of them, that their names have been handed down from age to age, and are regarded now with a veneration scarcely diminished by the splendid modern discoveries which have disproved some of their theories, and rendered useless many of their inventions.

But we must consider, on the other hand, that these men have generally flourished in older communities than ours; that the discoveries made, and the distinction obtained by many of them, were the fruits of a "learned leisure," which in Upper Canada hitherto scarcely any have enjoyed; and, besides, that these shining lights have commonly appeared at distant intervals in the course of centuries, with larger spaces of time perhaps between them than would cover our whole history as a people.

The more rapid and general spread of knowledge, too, has had the effect in our time of placing educated men upon more equal ground in regard to their attainments; so that a striking elevation is not so easily gained. And there has been another more formidable impediment peculiar to our condition as a new country, for Upper Canada may still be called such, though it is fast losing any claim to particular allowance upon that score—I refer here to the fact that among the million who now inhabit this upper portion of the Province, even those who came hither in mature years from other countries, with minds highly cultivated, have, with very few exceptions, been unavoidably engaged like the multitude around them, in the anxious labor of some profession or employment, by which their daily subsistence was to be earned. Those born in the country have had their time and their thoughts equally engaged by efforts to gain for themselves a competency which few have had the fortune to inherit from their fathers. And so it has happened, (though I think not entirely so) that Upper Canada, if I may assert this without seeming to disparage any just claim to excellence, and distinction, can not yet be pointed to as the birth place of any who have won for themselves the celebrity that waits on genius successfully cultivated, nor perhaps even of any who have greatly signalized themselves by an enthusiastic devotion to art or science. When I hesitate to say that we can wholly and clearly ascribe this want, which I think we must acknowledge, to the influence of any or all of the causes that I have mentioned, it is because I can not forget that in other countries we do see, every now and then, starting up, as if to relieve the monotony of life, poets, philosophers, mathematicians, mechanics, linguists, artists, whose very existence has seemed bound up in some one particular pursuit, who, under every disadvantage of position—oppressed by want—disheartened at times by neglect—unaided by instruction, and having access to no advantages which may not be enjoyed here, have worked their way to eminence, and have made their names like household words, likely to endure to the end of time—men

> Whose honors with increase of ages grow
> As streams roll down, enlarging as they flow.

I suppose after all, the solution is that we must look upon these prodigies as the gifts of GOD vouchsafed to a Country when he thinks fit; and that in the order of Providence, the day of Upper Canada has not yet come—for we must say of genius, as the Poet has said of taste,—

> —This nor gems, nor stores of gold
> Nor purple state, nor *culture* can bestow,
> But God alone, when first His active hand
> Imprints the secret bias of the soul.

It will not, however, I trust be long before Canada will have her sons whom future generations will have a pride in remembering, for as respects her political condition, and the public provision made for instruction, such is her actual state, and such the prospects of the future which are opening upon us, that we can scarcely name a country of which it can be said that those who are to be born in it will have fairer opportunity and freer scope, for the cultivation and use of their intellectual faculties.

KNOWLEDGE, POWER, AND GODLINESS

J. Dallas, *A Lecture on the Aims and Usefulness of Mechanics' Institutes* (Barrie, 1865), pp. 10-11.

To the young most especially are the objects and purposes of Mechanics' Institutes valuable. In them particularly may a foundation be laid for a life distinguished for that devotion to Science, that thirst for knowledge, and that honorable desire to be useful to the world, which has, in so many instances, conferred great and lasting benefit on society.

There is however one danger, not to be lost sight of, and that is a tendency to pride and vanity, which ought never to be the case with the Student of Philosophy. If he acquires more knowledge than falls to the lot of his fellow men, he is brought so much more into an acquaintance with the works of his Creator, and this ought to teach him humility. Is there a more illustrious name in the annals of Science than that of Newton? And yet Newton was remarkable for nothing more than for modesty and humility.

How many wonderful objects and processes do we meet with in our daily walk through life! How many are the various arts and manufactures invented by man! By what process, or series of processes is the wool from the Sheep's back wrought into the warm texture of our clothing! How is the tissue of the tiny worm converted into the rich and beautiful fabrics that adorn a well dressed lady! How is cotton, the production of the earth, converted into a cloth so useful and so generally worn! How does Hemp, a similar production, become a cable for the ship of war, and form the cords by which its sails are spread out to the breeze! By what curious and most ingenious process does the loom present to us figures so varied, so pleasing, so beautiful! Can you conceive of a mass of sand and salt or flint stone, being converted into the beautiful and transparent form of Glass? Can you tell the manner by which a rough ore taken from the bowels of the earth, is made to flow as a liquid, to become hard as adamant, and to receive a polish that vies with the mirror in brightness? How can we account for a mass of charcoal, sulphur, and saltpetre, each so powerless in itself, rendering asunder the solid rock—throwing projectiles of death for miles, and producing a total change in the mode of warfare through the wide extent of a world?

What do you know of that exquisite system of bones and muscle—nerves and sinews—brain and heart—with other of the great organs which compose the human body—a system so marvellous, displaying so powerfully the work of an Almighty hand, as to make us say with the Royal Psalmist, "We are fearfully and wonderfully made"?

Truly has it been said, that man left to himself, is the most helpless o all animals! How many hands have been employed in the forming of the clothes which you wear! And how many inventions of your predecessors are contributing to your present comfort. By knowledge man stands pre-eminently distinguished in the creation. The illustrious Bacon has truly said, "Knowledge is power"! Every object by which you are surrounded is a subject for the exercise of your talents. There is in fact no object in nature that does not, when rightly viewed and properly investigated, lead us to admire, adore, and praise that great Being, who with matchless wisdom, unbounded benevolence, and transcendent greatness, guides, governs, and preserves his creatures. We are led from Nature up to Nature's God!

THE IMPORTANCE OF MECHANICAL KNOWLEDGE TO THE WORKING CLASSES

J.C. Gallaway, *The Claims of Mechanics' Institutes* (Saint John, New Brunswick, 1844), pp. 12-14.

Next to virtue, it is laudable to aim at the improvement of our worldly condition. On this principle I ground another argument in favour of Mechanics' Institutes.

It does not, I apprehend, require much penetration to discover the connection that exists between the possession of knowledge and the improvement of one's finances. What workmen are most sought after; and who are most successful in fixing a high value upon their own labour? The dull, the ignorant, the unskilful? Allowing, of course, that with knowledge is associated those moral principles which are indispensable in turning this knowledge to a good account; and which moral principles are equally necessary in all the transactions of life—allowing this, the best informed operative is the best paid. Knowledge is an instrument in his hand, which renders him a more skilful, and therefore, more valuable workman than his ignorant companion.—Knowledge also operates in facilitating discoveries which may prove peculiarly profitable in a pecuniary respect. The history of the arts and sciences supplies us with several instances in which a happy invention lead to the acquisition of considerable wealth. The discovery of making patent shot, which cost Watts, a plumber in Bristol, the easy outlay of a dream, and the conveyance of a little heated lead to the top of a church tower, soon placed in the hands of its author the welcome present of ten thousand pounds. The renowned James Watt was in a small way of business as an instrument maker to the University of Glasgow, when he made his great improvement in the steam engine.

Really princely, as all persons who have visited Aston Hall, near Birmingham, well know, was the fortune which this wonderful discovery enabled its author to acquire, and transmit to another generation.

I dare not pledge myself, that if all of you will endeavour to improve your minds, and apply diligently to mechanical art, or other pursuits, that you will draw the prize of either ten thousand pounds, or another Aston Hall; nor would I venture to recommend you to attach any very great importance to such wealth, any further than it will enable you to realize the sublime aphorism of the Great Teacher: "it is more blessed to give than receive." But one thing I feel that I can safely pledge: it is this—knowledge, if it may not be the means of directly increasing your ordinary income, is very likely to suggest plans, and promote habits which will enable you to turn that income to the best advantage. Economy is often much more profitable than genius. Little savings generally tell up better than happy inventions. And so far, my auditors, as it is worthy of you to aim at the acquisition of property, I recommend to you the formation of those habits of reflection, forethought, temperance, and frugality, which the steady pursuit of knowledge is likely to engender.

The remarks which I have just made on the subject of invention, naturally suggest a fifth argument in favour of that diffusion of knowledge which is promoted by the Institutes for which I plead—I refer to the general progress of the arts and sciences.

It is a highly interesting and encouraging fact that most of the great improvements in these departments have originated in extremely trivial circumstances. Thus the renowned Galileo was lead to make his discoveries in the laws of motion, by observing the oscillation of a lamp suspended from a ceiling. Every one knows that the fall of an apple was the first circumstance that conducted the immortal Newton to his grand and comprehensive theory on the subject of gravitation. Cavallo, by means of a soap bubble, the plaything of children, was enabled to exhibit the most successful mode of aeriel navigation; and Franklin, who, for the encouragement of the working classes, it should ever be remembered, was himself an operative, made a discovery, by means of a kite, which has given a new nomenclature to science, has exploded many old theories, has afforded explanation to many most important phenomena, is daily leading to practical results of the greatest value, and has, in a word, secured for its author a name and place amongst "bards and sages old, immortal sons of praises."

From these facts, you may clearly perceive that the sphere of discovery is within your reach. The most every-day event of life, the oscillation of a lamp, the falling of an apple, the floating of a soap bubble, the flying of a kite, to which I may add the puffing of the tea-kettle, when contemplated with an intelligent eye, can lead to consequences of the utmost importance, in relation to the advancement of science, and the general comfort of the community. But, do not imagine that it is only requisite to gaze upon these trifles, and then be conducted, by a sudden leap, to some momentous discovery. Millions of minds had contemplated these facts before the period of Galileo, Cavallo, Newton, and Franklin. But the minds of these great men were previously stored with useful information. The general subject had been floating in their minds before these little events gave an impulse and direction to their inventive powers. They had made themselves somewhat familiar with the theories and experiments of others, and by these means were enabled to elicit such mighty results from such trivial beginnings.

Hence then the vast importance of furnishing your minds with general principles that you may apply them to the explanation of common facts; hence the value of becoming conversant with science that you may bring it to bear upon the improvements of art. Without such previous knowledge, you may waste your labours and consume your time in idle musing and in vain success. You may, after years of much toil, find that you have merely been acquiring what other minds had long known; and had it been your first aim to make yourselves familiar with their attainments, most of the time and labour that you may otherwise spend in reaching the position which they had previously attained, might have been employed, in carrying you into a new and wider field. It is not originality, it is a contemptible self-conceit that induces a man to disregard the views and improvements of other minds. He is the true genius, and I may add the true philanthropist who lays a broad foundation for his future inventions, in an extensive acquaintance with the success of others. . . .

Naturally arising from the view which I have just taken of the advantage of supplying mechanics with scientific knowledge, is the consideration of the benefit that will be secured to the community in general, by the better instruction of that portion of society, for whom such Institutes as these are expressly and primarily intended.

So far as the diffusion of knowledge among the working classes promotes their welfare, so far the community requires a direct benefit; and the very large numbers of that part of society, render such benefit correspondingly extensive. But we do not fairly estimate the benefit derived by the community at large from the better education of the working classes, if we limit our attention to the direct advantages which that section of the community separately enjoy. Society is held together by mutual dependence and vital relationship. One portion of the pyramid is not less essential to the constitution of the entire form, than is one section of the community to the stability, order, and beauty of the State. Nay, if we must allude to the question of mutual dependence, it would not be difficult to show that however important the upper classes of society may be; their importance, in relation to the welfare of the Empire is not by any means greater than that of the lower orders. And which is the direct and certain way of benefiting all the various grades of society? Is it by devoting our great effort to the further advancement of the higher, or by combining in an appropriate undertaking to raise the lower? Obviously the latter is the course marked out by reason and experience. The education of the rich does not necessarily involve the better education of the poor; but the intellectual improvement of the lower orders does necessitate a proportionate advancement in the higher. The wealthier sections of society have always better opportunities for intellectual and moral improvement, than those who are dependent for their daily sustenance on their daily toil. The motive too, to maintain their advanced portion will always be sufficiently strong to induce them to avail themselves of their better means. Hence there is no danger of the higher circles losing their position in society, whatever may be the progress of the lower. Every step in advance which is made by the working classes, necessitates a proportionate movement in those grades which occupy a more elevated position. A well-informed working population, will necessarily create a well-informed aristocracy. The raising of the upper tiers that form a part of the pyramid, will not necessarily raise the lower, but by placing the well adjusted machine beneath the lowest range, you elevate the whole. That man lays his plans for the amelioration of mankind, on the wisest principle, who directs his special attention to the masses of society, and endeavours to raise the character of the lowest. Our greatest, our perfect Exemplar displayed his wisdom as much as his benevolence in that feature of his public ministry, which was avowed in his well known declaration that "to the *poor* the Gospel is preached." The progress of human society hitherto, bears testimony to the soundness of this mode of procedure; and fully assured am I, that when that glorious era shall arrive, of which the page of inspiration speaks—a period when all mankind shall obtain the highest kind of knowledge, the movement toward that result will be found on a careful retrospect, to have been "from the least to the greatest."

TO LIGHTEN THE MECHANICS' LABOURS AND INFORM THE MANUFACTURER: *THE CANADIAN JOURNAL* INTRODUCES ITSELF

The Canadian Journal (August 1852), 5-6.

We cannot more appropriately introduce the *Canadian Journal* to the public, than by submitting a brief exposition of its claims to support, conjointly with an appeal to the professional men scattered throughout the country, whose experience and opportunities confer on them that power of co-operation upon which the ultimate success of this journal mainly rests.

If proof were wanting of the necessity which exists in this Province for a publication devoted to the Arts and Sciences of practical life, in addition to what is foreshadowed in the introduction to the present volume, it would suffice perhaps to enumerate the numerous foreign scientific and artistic periodicals which meet with a liberal patronage in Canada, and which are not unfrequently made the medium of communicating to the world the discoveries and inventions of the "sons of the soil". It might, with equal force, be urged that many useful additions to knowledge—especially the knowledge of our own country—are withheld from the light by the absence of that encouragement and assistance which the *Canadian Journal* aspires to contribute.

We do not, however, appeal to a spirit of nationality, deeply rooted, and most worthily so, as that sentiment is in the breasts of Canadians,—nor do we rest our claim to public encouragement upon the meritorious object of snatching original thought from obscurity, we have a more extended and far more practical design in view. We are endeavouring to supply such a publication as will afford a medium of communication between all engaged or interested in scientific or industrial pursuits, will assist, lighten and elevate the labours of the mechanic, will afford information to the manufacturer, and generally administer to the want of that already numerous and still increasing class in British America, who are desirous of becoming acquainted with the most recent inventions and improvements in the Arts, and those scientific changes and discoveries which are in progress throughout the world.

It were vain to suppose that the professional man generally, or the enterprising manufacturer, much less the scientific farmer, or the enquiring mechanic could command needful information respecting foreign or domestic progress in practical science and art from the pages of those publications which, out of the abundance of their resources, necessarily limit their range to one or two departments of industry or knowledge; which are not generally accessible on account of their expense, and which aim at a standard adapting them to the demands of a highly artificial and wealthy condition of society, rather than to the exigencies of a young and rapidly progressive people.

Even were the excellencies of foreign periodicals presented to the Canadian public in a form accessible to all classes, yet, such a publication would not meet the demands of the present day. As a thriving agricultural and commercial people—sprung, as it were, into existence during the last half century—we require special adaptation of many artifices and inventions to those unavoidable conditions which attach themselves to communities in new and extensive countries. We require information respecting many physical features of our territory, which, in the course of time, must impress with their influence our industry and prosperity. Our commercial relations demand an intimate and widely diffused acquaintance with the advantages we enjoy in relation to geographical position, soil, climate, productions, economic mineral resources and means of communication; and lastly, the imposing increase in the population of the Canadas, which numbers, while we write very nearly two million people, imperatively solicits that exertion which, if rightly directed, may place our literary and scientific achievements usefully and even prominently before the world.

Where may we hope to look for information relating to the Canadas if Canadians themselves do not supply the materials and furnish the record? How shall we elevate our position in the world of science and of letters if the "sons of the soil" do not arouse and exert themselves?

In every part of Canada men are to be found possessing high scientific attainments or profound practical knowledge. To many such we look for co-operation with confidence, now that a fitting medium for the publicity of the information they possess and are daily acquiring is hopefully offered to them.

The stupendous railway operations now in progress in many parts of both Provinces, present rare opportunities for obtaining much needed information respecting the geological features of the country through which they pass. The frosts of a single winter will, in many instances, obliterate all surface traces of strata possessing economic importance, until accident leads to their discovery at some future and perhaps distant period. We earnestly desire to enlist amongst the contributors to this journal the gentlemen engaged in the construction of those extensive lines of communication.

The ample opportunities for observations of the most useful description which are enjoyed by surveyors, induce us respectfully to solicit their correspondence on all matters relating to the physical features and natural history of the districts in which they may be engaged.

To the operative, deriving from experience a purely practical knowledge which experience alone can give, we address ourselves in the hope of obtaining assistance and counsel in matters wherein the busy lessons of the workshop are far more valuable than the unapplied speculations of retirement and study.

It is not our intention to trespass upon the field now occupied by our contemporary the Agriculturist, yet so vast and unexplored is the domain of Agricultural Science, that the rambler among its novelties may find, without encroachment, fruit and flowers in abundance wherewith to enrich our store and advance the public good.

To all who are interested in the objects of this journal we beg again to state, that the progressive improvement and extension of the work will be commensurate with the support which may be accorded to it by the public, and the degree to which the Canadian Institute and the promoters of the *Canadian Journal* may be successful in soliciting and combining the talents of those classes to which they appeal.

PROGRESS AS A RACE

R.B. Sullivan, *On the Connection between the Agriculture and Manufactures of Canada. Lecture, Delivered before the Mechanics' Institute of Hamilton* (Hamilton, 1848), pp. 4-6, 27-9.

As there is no condition of the individual man so happy as the one of improvement, so there is no state of a country so happy as the state of advancement. It scarcely matters what is the present condition of a community; the people are happy, if that condition is becoming better. In old states, and with crowded populations, the question as to the mode of advance is often perplexing and difficult; but it is, nevertheless, solved by the genius and intelligence of great communities. In new countries, like ours, the way is more obvious; in fact there are many ways leading directly or indirectly towards the same end. To arrive at the goal some time or another, it is not absolutely necessary that we should select the shortest road; but if we run a race with others who enjoy the same advantages with ourselves, and who have the power and judgment of proper choice, we must fall behind, if our choice be wrong. We have the elements of wealth, prosperity and advancement scattered around us; even with the use of a few of these we have a degree of success; but if others gather these elements with more judgment, industry and courage than ourselves; if they take a wider range, and exhibit more extended enterprize than we do, we are inevitably beaten in the competition. I fear this has been too much the case with our country hitherto. We are in the immediate neighborhood of great energy, activity and progress, which we have been far from equalling. We have in reality used but one of our native resources, at least one only has been used for our benefit; our only productive industry has been agriculture. Those who live amongst us, and who are not agriculturists, do not reciprocate the benefits they receive from it by productive industry of their own. Hence arises our want of progress, in comparison with that of our neighbors; and hence the danger of our falling into an inferior position, unworthy of the race from which we have sprung, of the Empire of which we form a part, and of the glorious land which has been given for our inheritance. . . .

If you ask me what interests me most in Hamilton, placing aside for the moment your railroad, which I wish was finished as well as commenced, (and I say this truly, without any disposition to doubt your success,)— but if you ask me in my small way, what interests me most,—it is this,— that every time I have visited your town, I have discovered at the foundry in James Street, the establishment, I believe, of Messrs. MacQuesten and Fisher, some great increase and improvement. Every time I come, I see more machinery at work, more buildings erected, more men employed, and a greater appearance of industry. Whether Hamilton or Toronto imports the most goods for the supply of the interior, is a question that interests me little; but I feel no such indifference on the question, whether the country is using more machinery, and whether that machinery can be manufactured by ourselves, by means of mechanics forming the population of our towns, and living and prospering amongst us. I look upon the success of that establishment, yet in its infancy, with interest, because it proves a problem in which the whole country is interested; and it is even now, the nucleus, around which capital earned, retained & reproductive in the country can gather. Small as the establishment is, in proportion to what such an one should be in a country like this, it will in the end have more substantial effect upon the prosperity of this town, and the neighboring farming population, than any five wholesale stores in Hamilton. And yet probably it has its difficulties; and when the import trade can command the purses of money lenders, and monopolise discounts at the banks, it is not unlikely that this establishment is left to work its own way, unaided. Knowing nothing of the facts, I may speculate in this mode without offence; what I mean to say is, that in Canada there is very little manufacturing enterprise, and very much unprofitable trade that is to say, unprofitable to the country; and that, generally speaking, the latter is the trade assisted and promoted, and that the former is too often considered visionary and uncertain, and unworthy of credit and support, until struggling against difficulty, it rises by its innate strength above suspicion.

I have a great regard for the town of Dundas, because more than any other place in Upper Canada, it appears to depend upon its factories; its situation in the midst of a fertile and beautiful country; its ever working stream, turning wheel after wheel, and keeping in movement factory after factory; the neat cottages of the artizans, and the snug, comfortable, and unpretending appearance of the whole place, are highly interesting to the stranger. Its growing wealth and importance is of particular interest to the farming community. As capital, created by industry, gathers there, you will find the fabrication of article after article now imported from abroad introduced; you will find, that successful enterprise in manufactures, reproduces itself, more naturally than any other kind of enterprise. The horse power in a country brewery, induces the steam engine;

the steam engine requires, in its construction, the founder, the turner, the machine maker; he brings the boiler maker; and so on by degrees, until every article belonging to the trade is made upon the spot. All this leads to the enquiry, in how many ways steam can be employed. The blacksmith who commences by shoeing horses, and tiring waggon wheels, finds that he can repair, and finally that he can make axes; from this he proceeds to the manufacture of other tools. Those who use the tools find that the home-manufactured articles are better than the imported; they learn that some of the cheapness of the latter is owing to their want of goodness, and they discover that there is no worse economy than the use of inferior implements however cheap. The common carding machine, adds to itself the spinning jenny, and the power loom; the place which begins as a manufactory for the immediate neighborhood, becomes a place for exportation: a large town arises by degrees, peopled by ingenious, skilful mechanics, who are ever plotting how they can set their newly-gained capital at work, in the increase of the old, or the establishment of new works. Improvements adopted in other countries are sought after, and adopted; strange mechanics come to examine and set up for themselves: thus the manufacturing city arises, and the farmers around find a market for all their produce; they raise new articles; hemp, because of the new rope walks, and the certain market; flax, because of the linen factory; land is turned to better account; agricultural machinery is introduced; more hands are employed in agriculture; the country becomes thickly populated; there are more tax payers, and less taxes upon each; better roads, and lower tolls, because there are more persons to use & pay for them; civilization, wealth, refinement, and accumulated capital follow; and we have a rich country, because it contains the two elements of riches, namely, a town and country population. As we are now situated, we are like a man who would make an effervescing draught with the soda or the acid, without the other ingredient; his drink may be as sour, or as salt as he likes, but it would never be soda water.

TO DISPLAY THE FRUITS OF PROGRESS

THE MORAL EFFECT OF INDUSTRIAL EXHIBITIONS

Charles D. Day, *Address Delivered at the Provincial Industrial Exhibition, Montreal, on Saturday, Oct. 19, 1850* (Montreal, 1850), pp. 6-8, 22-5.

You come but now from the interesting display of these productions of man's ingenuity in another hall; you have surveyed them there: did you see in them nothing but wood and iron, and brass and leather? Look at them again, and they will tell you of hours of deep, laborious, persevering meditation—of weariness of body—of exhaustion of spirits—discouragement, almost despair—of revived hope and energy, and victories—glorious victories of mind, won inch by inch over the strong, although inert, resistance of matter and its laws. And how won? By the patient industry which dares and conquers all. The truth is, that these things are the handwriting of the inventor and the mechanic: they are, to his mind, the expression of its efforts and its power, as fully as the exact language of the philosopher, and the eloquent and glowing sentences of the poet, are the expression of theirs. We are apt to overlook or underrate the intelligence which is not recorded in books, and to forget that the faculties which are every day called into exercise, not only in mechanical inventions, but in many of the arts of life, are closely allied to those, which, under different training and with another direction, give literary and scientific fame. There must be in the head of the inventor, as close a logic, as in that of the mathematician; a creative power similar in kind, if not equal in degree, to that of the poet; and the patent office of most countries, nay, this Exhibition, indicates the extent to which these qualities have been possessed, and the intensity and perseverance with which they have been exerted. The steadfast resolute application of the mental energies, in a certain direction, and with a fixed object, makes the difference, perhaps all the difference, between civilized and savage man. . . .

I say, that if this great Industrial Exhibition excite the interest, and meet the wide success which it deserves, it will be a noble evidence of a lofty civilization, which no time before has equalled, or approached; an expression of the spirit of our age, which every living man, who has not lived in vain, may hail with honest pride. There is a grandeur in the spectacle of this universal and spontaneous contribution, selected from all that in the lapse of centuries—upon the varied surface of the ample earth—in cold or heat—in all modes of social life, and all varieties of human circumstance, have been elaborated from the teeming brain of man, to be displayed, compared, and judged in friendly rivalry. There is in it an earnest of moral progress—of the growth of a right standard of the true and good—and of an upward spring in man's best nature. No event has ever occurred, which is so emphatic a declaration to the world, of the spirit of peace. And to those philanthropists, who have striven to enlist mankind, in one great compact for its universal diffusion—it must be a welcome harbinger. I know that the views of these men have been frowned upon as visionary and impracticable, and the convictions from which they spring called mawkish sentiment: but it is no new thing in the upward progress of morality; for the conventional and the false to deal out words of discouragement and contumely, upon the unwelcome and the true. Yet likely as this is to happen, it is no less certain, that the upright act, born of the pure emotions which have their dwelling in the soul's deep sanctuary is never lost; and now they have an assurance that in their so-called visionary views and mawkish sentiment, they are not alone. Let them then take courage, and remember that with strong and faithful effort the difficult is not the impossible, and the remote soon ceases to be the unattainable. Who can say, that this dove of peace, which year after year has been sent forth, amid the clouds and storms and raging ocean of men's passions, and seen no place of rest, may not, ere long, behold a subsidence of the dark waters; and a broad mountain top on which her weary foot may find repose?

But I try your patience, and will add but little more. I know not if I have made myself fully understood; but my design has been, to draw from these Industrial Exhibitions, some two or three conclusions. The first of these is, that the productions of mechanical contrivance ought to be regarded by us with an interest deeper than a mere passing curiosity—as a record of civilization; because they are a history of intelligent labor, that is, of that discipline of men's faculties, which itself is the essential element of civilization. By the word labor, I do not intend the mere corporeal toil, which the reformers of a certain school seem to consider as alone entitled to regard; nor do I mean entirely to exclude it; for no form of cheerful diligence, in the fulfilment of our mission here on earth, is without its power and dignity. A pervading earnestness of spirit informs and elevates all conditions of human exertion. But its noblest exhibition, is that which tasks the energies of heart and brain; and stirs within us the impulses of a high intelligence, and something higher still—the moral sense which binds us to another world. I would again insist upon this plain and hacknied, but unheeded truth, that where this spirit of labor is not, no gift of nature or of fortune can avail. Genius can rear no monument without its aid. It is the condition, imposed by God himself, upon the attainment of all excellence and happiness by man.

A second conclusion which I have endeavored to enforce is, that these Exhibitions are significant of a civilization, high in degree, and different in principle, from that which any other age has offered;—their vital principle is a spirit of peace. It is not that there is to be no more war; such a consummation is not yet near, for slow and painful is the ascent of nations in the scale of virtue. But the supremacy of that great evil is abated. The sounding words and glittering pomp, which have so long misled the world, are beginning to be understood; and the thoughtful and the just have learned, and are declaring, that war, and its miscalled glory, are the offspring of those baser instincts, which are nearest earth, and most remote from heaven. The lowest and worst point is turned, and this tyrant power is yielding, heavily and sullenly, but visibly yielding, and let us hope forever, before the vigor of a sound and healthful tone of public sentiment. It is this increasing and fundamental change, by the substitution of the predominance of peace for the supremacy of war, as an element in the construction of society, and as its presiding genius, which I have endeavored to render the prominent feature of this discourse, and would submit as a worthy subject for your sober contemplation. Of such a change these Exhibitions are a loud and unequivocal assertion. The spirit which they breathe, is of a noble essence, combined of patient industry—of high intelligence—and of universal peace. May it be the growing and pervading, and abiding spirit of our country and the world!

LESSONS FROM AN EXHIBITION

The Canadian Journal (October 1852), 56-7.

In Agricultural Machines were to be found ploughs, drills, harrows, reaping and mowing machines, chaff and straw cutters, grain and root crushers and cutters, thrashing machines of various construction, agricultural horse-power, (occupying wonderfully small space for the power exerted), cultivators, fanning mills, churns and cheese presses, and various other labour-saving machines; a clover seed gatherer; a cross-cutting saw mill also attracted particular attention. All these machines bore a high stamp of excellence, and were not surpassed by those of English and American make. The subsoil plough was, in the foreign department, prominent, thus shewing a decided approval of the latest improvements in English and Scotch agriculture; there were wanted but the draining plough, and draining tile and pipe machine to represent the latest and most permanent improvements which British ingenuity has produced in her struggle against the world.

Though not evincing so great an improvement over former exhibitions as we had hoped to see, the collection of Canadian Agricultural Machinery presented many encouraging facts to our notice; and chiefly so is the very favourable manner in which it compared with similar productions exhibited by our neighbours. It has been generally admitted, though almost without enquiry, that the older hands on the *"other side"* as a matter of course, produce implements so superior to those manufactured in Canada as to put all attempts at successful competition out of the question. It is to be regretted that our mechanics have so long tacitly admitted the truth of that assumption; it needed but an impartial examination of the machines exhibited last month to prove its fallacy, and to demonstrate that we need but a fair field—and no favours—beyond a fair trial, to enable us of Canada to compete successfully in the manufacture of Agricultural implements with our older established brethren across the border. Let us not be understood here as repudiating our obligations to our very energetic neighbours: we owe them a *turn* for rubbing off our rusty spots. . . .

A Threshing Machine and Horse-power by Medcalf of Toronto, appears to leave but little to desire in this class of implements; the arrangements and character of workmanship is equal to anything we have seen. We much regretted the bad taste which induced the attempt at ornamental [daubing?] painting displayed on this excellent piece of mechanism; the real wood or plain white colours always look appropriate, while the wretched attempts which are sometimes made at imitating a mahogany panel on a Fanning Mill, with perhaps satinwood framing and rosewood mouldings, are truly distressing: in equally bad taste we noticed some Farm Waggons bedaubed with all the colours of the rainbow. Commend to us the mechanic whose work will bear inspection without such wretched aid. How well the natural grain of the tough ash, hickory, and oak, of some of the American machines contrasted with the gaudy colours of our own.

THE MISCELLANY OF PROGRESS

Provincial Exhibition, Toronto, 1858 (n.p., n.d.), pp. 6-7.

We will commence our tour of observation at the Eastern Entrance. Beginning at the head of the stand on the north side of the eastern wing are a number of scales and weights, the former exhibited by Messrs. Dally, Ware & Co., of Hamilton, the latter by Messrs. H. Piper & Bro., Inspector of Weights and Measures, Toronto. The scales are well worthy attention, both on account of the excellence of the materials and finish, and also because of the nicety with which they are balanced, the bearings being of steel. In this latter respect they are superior to the celebrated scales of Fairbanks, of the States. The large platform scales will weigh from half a pound to 25 cwt. Mr. John Mills, of Hamilton, exhibited an improvement upon his last air furnace, containing as it does 200 feet of heating surface. The furnace contains 15 different flues, and is adapted to the heating of churches and other public buildings. Either wood or coal may be used as fuel, and the stove is admirably suited to the maintenance of an even temperature. A first-rate case of rifles was shown by Mr. John Grainger, Toronto, No. 1 of which, a double elliptic rifle, was considered a decided improvement on the Lancaster gun. Coal oil lamps were shewn by Messrs. Parson Brothers, who claimed that in the diffusion of the light they were superior to those of English or American manufacture. Mr. H.G. Booth, Toronto, had a creditable stand of tin, copper, and brass, whilst Messrs. Moore & Co., of Hamilton, showed some good Japan ware. Mr. Wm. H. Rice, of Toronto, excelled in wire work, one of the best specimens of which was an ingenious rat-trap, well calculated to deceive the most wary of those very troublesome customers. Mr. Rice also shewed wire cloth and wire hoop of capital workmanship. Mr. D.R. Wallace, of Montreal, a sewing machine. Mr. H. Yates, of Brantford, a slide valve indicator for a locomotive. Mixed oils—both vegetable and animal—so as to constitute what the exhibitor denominated "anti-friction grease," were shewn by Mr. Joseph Archer, of Toronto, who states that they neither freeze on the machinery in winter nor drop off it during the hottest days of summer—a rare combination of qualities. Mr. Israel Seaman shewed a good rotary grain separator, and also a bran duster and smut mill. Mr. Geo. Campbell, of Toronto, blacksmith's portable iron forges. A new sewing machine—an improvement on the many improvements made on stitching machinery since the "song of the shirt" saw the light—was busily at work under the direction of Messrs. Butler & Co. of Newmarket, its inventors. It is designed for family use, and does single stitching in a manner which is almost faultless. Mr. John O'Malley, of Toronto, a shingle edging machine. Mr. John Gartshaw, of Dundas, specimens of finishing in iron. We arrive next at the north-east corner of the Palace, which is largely occupied by the goods of Messrs. Thomson, Keith & Co., Toronto. The chief articles in the space allotted to them are a gasometer and fittings, employed in the manufacture of gas from rosin oil, and which it produces at $2 per 1000 feet. If applied to detached country dwellings, it would entirely relieve the inmates thereof of the miseries incident to a state of semi-darkness during our long winter nights. It might also be used with advantage and profit in some of the imperfectly lighted hotels with which the Province abounds. The same firm also exhibited a fine assortment of chandeliers, and some very excellent baths, &c. Mr. Wm. Hodson, of Toronto, brought specimens of handiwork in the shape of window sashes, doors, blinds, &c., whose chief merit were that they had been made to assume a beautifully smooth surface without the aid of sand paper. Mr. Wm. Tait, of Duart, a set of agricultural rakes and forks. C.R. Parkes, of Toronto, wood turnings. The prisoners in the Penitentiary at Kingston sent the results of their industry in the form of rakes and cradles and washing boards, all of which were very creditable specimens of workmanship. The goods were shewn by Messrs. Thomson & Burns, Toronto, agents for Messrs. Drummond & Co., Kingston. Mr. M.B. Veasley, of Hamilton, and Messrs. Smith & Caulkins, exhibited clean sweeping brooms.

CANADA AT THE CRYSTAL PALACE, LONDON, 1851

Tallis's History and Description of the Crystal Palace, and the Exhibition of the World's Industry in 1851 (London, 1851), pp. 51-2.

Canada made the best display, as was to be expected from the energetic character of the people, the means they had of obtaining early intelligence, of conveying their goods to this country, and obtaining the cooperation of the governor, the earl of Elgin, and their local authorities. The Canadians held a preliminary exhibition of native produce, and selected from that exhibition the best, as specimens of raw produce and manufactures. The most prominent object was a fire-engine from Montreal, which carried off the first prize at the Canadian exhibition of industry, and was sent, by subscription among a few patriotic Canadians, to show what the mechanics of that fine colony could do. As a carriage, it was extremely handsome. The panels were adorned with paintings of Canadian scenery, views of a great fire at Montreal, the principal churches, banks, and other public buildings, and figures of an Indian in snow shoes in winter costume, of a fireman, &c., executed with a spirit and feeling of reality which raised them above the class of ordinary coach-painting. The body was of copper, from the rich copper mines of Lake Superior, lined with wood. The tool-box was of mahogany. The mechanical arrangements seemed good, and the finish of both the wood and metal work was most creditable to Canadian workmen. It was followed by a hose-box on two wheels, to carry 300 feet of hose, and weighed altogether 25 cwt. It would pump up water from a depth of 27 feet; and according to the statement of the gentleman who manufactured it, would throw 170 feet high from 300 feet of hose. Fire-engines throughout both British and republican America are drawn by men, and not by horses. They are usually the property of young men associated into voluntary companies, who take great pride in adorning their respective engines. Hence the profusion of painting and other ornamental decorations. Over the fire-engine was suspended a canoe of white birch, which presented no especial difference from canoes we have seen a hundred times, except its size; but this canoe was actually paddled 3,000 miles of lake and river navigation, with a crew of twenty men, before being placed on board a steamer for England. It was the same description of canoe employed by the Hudson's Bay Company in their annual journeys to the vast preserves of fur-bearing animals under their command. We should have been pleased if it had been accompanied by one of the *voyageurs*, whose gay costume, and songs, and semi-savage manners, have been described in the book of Sir George Simpson, late resident governor of Hudson's Bay, or as it is now officially named, Rupert's Land, and several North American travellers. A piano, a large

French bedstead, a set of tables and chairs, all elaborately carved out of Canadian black walnut, next came under our notice, as remarkable specimens of a wood as yet little known in this country. In colour, size, beauty of grain, and polish, it was equal, if not superior to the best specimens of French and Italian walnut. A slab, which formed part of the Canadian trophy in the central avenue, was cut from a tree which made 27,000 feet of available timber. The workmanship of this furniture, although very fair, offered nothing remarkable for praise or blame. We liked the emblematic beavers carved round the edge of the table; but not the same animals crawling like rats on the cross bars of the legs. Among the chairs were a set unpolished, and fashioned after some introduced into America by the earliest settlers. It was reported that her majesty had condescended to accept them. One Canadian gentleman was under the impression that the originals had been imported from England in the sixteenth century, by Sebastian Cabot; but that is unlikely, because, although Cabot discovered Labrador, there is no evidence that he formed any settlement in Canada at all. The originals are probably of French origin, and not older than the time of Louis Quatorze. Around the fire-engine were arranged a set of Canadian sleighs. The white one was a cutter for one horse; the next, an elegant long carriage of very graceful curves, was a tandem sleigh; the largest was for a pair of four horses, and was made after the fashion approved by the Military Tandem Club. With the sleighs, we must notice a set of harness that hung on the wall, the saddles covered with bells, and adorned with pendent plumes of blue horse-hair: white plumes of the same material were arranged to wave from brass spikes between the ears of the prancing horses. On a bright winter's day we can imagine no prettier sight than the whole turn-out, with its blood horses, ringing bells, fair ladies wrapped in furs, and dashing fur-wrapped driver, careering across the hard snow or the sounding ice of a frozen river. Furs, skins, horns, and Indian curiosities filled up the interstices of the Canadian collection. The head and wide-spreading horns of a gigantic moose, or elk, might be compared with the European variety of the same species, from the Lithuanian forests, exhibited in the Russian section.

LET US BE HONEST AND MODEST

J.A. Chisholm, ed., *The Speeches and Public Letters of Joseph Howe*, vol. II (Halifax, 1909), pp. 369-70.

Now, I wandered for a week through the great Exhibition held in Paris in 1854; and I declare to my countrymen and countrywomen that up to the hour I crossed the threshold I had no expectation of what the civilization and the industry of the world had produced. Then I saw what the great European nations could do. I saw the most minute and delicate industry represented; I saw what man had done upon the face of the created universe there represented in all the departments of life and industry. I could scarcely conceive that the civilization of the globe had risen to so high a pitch. It was a perfect storehouse of information; and when for a week I had examined its countless treasures, I not only felt that I had seen a marvellous display, but at times there came to me a thought of the delight that would be felt by many far over the Atlantic wave if they could but be present at the spectacle. But there is one saddening reflection that I have not forgotten. After wandering through the galleries of art—after looking at the vast building devoted to them—after having seen everything, from the crown jewels of the European sovereigns down to the minutest instrument which a lady handles when she is doing her ordinary work—after having seen in wood and iron and bronze and ten thousand substances the industry of the world exhibited, I came to two or three compartments having the names of New Brunswick and Nova Scotia painted in large letters above them, and beneath nothing at all. Then I bowed my head and thanked God that nobody knew me; I was glad that there was a reasonable prospect of my being able to skulk out with the conviction that nobody knew where I came from. And when I went back to London I said nothing about Nova Scotia that season; I passed for an Englishman, and got home as quickly as I could. Let us not exhibit ourselves in such a plight again. . . . Let us be honest and modest, and not attempt too much, but go to the next World's Fair with what we have, and send, as we shall send, in pamphlet form, a fair, candid account, not too voluminous, of the Province, to show every man who may wish to emigrate, what sort of country this is. We will not pretend to rival the neighbouring States, but this we can say: that this country only began to be settled very many years after the old colonies; that we commenced with nothing in the wilderness, and all we have made has been made in little over a century. It has been said that the moose and caribou roamed through the forests a hundred years ago; and yet look what the efforts of man have done since that time!

TO GO OR NOT TO GO: THE AMERICAN CENTENNIAL EXHIBITION, 1876

The Monetary Times and Trade Review, August 20, 1875.

So far as the United States is concerned, there are no special reasons why the people of Canada should take part in the Philadelphia Centennial Exhibition. To hold such an exhibition of the productions of all nations, whilst at the same time they continue their policy of commercial exclusion, is a curious inconsistency on the part of our neighbours, which merited the caustic reference of John Bright in his letter of a few months ago. Such gatherings have at their foundation Free Trade ideas, and what use is it for other nations to send samples of their productions to Philadelphia next year, if the United States is bent on excluding them on all other occasions by prohibitory tariffs? So far as encouraging *trade* with that country itself is concerned, there would be little object gained in exhibiting at all, for whilst the Government is willing to let it's people *see* what articles they could purchase better and cheaper from other nations, they take care by their commercial policy to prevent them from *buying* them whenever it can possibly be done.

Looked at from this particular standpoint, we are not surprised to learn that some English manufacturers have declined to send articles to the Centennial Exhibition next year, and that some Canadians feel very much in the same way. There is, however, another side to the question, more particularly in regard to Canada, and one which, in our opinion, every intelligent, patriotic citizen must see renders it imperative in the interests of this Dominion, that the very best possible display of our national resources should be made.

Whether we take part in the gathering at Philadelphia or not, it will take place, and the nations which have promised to take part in it, the magnificent buildings erected, and the excellence of the arrangements generally, all indicate that it will be one of the grandest displays of the kind which the world has ever seen. Millions of the most active and intelligent of Europe, the West Indies, South America, and more distant parts of the globe will be present, and tens of millions will read in their own homes in every nook and valley of civilization the story of the exhibition. What would the effect be upon the growing interests of Canada if, situated alongside of the United States, and boasting as we do of the great resources and future of our country, we took no part in the exhibition, or made a shabby display? The effects would be most disastrous. Our course would give a deadly blow to the increasing favour with which the Dominion is now being regarded in Europe and throughout the world, from which we would be fortunate if we recovered in one or two decades.

If we put in no appearance at Philadelphia at all, it would be alleged in every paper in the United States, and very many in other parts of the world, that Canada did not exhibit because afraid of the contrast between her productions and those of the Republic. The story would be revived with greater force than ever, that Canada is a cold, ice-bound, hyperborean region, and we know from past experience how difficult it is to eradicate that absurdity from the European mind, when once it finds a lodgement. The millions who attend at Philadelphia would be irresistibly led to the conclusion that if we could have made a good display we would certainly have done it, and that our failing to do so was *prima faciae* evidence that the Dominion was of very little account, either as regards resources or enterprise. It would afterwards be thrown up to our emigration agents at every turn—in short, a score of ways might be mentioned in which it could and would be used to the injury of the Dominion for many years thereafter.

To take part in the Centennial and make a poor appearance, would be a still more fatal mistake. We know that the United States is sparing no efforts to make a grand display; for Canada to appear paltry and shabby by its side, would be to inflict an almost irreparable blow upon our prosperity. We look upon the occasion consequently as of the greatest possible moment to this country; we shall have much at stake at Philadelphia next year, and we trust our Federal and Provincial Governments, and the Commissioners and Advisory Boards who have been appointed, will be found equal to the importance of the occasion. We are pleased to observe that active, energetic men have been appointed, irrespective of political leanings, and certainly their position will be no sinecure. Canada has so much at stake in the matter that they cannot but feel their responsibility, and we call upon all classes to patriotically aid them in making the Canadian display at Philadelphia such as will redound to the honour and credit of our common country.

KUDOS FROM PHILADELPHIA

Francis A. Walker, *The World's Fair. Philadelphia, 1876. A Critical Account* (New York, 1878), p. 46.

Next to Russia, perhaps the greatest of the surprises of the Exhibition was found in the displays made by the British colonies, and pre-eminently by Canada. The commercial instinct in these new countries is exceedingly active and adventurous, and it was well directed and reinforced by the colonial commissions appointed for the purpose. For the wealth of natural resources shown by Australia the American people were in a considerable degree prepared, though the impression produced upon every careful observer as to the future of that continent was profound. But for the Canadian display neither the American people, though so close neighbors, nor the judges of the Exhibition were prepared. Here it was not alone the richness of natural endowment, as shown in cereals and fruits, lumber, cattle, and horses, often surpassing the corresponding products of the most favored regions of the United States, which witnessed to the present wealth and future growth of Canada; but the artfulness of mechanical contrivance, quite New-England-like, the spirit of industrial enterprise, active and penetrating, and the admirable educational system of at least one of the provinces, were in the best sense American.

MEASURING NATIONAL PROGRESS

SCIENCE AND THE FARMER

The Canada Farmer, vol. 1 (January 29, 1847), 2.

Those however who see and feel the evils and burdens with which the agriculture of Canada is oppressed; those who have some knowledge of the wondrous achievements which science and experience combined have accomplished in this grand department of human labour, in other countries; those in a word who, whether native or foreign born, can realize the existence of a peculiar influence in the talismanic words "my country", must and will hail with gladness the appearance of an agency so all-powerful for good and so unproductive of evil as the *press* becomes, when applied to the objects we seek. The number of such persons we believe is rapidly increasing in Canada. The lines of demarcation between classes, sections and parties, which have hitherto been so plain to every eye, so offensive to, and so regretted by every generous well wisher of his country, are becoming shadowy and indistinct. Soon, very soon it is to be hoped, they will have left no trace behind. The time has arrived when we must think and feel ourselves *Canadians*. This is no longer a matter of choice or indifference. We have stood calling upon Jupiter for a long time, and we have at last been told very significantly to put our *own shoulders to the wheel*. There is no doubt we shall get out of the mire much quicker for it; we must *lift* however, and not only so, but we must seek out every advantage our position affords; avail ourselves of every discovery of science; every invention of ingenuity; and every acquisition of experience. If we are hereafter obliged to go into the world's markets without any *protection*; to be jostled by the busy crowds, and underbid by the active, enterprising, intelligent, and in some cases, more fortunate producers we shall meet with there, it must be plain to the simplest mind, that we shall have to adopt different plans from those heretofore followed . . . what then is to be done? Shall we travel on in the old mill-house round? Shall we stick to our old ways, and shut our ears against all improvement because "our *fathers* never did so"? We are already years behind our neighbours. As a people we are wholly unacquainted with many modern discoveries and improvements which enable the farmer with no more labour than before to obtain *double* the profit. It is true there is here and there among us a farmer, who might safely compete with the best of any country. But they have not been made here. They have come from a country where science has freely given out the richest treasures of her vast store-house; where the laboratory of the chemist has been applied to a better purpose than the transmutation of metals, or the discovery of the philosopher's stone. These farmers may be perfectly ignorant of the rationale of the thing, the "why and the wherefore" yet they have been instructed in the *results*, and in the way to produce them.—They have not obtained the knowledge they possess from experience alone. The establishment of agricultural societies, model and experimental farms; the labours of such men as Johnston, Louden, Liebig and others; and the newspapers and periodicals expressly devoted to the improvement of agriculture which have been spread broad-cast over all those countries in which any considerable advance has been made, have given, even to the *un*reading, labouring farmer, that knowledge which he turns to so good an account. He may not have derived his skill *directly* from any of these sources, but he has been taught it by those who did. In other words, had it not been for the discoveries of science, he would now be in total ignorance of what he well knows cannot be too highly estimated.

AN ELEMENTARY CATECHISM

Manuel Elémentaire et Pratique de l'Art Agricole, par membre du clergé Canadien (Montreal, 1853), pp. 7-12.

QUESTION.—What is Agriculture?

ANSWER.—Agriculture is the art of cultivating the fields and making them fertile.

Q. What are the means of arriving at this end?

A. One arrives there by study, thought, and experience, as well as with the assistance of the animals that provide man with his food and clothing, and a host of useful benefits, necessary or purely for enjoyment.

Q. What rank ought agriculture be assigned among the arts in general?

A. Agriculture can, with justice, be placed at the head of the arts, for it certainly has two advantages over all the others: its antiquity and its utility.

Q. In these modern times is agriculture still held in honor?

A. Modern times profit today from the experience of past centuries: thus the art of agriculture is greatly honored in those states where the government deigns to occupy itself seriously with means of assuring the well being of the governed, and consequently, the prosperity of the commonwealth. Above all, it is appropriate in our epoch and even in this country to consider agriculture as the mother of manufactures—of industry and commerce—and as the intermediary that ought powerfully to assist the true Canadian to keep intact his faith, his way of life and his nationality.

Q. Can you cite several examples of encouragement given to agriculture in our epoch?

A. Other than that agriculture is flowering remarkably today in the United States of America, in England and in the advanced countries of the old world, it is in China still the object of a kind of cult. The emperor of China provides all other sovereigns an example that deserves to be imitated. Every year, on the same day, he presides in person over a great festival of agriculture. Followed by three princes of the court and the principal magistrates of the empire, he first offers a sacrifice for the prosperity and preservation of the goods of the land. The ceremony finished, he goes down to the fields, in the presence of all of his court, and starts to plough the field in the midst of a religious silence. The dignitaries who accompany him work with him. They themselves carry the precious boxes containing the seeds to be sown. After having guided the plough over various places, the emperor sows the seeds. He then distributes prizes to professional ploughmen who have distinguished themselves by their work. Also in China, honor and encouragement is accorded to whoever reclaims uncultivated land in the deserts of Tartary.

In France, it is often a question of agricultural groups. There are more than 120 agricultural societies there, which make commendable efforts to improve the work, and offer annual prizes in order to encourage useful discoveries.

In Canada, agriculture has, in our day, shown progress worthy of the encouragement with which our legislature has favoured it, by stimulating competition by a system of rewards. Among the farmers of this country progress that is more and more noticeable will not fail to be the result of the impetus given today to this noble profession not only by the Legislative Assembly, but also by public opinion, the press, and, in general, all the true friends of local prosperity.

Q. Under what form of government is agriculture susceptible to the greatest advancement?

A. Agriculture can make no greater progress than under a liberal government that, on the one hand, protects its interests and, on the other, gives a latitude to public liberty which cannot fail to be turned to the advantage of agriculture.

Q. Can one hope for effective progress in Canadian agriculture?

A. Yes: Canada possesses fertile lands of immense extent, that can amply suffice for the needs of a people even much more numerous than those who inhabit it.

Q. Would you please give the reasons of utility that determine the preeminence agriculture must be given over the other arts?

A. These reasons of utility are deduced from the fact that agriculture is the mother and the nurse of the human species. It is, in effect, the source of real wealth, of riches that have a real price and are not dependent upon the opinions of men; it satisfies the demands of necessity without ceasing to be a source of delights: because of it, a people need not be dependent on foreigners, and may even be able to supply [foreigners with produce]. Finally, agriculture is the principal revenue of a state, revenue that takes the place of all others if it should lack them.

AN 1865 PLEA FOR EDUCATIONAL REFORM

Arthur Buies, *Textes présentés et annotés*, ed., Léopold Lamontagne (Montreal, 1959), pp. 71-5. Reprinted by permission of Les Editions Fides.

There comes a moment in the life of each man when ideas, long combatted, suddenly impose themselves upon the mind, and become the law of opinions and conduct. Before becoming applicable, they had to find a mind matured and prepared to receive them. This is the reason for the slowness with which the simplest ideas penetrate into the crowd, and for the eagerness with which they are adopted as soon as they have become necessary. Canada has arrived at the phase of its existence where the postponement of reforms is no longer possible, where retarding certain advancements would be nonsense and a proof of ineptitude. Important questions press, accumulate during delays, grow by the influence they more and more hold in the mind. These questions have become necessities. They demand a solution, and without this solution, it is useless to pretend to something, and to pursue our destiny.

I want to say that it is time profoundly to modify our system of education. It is time to bring the aid of reason to the impotence of this system. It is time to rid the public intelligence of that incoherent mass of obstacles that arrest our progress.

It is not a question of raising the level of studies; they must be specialized and above all they must be put in harmony with the ideas of our century—the only way of making them profitable.

Exclusively classical studies had their *raison d'être* as long as one limited one's learning to literature and metaphysics. They have had a goal in so far as one has thought that the rhetoric of Aristotle was the "nec plus ultra" of human perfection; in so far as men had no idea of progress and had placed their interest in life in speculations and hypotheses. But our century wants something else. It has shown that there was a side to human intelligence which had been forgotten, and that this side contained a whole world of indispensable knowledge, all the seeds of the future; and it is before the pressure and development of these previously under-estimated faculties that the prejudices, the old routines, the systems of pure convention, the absurdities of all kinds that block the march of humanity, are toppled.

Very well! This pressing indispensable thing that summarizes all the instincts and all the ideas of our epoch, and that is called industry, finds only indifference among us and often even disdain. Industry, which is, so to speak, the only future that we can promise ourselves, because we are placed under an ungrateful heaven, in the bosom of a climate that refuses us almost all the powers of nature—industry which is a need "sine qua non" of our existence and of our progress—industry, is the only thing that is not thought over, that is not appreciated, that is not studied in the colleges.

What! Must we then persist in living sixty years back, in transporting ourselves into a world that is no longer ours and in gratuitously making ourselves the conservers of outdated theories? Must we persist in failing to recognize the results accomplished by industry, and the necessities imposed upon us by the situation of our country and by our own inter-ests? Must we wait until our indifference to indispensable knowledge has become a disgrace to the Canadian people before we judge ourselves capable of learning it? When will we have our fill of the sad results of our inertia, and must we wait until disgust suggests the remedy?

I hear everyone saying: "We are young, let time take its course; are we not advancing? Look at the land that has been cleared, the progress of the cities." And it is with these banalities that we perpetuate our own inaction. But look at the United States, see if they are content to call themselves young, or if they have not taken advantage of their youth to make the immense steps that one needs in the career of progress.

With respect to a people who have need of immediate reforms, is youth then a reason for not adopting them, and for leaving time to do the work of men?

It is the nature of progress, as it is of all things, to be accomplished when its hour has come. Why then should we retard it at the moment it is applicable, under the pretext that our development is not that of the greatest nations? We have found place for a host of studies that are no doubt useful, even necessary, but of less importance than that of industry; we were not too young to devote a large part of our time and our intelli-gence to these secondary studies; why should we be too young to do the same for a branch of education that is more indispensable to us? What people are too young to be enlightened as to their interests, and how long must we be made impotent by the phantom of a word? How much time is required for our youth to arrive at the age of reason? There is, mean-while, a limit to this tutelage, and does it not find itself in general aspira-tions, in the universally felt need for reforms? The boundary of youth is experience; now, experience has shown us that this state of things can-not last any longer. It is time to leave it. A remedy must be found for the defects in our system of education, defects that have already caused much harm, and that can only increase because of the developments taking place in the country. It is time to spread industrial education amongst ourselves, and especially the teaching of political economy, which rules it, and without which industrial development leads often only to disaster. It is political economy that enlightens people to their true needs and prevents the sacrifice of the general interest to transient indi-vidual interests. [...]

I sum up. Elementary schools of industry must be set up, along with special schools of industry.

If we wish to stop the continual sacrifice of the national honour, if we wish to face the needs that multiply everywhere around us, we must do it. Let us no longer look abroad for our engineers, let us form them ourselves. It will cost the public pocket less.

Let us have artisans who can work in the manufactures, and industrial-ists who can run them without having to go to the United States to learn all these various arts. Let us have men, finally, useful citizens, who can serve their country, and who are not forced to abandon it to seek their fortunes elsewhere because careers are not available for their aptitudes and because there are no industrial establishments that can turn our national resources into profit.

THE CREAMERY AS SYMBOL OF PROGRESS

F.E.A. Gagnon, *Choses d'Autrefois, feuilles éparses* (Montreal, 1905), pp. 51-3.

Athenians, Athenians, where are you leading us?

Where? . . . . but simply to wealth, and that to the rhythmic sound of melodic phrases and with a speed, of which the centrifugal machine at the Sainte-Marie (Nouvelle-Beauce) creamery, with its 1900 revolutions per minute, is a lively and striking image.

This centrifugal machine is truly marvelous: it separates the cream from the milk at a rate of 1000 pounds per hour. Thanks to its use, the one hundred and six farmers who supply the creamery, of which MM.

Duchesnay, Lindsay, Chaperon, and others are the owners, need only transport their milk once a day. The evening milk is mixed with the morning milk. The light cream formed during the night is remixed with the milk during transport, but the centrifugal separator undoes all that.

The factory of Sainte-Marie de la Beauce is a real Danish factory. The apparatus is put into motion by a six-horsepower steam engine, a jewel! You must go see the separator work, the mixer, the vacuum suction devices, etc. Above all, be sure to have every thing explained to you by the intelligent director of the school-factory, Mr. Stanislas Barré.

Go and see. I tell you just this, because one must always be careful not to promise more butter than bread.

A SUMMARY OF CANADIAN PROGRESS

Charles Legge, *A Glance at the Victoria Bridge and the Men Who Built It* (Montreal, 1860), pp. 24-9.

The tide of immigration continued to flow; those trials and difficulties became less from year to year, as the country became opened up. Montreal was brought within four weeks' journey of Toronto and that harbinger of progress, a newspaper, started. Slavery was declared in both provinces incompatible with the institutions growing up, and was at once and forever abolished; the fetters which bound slaves then in the country were knocked off and the liberated Africans declared British subjects, and as such free men. The second steamboat in the New World, first ploughed the blue waters of the St. Lawrence about the year 1809, reducing the journey between Montreal and Quebec to 36 hours, and was quickly followed by additional ones in both provinces. A fierce and deadly struggle for British supremacy, against almost overwhelming odds, was brought to a successful termination, and the neighbouring power taught a lesson they have not yet forgotten. Commerce increased, manufactures were established, schools opened and churches built, even in defiance of obstacles thrown in the way by a government at the distance of 3000 miles, whose officials were profoundly ignorant of the resources and growing importance of the rising colony, as may be inferred from a single illustration. So late as the year 1812 the wood-work of the Psyche frigate, intended for naval operations on Lake Ontario, was sent out from England, to a country where it could be provided on the spot in one tenth of the time necessary to carry it from Montreal to Kingston, and at the twentieth part of the expense; even wedges were included in the stock sent. And to exemplify more completely the information possessed at that time by the Admiralty, full supplies of water-casks were forwarded for the use of the ships of war on Lake Ontario, when it was only necessary to throw a bucket overboard to draw up water of the best quality. An amount of ignorance like this, when shewn by this department of government, that should have been better posted up, was bad enough even though the money squandered did not directly affect the people's interest, but when, from the numerous suicidal acts that emanated in the Colonial Office, the shoe commenced to pinch, petitions, addresses, remonstrances, and at last armed rebellion, opened the eyes of the mother country to the injury and injustice her children in the West were suffering, and, after crushing the unconstitutional movement, at once proceeded to devise a system of responsible self-government, and, with a generous confidence in the attachment of her sons in Canada, and assurance in their ability to take care of themselves, slipped the leash, and left her full fledged offspring to go on its journey for weal or for woe.

But a few years have elapsed since this boon was granted, and already Canada can point to the enormous strides made in every direction, as a proof that for the Anglo Saxon race self-government is requisite. She can proudly make known the fact that as the commencement of the century saw her with a population of 150,000 inhabitants, she now claims the allegiance of 3,000,000, a case of rapid increase without a parallel, if the auriferous countries are excepted, and point to her broad expanse of unoccupied territory stretching far north and westward to the Pacific Ocean, with her noble lakes and unrivalled rivers, to her rich soil and healthy climate, in all its different variations, together with inexhaustible mines of iron, copper, lead, and other minerals, as the future homes and means of support for hundred millions more.

She can at the present time show a chain of inland lakes and rivers, connected together for commercial purposes, by a series of the most magnificent canals in the world, enabling vessels of 800 tons to ascend from the Ocean to Lake Ontario, and vessels of 400 tons from thence to Lake Erie, with an increased commerce from about $3,000,000 in the year 1800, to $75,631,404 in 1856. But a few years since, where the solemn silence of the forest was interrupted but by the wandering Indian or wild animal, and where the foot of a white man had rarely or never trod, she can now point out numerous cities, towns, and villages, with populations ranging from 40,000 downwards; many of them second to none on the continent for the enterprise and public spirit of their inhabitants, the architectural ornament and solidity of public and private buildings, for the extensive works of utility they have completed, and to their mammoth warehouses and harbours filled with the produce of a still further west; and exult in those busy marts of commerce as evidence that she is on the high-way to prosperity. She can show extensive regions once the scene of the beaver's labours, and the home of the sickening fever, from which the forests have fled as if by magic, now converted into smiling fields of plenty and peace, and filling the land with the ceaseless hum of industry and happiness. She has produced a system of railways extending over the entire country, unequalled for solidity and permanency of construction on this continent, amounting to about 2093 miles, nearly all of which have been put in operation within the last ten years, bringing the extreme portions of the province within a few hours of each other. The large number of 1,613,935 persons have travelled by this means a total distance of 91,027,299 miles, or an average for each passenger of 56½ miles, at the rate of 26 miles an hour, with only one passenger killed for every 13,003,900 miles travelled during the year 1858, but which is regarded by the Government Railway Inspector as being unusually severe in so far as loss of human life is concerned. It will be remembered that during the summer season those floating palaces the steamboats attract nearly all the pleasure travel, which would otherwise swell the number by railway to an enormous extent. Distance and time are completely annihilated by the flashing of the electric fluid along the telegraphic wires and bring all sections of the country within a moment's distance of every portion of the continent connected by the magic wire. That great engine of popular instruction and freedom the press has increased beyond calculation from the days of its infancy, when the solitary Government Gazette in 1795 sent forth its 100 copies per week, with the latest intelligence from New York and Quebec a month old, to the present time, when from the city mammoth daily to the village modest weekly, the country is deluged with reading matter on all conceivable subjects and with intelligence a few hours old from all parts of America. This enormous power is controlled and directed by men from the highest order of newspaper talent, down to those possessing only a mediocrity, but all working with the common view of instructing and improving their readers. With still greater pride can Canada point out the high position she has attained in the education of her children both spiritually and intellectually; to the complete religious toleration which prevails, allowing every man to worship his Maker according to the dictates of his conscience, none daring to make him afraid; to the countless spires rising towards heaven from one end of the land to the other, all uniting on the calm Sabbath morning in a melodious but solemn summons for the people to attend the house of God. With just exultation she may also call attention to the universities, academies, common schools, and mechanics' institutes, which stud the whole face of the country, and attended during the year 1858 by 463,288 pupils, at an expense of $2,493,811, furnishing a system of education embracing classics, belles-lettres, law, medicine, mathematics, and the whole range of sciences, down to rudimentary instruction in the English language. These institutions are open to all, from the highest to the lowest on the same terms, with no merit recognised but ability. She can point to the upright, learned and eloquent men who grace the ermine they wear, and as fountains of justice distributing it in streams, as clear and irresistible as the limpid waters of the mighty St. Lawrence in its majestic flow; to her men of science, her Logans, Dawsons, Hunts, Smallwoods, Billingses, and a host of others with world-wide reputations, all actively engaged in bringing their knowledge to bear on her physical development; to her Keefers, Pages, Shanleys, and others, as engineers who have made themselves eminent and their country celebrated for the colossal public works they have planned and executed; to the free and elective government with its constitutional opposition, to guarantee that the rights of the people shall not be invaded nor the public funds mis-appropriated, and, when in the course of time changing places, to see the late ministers converted into watchful sentinels on their successful adver-saries taking the helm of state,—all equally zealous in the maintenance of their country's credit, honour, and prosperity; and above all, to the feel-ing of loyalty and devoted attachment to the land of their forefathers, burning as brightly as the patriotic flame on their own country's altar,—to the thrill of joy and pride which pervaded all classes on the glorious termination of England's conflicts—to the gratification felt on being al-lowed to contribute a regiment to her army, with a contribution to the widows and orphans of her brave defenders, and able, in the event of an emergency, to send into the field a hundred thousand of her sons with the deadly minie-rifle to sustain the prestige of "the flag that's braved a thousand years the battle and the breeze," with arms as strong and spirits as brave, as those of their common ancestors who conquered on the fields of Agincourt and Waterloo.

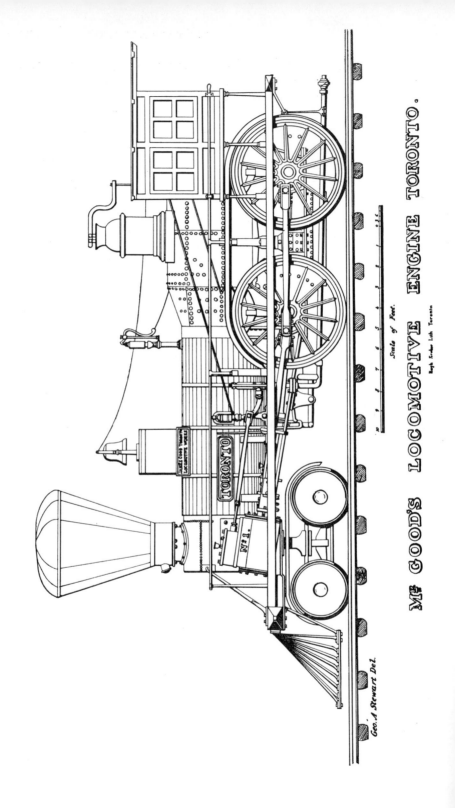

Geo. A. Stewart Del.

Roph. Krober Lith Toronto.

Scale of Feet.

MR GOOD'S LOCOMOTIVE ENGINE TORONTO.

The Growth of Industry | 5

Until very recently, most Canadians regarded the smoke from factory chimneys as a sign of well-being. The lithographic city views so popular in the nineteenth century reflected that idea. Busy smokestacks meant employment and a happy prosperous community. The production of agricultural implements proved to be one of the most successful lines of early industrial activity. Agriculture required a great deal of hard work, and in the nineteenth century machines to reduce drudgery were regarded as signs of man's continuing ascent to a higher level of civilization. Agricultural writers of the period emphasized the use of machinery and of efficient methods of production. In that context, simple devices to cut wood or easier methods of performing ordinary tasks marked the dividing line between economic success or failure.

The 'horsepower' was just such an implement. Essentially a power take-off device, it used a horse as the prime mover for a variety of machines, much as farmers later used Model T Fords for more than driving to town. Uncomplicated, flexible, and inexpensive, it became a stock item in the catalogues of farm-implement manufacturers. The production of horsepowers, threshers, ploughs, and other devices became one of Canada's earliest manufacturing industries. Many firms were small and not all enjoyed long life. But they provided a school for training in iron working and machine skills, and stimulated the growth of related manufactures.

Scattered deposits of bog iron ore and a practically unrestricted supply of timber for fuel provided the basis for Canada's early iron industry. However, John Mason's experience demonstrated that the successful exploitation of these natural resources depended on technical skill and capital. In time, local furnaces and forges brought a modest prosperity to their communities by the production of ironware suited to the needs of an agricultural society. Neighbourhood supplies of ore were soon exhausted, however, or rendered unprofitable by technical advances—particularly in the U.S.—that made it cheaper to import castings. The discovery of large nickel ore deposits in Ontario raised new hopes for industrial development and made Canadians increasingly aware of the fact that the ability to process their own natural resources was the key to wealth.

Steam power was first and most dramatically employed in North America to solve transportation problems. But by the 1830s Canadian

foundries and machine shops were turning out steam engines for industrial purposes. In urban centres, newspapers triumphantly heralded
the shops and skills of local engine builders, and Elijah Leonard recalled
that his first steam engine in London, Ontario drew crowds of curious
onlookers. The building of steam locomotives became an important industry in its own right at Montreal, Kingston, and Hamilton, providing
Canadians with still further opportunity to celebrate the advances possible in the age of steam.

Manufacturing played a more important role in Canada's nineteenth-
century development than is commonly supposed. There were large numbers of factories and they produced a remarkable variety of goods. Just
as in agriculture, labour costs stimulated mechanization and more efficient
use of power. The relatively small size of Canadian markets led many
mill-owners to advocate protective tariffs. Since most people won their
livelihood from the land, however, the advantages of manufacturing had
to be linked in a system that also promised rewards for the farmer. Jacob
de Witt's answer was that industry offered a market for agricultural
products, a theme later dramatized in political posters during Macdonald's
campaign for the National Policy. The Bowmanville Cabinet Factory
seemed to prove the benefits of protection; neighbourhood resources and
people found employment in production of the furniture that could be
sold more cheaply than imported ware.

The search for profit made manufacturers sensitive to the peculiarities
of the Canadian scene. Hart Massey's correspondence reveals that in his
case success depended on a combination of American designs and business methods suited to his own economic environment. Foreign influences
in general were a pervasive and significant factor, whether in providing
a model for emulation or a source of competition. As the century wore on,
the problem of direct foreign ownership became increasingly apparent.

AGRICULTURAL IMPLEMENTS

MACHINES FOR THE FARMER

The Canadian Agricultural Reader (Niagara, 1845), pp. 206-8.

1. FARM IMPLEMENTS AND LABOUR-SAVING MACHINES.

—As farmers generally have more leisure at the present season (February) than at any other time of the year, we would recommend to their
attention procuring and repairing such farming implements as they may
need for use during the ensuing season. Ploughs, harrows, rakes, hoes,

shovels, forks, carts, hay racks, scythes, cradles, and many other things, should be examined and put in order; and if there is a probability of there not being a sufficient number for performing conveniently the required work, it will be proper to procure additional ones to supply the deficiency.

2. We do not wish to advocate a lavish waste of money in buying what would be unnecessary, but to direct the attention of farmers to the importance of always having at hand a sufficient number of tools. It is no evidence of economy to save a few shillings by refraining from the purchase of a rake or a hoe, and afterwards lose a day's work or more, in a hurrying season, in consequence of the deficiency thus occasioned. Neither is it a proof of economy to purchase the cheapest implements only.

3. The cheapest are generally the worst made, and are either weak or clumsy. We have known active men to waste nearly half their strength in using such—in performing, day after day, not more than two-thirds of the labor they might have done, had they used strong, neat, and well-made tools. As it is impossible to work *without* tools, so it is impossible to do work well and expeditiously, without *good* tools.

4. Another important subject, is that of labour-saving implements and machines. There is one great advantage in these, which is generally overlooked. By enabling the farmer to despatch his business, his work is more completely under his control; and he is enabled to guard against loss or damage which might be the consequence of more protracted operations.

5. Thus, for instance, in using the horse rake, he is not only enabled to accomplish the same work with one quarter of the expense he would otherwise have to employ; but by enabling him to perform it so much more expeditiously, he can take advantage of the weather, and have many acres of hay upon the ground without the danger of having it spoiled by rain; as the speed with which he may collect it with a horse rake, enables him to anticipate wet weather.

6. Thus, independently of the *immediate* amount of labor it saves, it prevents the troublesome operation of drying wet hay, after it has once before become fit for the mow or stack. Again, by the use of the planting or drilling machine one man is enabled to do the work of several: this is one item of saving; but in addition to this, it very often happens that a crop may be planted with it during a favorable season, and while the ground is in the best possible condition; while, without it, the work might be protracted till the ground is rendered unfit by heavy rains; and a loss of many bushels to the acre sometimes arises from crops being planted out of season.

7. A vast amount of labor might be saved by employing a moderate share of thought and contrivance in constructing or procuring and arranging, some of the simpler and more common kinds of labor-saving machinery. Thrashing machines have become very common, and many are connected with a portable horse power, which may be separated from the

machine and applied to other purposes. This may be easily, and it some-times is, attached to a circular saw, (the cost of which is comparatively small), and the expensive and laborious operation of sawing wood by hand, is rendered expeditious and easy.

8. It may also with a little contrivance, be made to work a straw-cutting machine, a turnip and potato slicer, a corn sheller, and other similar machines, which are commonly worked by hand; and this may be fre-quently done while it is driving a thrashing machine, or performing other work. We have known a fanning mill to be connected with it, and worked by it, the thrashing machine being situated on a floor above, so that the wheat fell directly from it into the hopper of the fanning mill, and passed out ready for market.

9. We have also heard of a pair of buhr-stones placed in a barn, which could be driven by the horse power of a thrashing machine, and used for grinding food for domestic animals. By a little attention and thinking, numberless similar conveniences may be devised. Improvements of this kind should not however be adopted, until calculation has proved that from the amount of labor they will be required to perform, the ultimate saving will more than counterbalance the immediate cost.

AN IMPROVED SAWING MACHINE

Canadian Illustrated News (November 22, 1862), 21.

NOXON'S IMPROVED SAWING MACHINE.

THIS Machine is known as Noxon's Patent Improved Sawing Machine, and took the 'Extra Prize' at the Provincial Exhibition, held in Toronto. It is simple in construction and will not be easy to put out of order. It can be attached to any ordinary horse-power thrashing machine, and is almost self-acting. By an ingenious contrivance in the Machinery the saw raises itself to admit the movement of the log for the next cut. The cuts can be made at any length, and the Patentee warrants it capable of cutting 60 cords of wood per day. It is certainly superior to anything of the kind that has yet been invented both in the simplicity of its arrangement and the ease with which it can be wrought. Any further information can be obtained from J. & S. Noxon, at Ingersoll.

TWO CANADIAN IMPLEMENT MANUFACTURERS

Canadian Illustrated News (October 3, 1863), 245.

WE give here a cut of an improved thrashing machine, designed and manufactured at the establishment of John Watson, Esq., at Ayr, C. W. Mr. Watson has carried on the Foundry and Agricultural Implement Manufacturing business there now for some twenty years or so, and being a man of enterprise and management, his establishment is now among the

PITT'S HORSE POWER WITH WATSON'S IMPROVEMENT

leading ones in its line in the western part of the Province. He makes a splendid combined reaper and mower, of which over sixty were sold this season. For eight years past, Mr. W. has been at work at improvements in the construction of the Separating Thrashing Machine. He offers one now which he claims will thrash and clean faster than any other in the Province. For durability, ease of draught, and general efficiency, he claims that his machine cannot be surpassed; and in this he is backed by the testimony of those who have tried and proved it.

His Horse power (Pitt's patent, with his own improvement) is celebrated for simplicity, ease of draught and effective power, and is a strong and durable article, warranted of sufficient strength for the power at which it is rated. This power is universally admitted by threshers to be the best that is made. Mr. W. supplies them for 8 or 10 horse power, and with lever boxes or draw rods to suit purchasers. It is well adapted for driving any kind of Machinery, but is designed particularly for Threshing Machines.

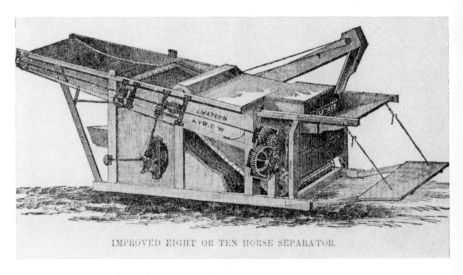

IMPROVED EIGHT OR TEN HORSE SEPARATOR.

Canadian Illustrated News (November 21, 1863), 357.

The engraving on [the facing] page is a representation of the agricultural implement manufactory of Messrs. L. & P. Sawyer, situated at the foot of Wellington street, in this city. It was formerly conducted by Messrs. McQuestin & Co.; but has been in the hands of the present proprietors about six years. It is said to be the largest establishment of the kind in Canada.

The principal building is a stone structure one hundred and sixty feet long, eighty feet wide and three stories high. The wood-work department and the machine shop are both included in one room eighty feet square. Here the wood-work of the implements is made, and the iron portion of the

AGRICULTURAL IMPLEMENT MANUFACTORY OF MESSRS. L. & P. SAWYER, HAMILTON, C.W.

machinery finished. The moulding shop in the rear is of the same size. In the rear of the moulding shop, is a frame building ninety feet square, the lower story of which is used as a finishing shop, the second story for storage, and the third for patterns. The blacksmith shop in the east wing of the building is forty feet square, with a pattern shop of the same dimensions adjoining. The engine is of twenty-five horse power, and was built by the proprietors themselves. Formerly stoves in large quantities were manufactured by Messrs. Sawyer, but they have now almost entirely abandoned this branch of business. All kinds of general machinery and agricultural implements are also made here. Messrs. Sawyer now confine themselves chiefly to the construction of threshing machines, mowing and reaping machines, straw cutters, fanning mills and the more costly articles used on the farm. At this establishment Ball's celebrated combined mower and reaper is manufactured in great numbers. It is generally considered to be the best machine of the kind yet constructed; it is simpler in construction, more durable or less liable to get out of order, and does its work better than any other in use.

The distinguishing feature of this machine is a flexible, folding cutting-bar, which adapts itself to uneven surfaces, and cuts on hill sides as easily as on a level. It is also useful in fields where there are ditches, as the operator may work lengthwise or across the furrows. The bar is made of steel, and the guards of wrought iron, inlaid with steel. The machine has two driving-wheels, so that the knife, is always in motion, even while turning in either direction. It is worked very easily, one span of horses being able to work it all day. It is capable of cutting from ten to fifteen acres of grass in a day, and from twelve to twenty acres of grain. We are informed that at nine different trials with a variety of other combined instruments of the same kind, Ball's were decided by competent judges to be the best.

Thirty men receive constant employment at the establishment, whose aggregate wages amount to ten thousand dollars a year. The capital employed, including the value of the buildings, &c., is estimated at about thirty thousand dollars, and the total value of the annual product at about the same sum. The implements made here are quite as good as any made in the United States, and with a duty of 20 per cent in favor of the Canadian manufacturer, it is quite easy to understand why the importation of agricultural implements has diminished, and the home demand been supplied by our own manufacturers.

About one hundred tons of Scotch pig iron, a large quantity of wrought iron, and sixty thousand feet of lumber, are used annually by Messrs. Sawyer & Co., in the manufacture of agricultural implements. We were also shown some iron, which is largely used by Messrs. Sawyer, peculiarly adapted for castings for such work, as it has greater tenacity, probably, than any other iron known. A large pig of the best Scotch iron was easily broken by a single blow from an ordinary sledge, while repeated blows were required to break a much smaller pig of this metal. It is obtained at Salisbury, Conn. We are informed that the United States Government has purchased all the iron of this description in the market for the manufacture of guns, for which it is peculiarly adapted. When their supply of this iron is exhausted Messrs. Sawyer will use Canadian iron for their castings, which is nearly, if not quite as good as the Salisbury iron.

THE DETAILS OF BUSINESS

Hart A. Massey Correspondence, Massey-Ferguson Archives, Toronto. Reprinted by permission.

Messers Weed, Parsons and Co. Newcastle, Feb. 10th, 1862.
Albany, N.Y.

Gentlemen:
I am desirous of getting up a catalogue of Agricultural Implements, say about thirty pages, similar to those that you get up for Mr. W.A. Wood of Hoosick Falls, with the exception that I want to use a cut of most of the implements recommended on most of the pages. I would want you to get the use of Mr. Woods cuts for his mower and combined mower and reaper. He has promised them to me, as I got my patterns off him. You will please inform me, by an early mail, of your lowest price and terms per thousand, say for 2,000.
Yours truly,
H.A.Massey.

Mr. J. Gartshore, Newcastle, Feb. 13th, 1862.
Dundas, C.W.

Dear Sir:
I am informed that you manufacture or can repair the lathes made by Wm. H. Gibson, who was, at one time, in your place.
I want one of the small gear pinions, diameter, 2 3/16th of an inch, 19

cogs and 1 inch face, which you will please send me by train or express. If you have not got one on hand, perhaps you can cut one for me?
Yours truly,
H.A. Massey.

Mr. A.S. Edmunston,   Newcastle, Dec. 18th, 1861.
Rochester, N.Y.

Dear Sir;
Yours of the 10th instant is just received. I can get along very well without you until the first of next month, but would like you to be sure to come then, as it would disappoint me much to wait till then, and then have you not come. I shall therefore expect you the first or second week in January. As I do not wish to have another person commence the machines, you will therefore please try to be here as soon after the New Year as you can.
I want to get a small, cheap iron lathe. If you see any good second hand ones, let me know. I also want a good plough wooder if you hear of one. I have a stereotype cut of a threshing machine at the Engravers in the Rural New York Office in Rochester, which I wish you to bring. The price of it was to be $4.00. If you do not have the money to spare to pay for it, I will send it to you. . . .
Yours truly,
H.A. Massey.

Messers Johnson, Thompson Co.   Newcastle, Feb. 24th, 1862.
Montreal, L.C.

Gentlemen:
Mr. Lyman of this place, who gave you a sample of malleable iron that I wished made has just handed me your card on which you state 9—10 cents per lb. and asked $1.30 to make the pattern. These I have already had made at Troy, where I have been getting my malleable castings, and only paid 8½ cents per lb.; and they were very good castings. I should not like to pay for patterns as I can get them at the same place as before, but I prefer home manufactures if as good.
I will send you my order at 9—9½ cents per lb. and you make your own patterns. The wrench pattern is one that you will find great sale for; I could send you a wrench to make one by. . . .
Your early reply will much oblige,
Yours truly,
H.A. Massey.

Mr. A. Richardson,   Newcastle, Jan. 2nd, 1862
Grafton, C.W.

Dear Sir:
I want to get a few thousand feet of dry oak 2x3 inch plank. Have you
got it or could you tell me where to get it? If you have it, what is your best
price delivered at Grafton station?
Do you want a machine this year and to pay me in lumber?
Yours truly,
H.A. Massey.

Messers Chuvett and Co.   Newcastle, June 19th, 1861
Kingston, C.W.

Gentlemen:
The 16 bars, $\frac{7}{8} \times \frac{3}{4}$ of an inch have arrived and I find I made a mistake in
ordering—it should have been $\frac{7}{8} \times \frac{1}{2}$ of an inch. Will you change it for me
and send me 500 lbs. of $\frac{7}{8} \times \frac{1}{2}$? If you will take the other back I would
rather you do so as it is unsizable and can only be used for harrow teeth.
Send the very best iron.
Yours truly,
H.A. Massey

IRON AND STEEL MANUFACTURE

THE DIFFICULTIES OF TRANSPLANTNG IRON-MAKING
TECHNOLOGY

Robert Gourlay, *Statistical Account of Upper Canada*, 2 vols (London,
Simpkin and Marshall, 1822), vol. I, pp. 324-6.

"POTTER'S CREEK, Dec. 4th, 1817.

"SIR,
    "You desired me to give you every information in my power of the

probability or certainty of making iron in this part of the province, so as to be beneficial to the manufacturer and the public. I will state to you what is for and what against. In favor of iron-works is the high price of iron and plenty of timber for coal; everything but these is against the first beginner. The bog-ore is scattered over the whole country, but I do not know of any one bed of ore that will exceed 120 tons. I spent three months in examining the country for ore, and I calculate that it will take all the ore I found within twenty miles of this place to supply a small furnace for seven years; but I believe considerable quantities within that space are not yet found. No rock ore has as yet been found in this part of the province, and if there is any, it must be at considerable depth from the surface of the ground and will be difficult to find, as the strata lie horizontal. Another thing against iron-works is that it will require many experiments before we can know the best method of working the ore, and there is not any stone in this part of the province that will stand the fire, and I believe it will be best if it comes from three different places in the United States. I want five or six pieces of iron, each 30 cwt., these will come to an enormous expense. I intended to ask the Government to give or lend me five or six disabled cannon for this. I asked the Government to pay the passage of five or six families from England to work in the furnace. This could not be granted, and therefore I would not ask for the cannon. Another thing against me is that there is not a man in the country that I know capable of working in the furnace. But the greatest difficulty I have to overcome is iron-men, as we call them, who are the very worst sort of men, colliers not excepted. Not one of a hundred of them but will take every advantage of his master in his power. If I have just the number of hands for the work, every one of them will know that I cannot do without every one of them, therefore everyone of them will be my master. Anxiety and trouble will be the consequence; and if I keep more hands than are necessary, so as to have it in my power to turn those away who will not do right, this will be expensive. But, after all, if the ore is as good as I expect, I hope to reduce the price of iron very considerably. The place where I am is a reserve lot. Governor Gore has promised encouragement to the works, when the Government is satisfied they will answer a good purpose. If Governor Gore does not return to this country, and what he promises should be refused me, iron-works will be at an end with me and at this place; but I shall not ask for the promise until the inhabitants of the country will be my bondsmen for the benefits arising from the iron-works. When I saw you I offered a considerable sum of money to take them off my hands; this I repeat, not but what I believe they will answer, but the trouble will be more than equal to any profit from them. Those who begin iron-works in this country after me will start many thousand dollars ahead of me, everything they want except stone will be had here,

the best method of working the ore will be known, and men will be
learned to work it.

"I am, sir,
"Your obedient servant,
"JOHN MASON."

EARLY IRON SMELTING

Elijah Leonard, *A Memoir* (London, Ontario, 1894), pp. 6-7.

We lived on the east bluff in a frame house on a lot owned for many years
by Mr. Tolmie, but the building has long since disappeared. The Normandale Furnace, as it was called, was established by an Englishman named
Capron some years before. He did not make the business pay, and sold
out to the Messrs. VanNorman. The furnace consisted of a brick stack or
chimney about thirty feet high and five feet bosh, built on the side of a
hill. Motive power was obtained from the fine stream of water running
through the village, which kept in motion an overshot wheel about fourteen feet in diameter, that in turn drove a double piston bellows by means
of cranks. Only one tuyere was employed to admit the blast. The charcoal was made back in the bush, and the iron ore teamed in from a swamp
about seven miles west. My father had charge of the works, and directed
the mixing of ore and charcoal in the top house. The material was dumped
into the furnace by barrows and the iron, when melted, ran down into a
hearth about two feet wide and five feet long. Into this receptacle we
dipped our ladles and carried off the product direct to the flasks. When
in full blast we took off two heats in twenty-four hours, consisting of
plows, stoves, kettles, sleigh shoes, and all kinds of castings required in
a new country. One of the stoves made at these works is at present in use
in the Art School-room, Mechanics' Institute in this city. At this time
Normandale was a thriving place, the furnace requiring about four hundred men directly and indirectly getting out and teaming ore, burning
charcoal, working about the furnace, and attending to the mercantile part
of the establishment. Normandale has receded since those days and contains about eighty inhabitants now. The site of the furnace can yet be
located, but in place of smoke, and glare, and heat, and the throb of the
bellows, all is quiet save the noise of the ever-running stream. A vegetable
garden takes the place of the top house and the side hill is covered by a
goodly sized orchard.

The ore we used was bog ore, which was gathered from the neighboring swamps and brought to the furnace with teams. This supply lasted a good while, but played out finally, and the furnace, then in charge of Mr. Romaine VanNorman, was abandoned about 1853, after having supplied for years the whole of Western Canada with castings. I understand there is yet plenty of this ore in the same locality, but it does not pay to work it at the present price of pig iron.

THE MARMORA IRONWORKS

William H. Smith, *Canada: Past, Present and Future* (Toronto, 1851), p. 247.

A company was formed in Belleville for the purpose of purchasing the property and making another attempt to work the mines. The Marmora Iron-works, the property of the Marmora Foundry Company, are situated on Lots. Nos. 9 and 10, in the fourth concession of that township. The works, which are erected on the bank of the Crow River, a short distance from the foot of Crow Lake, are very extensive, and consist of two blast-furnaces of good size, one of which has been within a few months almost newly built and lined with Stourbridge brick, and is ready for use at any time when the operations of the company may be resumed. The blast (which is called the 'hot-blast') is furnished by a new and improved cylinder apparatus with air-heating ovens on the most approved principle, and is driven by a powerful and never-failing stream of water. This furnace has been in blast but for a short period, and that only for the purpose of testing the practicability of working the ore, so as to produce such a quantity of iron per diem, as would leave reasonable expectations of the manufacture proving profitable. The company therefore spared no expense in fitting up the furnace, which was done under the superintendence of an eminent iron-founder and practical assistants. The quantity of iron (pig) produced from this furnace was five tons per day of very superior quality, and it was found that the probable cost of manufacture in a blast of longer duration would not exceed three pounds, or three pounds five shillings per ton.

Owing to some difficulty between the directors and a portion of the stockholders, who had refused payment of their stock, the works were stopped after this experiment, and will not probably be resumed for a year or two unless the company succeed in leasing the premises to some practical person, a course which they would prefer rather than carry them on in future on their own account.

The premises of the company are very extensive, and comprise (in addition to the blast-furnaces and several large houses for storing charcoal), a large stone building with trip-hammer, for the manufacture of bar-iron, several stone buildings and houses, used for shops, boarding-houses, etc., and about twelve frame dwelling-houses occupied formerly by the work-people of the establishment, which are now rented out to various parties. There are also a flouring-mill, a saw-mill, and a building formerly a tannery, but now about to be converted into a clothing- and fulling-factory, all driven by the same stream (which is capable of propelling three or four times as much machinery from the same head) over which a very hand-some and suitable bridge was built last year. A church (Roman Catholic), built of stone and of very neat construction, is situated nearly opposite the bridge, on the western bank of the stream. All of these buildings are on the property of the company, and form together a compact and flourishing village, in which is a post office. On the north side of the village, and also on the property of the company, a town-plot has been laid out, and a few lots sold, on which buildings are now being erected by the purchasers; but the whole of the grounds on which the buildings above described stand is intended by the company to be reserved for the purpose of leasing to tenants. On the south side of the village is a well-cultivated farm, with handsome dwelling-houses and suitable out-houses, gardens, etc., also the property of the company.

The ore-bed (or rather the main ore-bed from which the furnace was supplied, for there are many valuable beds of magnetic iron-ore in the neighbourhood and some of bog-ore) is situated on a high bank on the shore of Crow Lake; it is mined easily and loaded on board scows for transport to the works, from which the ore bed is distant about three miles and a half. The ore is a magnetic oxide, very rich, three tons yielding two tons of iron. Excellent as the cast-iron made from this ore, it is still more suitable for bar-iron, the toughness and ductility of that which has been made there giving it a preference to the best Swedish iron. Marble and lithographic stone are also on the property of the company; samples of the latter were sent to the great exhibition at London and received (as did also the iron and specimens of ore sent) favorable notices from the English press.

THE CASE FOR A NICKEL STEEL INDUSTRY IN ONTARIO

'Statement of Samuel J. Ritchie', *Ontario Department of Mines Annual Report, 1892* (Toronto, 1892), pp. 110-11.

I think the iron industry can be most successfully established in this country in combination with the nickel industry. I do not see how it could live here alone. There would be no use in anyone trying to send iron from here to any other country, whereas nickel steel could be sent to England or the continent, or anywhere in the world. There is no question that the demand for nickel steel will be a large and permanent one. I can quote what Sir James Kitson told me the last time I saw him; he said that every boiler in Her Majesty's war vessels would be superseded by nickel steel plates, and this not only for first class, but even for second and third class vessels. Sir James is ex-president of the Iron and Steel Institute. There is no doubt that nickel steel must be preferred for any purpose where great strength, elasticity, and resistance are required. There is a market in the United States for this ore when treated in the way I have described, and the difference between the freight you would have to pay, for instance, from anywhere on the Central Ontario to points east of the Allegheny mountains and the freight you would have to pay from Lake Superior ought to more than offset the duty. Canada ought to have a large market of her own. She has upwards of 13,000 miles of railway—a larger percentage of mileage per head than the United States—and there is no reason why she should not produce the highest grade of material for all her locomotives, cars and car-wheels which she now buys of Krupp. Krupp has got to go to Africa for his ore and ship and haul it by rail. If he gets any nickel he must go to New Caledonia or Canada for it. There is no reason why all these things should not be manufactured here. There is no such difference in labor, fuel or tariff as to prevent it. I am certainly of opinion, from observation in my own country of such towns as Pittsburgh, Chicago, Cleveland, Reading, and Bethlehem, that by the establishing of various branches of the iron industry you create a local market for pig iron, and in that way you put the industry on a better basis. I do not know any country that ever got rich by selling raw material and buying manufactured, and I do not think that Canada will prove an exception. She needs to manufacture for herself; she cannot sell grain from the farm and buy manufactured articles, paying 30 to 40 per cent. duty on them, and prosper very well.

There is no reason in the world why the iron industry should not be established in Ontario. The Illinois manufacturers haul their coke over five hundred miles; you do not need to haul yours over three hundred. These companies do not have any return cargoes; the cars in which the coke is shipped go back empty. No grain or anything of that kind is shipped in them. The cars are owned by the companies themselves. Train after train comes to the Illinois Steel Company with coke, and goes back empty. The copper mines at Butte, Montana, get their coke from Connellsville, and pay $18 or $19 a ton for it. I have not the figures with me which would enable me to say what amount of freight the establishment of such an industry would contribute to the railways, but I can say this, that if the mineral business were taken away from the Pennsylvania system of railroads it would bankrupt it in four months, and the case is similar with all the railroads in the United States. The only wonder is how the roads here can live without such a business at all.

The iron business would afford employment for all classes of labor, from the most skilled artisan to the common navvy. A great number of the iron workers in the States are paid high wages, higher than any form of labor employed in Canada. Labor in the iron and steel mills and iron furnaces of the United States is better paid than labor in the mines or on the farm—more than twice as much as farm labor.

For the manufacture of nickel steel it does not matter much whether you have protection or not. Steel rails I think now come into Canada free. You have no industry to protect, if protection pure and simple is what is aimed at. What you want to do here is to produce an article which you can not only sell at home, but export it abroad and keep your balance of trade right. If you make nickel steel you do not need to swap it for anything. You could not sell iron alone in England; carrying coals to Newcastle would be an easy task compared with that. I do not know how they could manufacture nickel steel more cheaply in England than we could here. They cannot manufacture for nothing there any more than we can here. Their coke costs as much as your coke would cost. When I was over there last, coke was higher a good deal than it was in the United States. I think that there is little doubt that you could lay down coke here just as cheap as the majority of manufacturers in England get it. I do not think there is anything lacking now to enable the industry to be established, since a process has been invented to treat such ores as you have here. If you were going in, depending wholly on the ore as it is taken from the ground, it would be another story. There is plenty of ore where there is no railway. Between the end of our railway and the Northern there are large deposits of ore containing no sulphur. But as you are able to treat the entire output of the mine by this process and get a superior class of ore, especially after roasting it, it is not so essential that a first class ore be provided by nature as it used to be.

I think if your moneyed men who have invested so largely in loan societies, etc., wish to protect their investments they cannot do better than set about establishing this industry. No country can ignore such a natural storehouse of wealth and expect to prosper. Compare the Southern States of today with what they were before the war, when they used to purchase everything with cotton, even the bacon they used, from the north, and see what a change has been brought about by the development of their mineral resources. Lands around Birmingham [Alabama] that were offered to me for fifty cents, or $1 per acre could not be bought now for $5,000 or even $10,000 per acre.

THE AGE OF STEEL

Iron and Steel of Canada, vol. I, (1918), pp. 1-3.

The present century is surely an age of steel. During the thirteen and a half years of industrial expansion which proceeded the outbreak of the war no other commodity played so conspicuous a part as did steel. In the last three and a half years it has measured the offensive and defensive powers of nations, and from all appearances it will continue to play an equally important role for years after peace is declared. From all appearances the engines of peace no less than the engines of war must continue to be moulded from this metal, and the progress of any country will be proportionate to the use she is able to make of it.

Canada possesses, or can easily acquire the necessary raw material of iron ore and fuel. She has the electrical energy and the latent ability in her human forces. She lacks only a national awakening that will inspire in her people a due appreciation of the importance of her Iron and Steel industry, and provide her laboratories, furnaces, forges, rolling mills, foundries and machine shops with well trained metallurgists, chemists and mechanics....

What then is the solution? If we search for it among the experiences of older countries that have attained industrial preeminence, there is much to support the conviction that efficient organization of industrial skill and technical literature has played a most important role. The Iron and Steel and other metallurgical institutes and associations of the United States, Great Britain and other European countries, together with many excellent trade and technical periodicals, have done much to attract brain power, awaken latent ability, encourage the establishment of facilities for technical education, and inculcate the most advanced methods in the iron and steel industry of these countries. There are only two ways of acquiring knowledge, namely, by personal instruction and by literature; and technical organization and technical literature are the best means towards this end. The establishment of technical schools is of little value without some local and national awakening force that arouses the interest of those to be benefited thereby and sets the goal for both students and teachers.

At first thought it may occur that the existing organizations and periodicals of other countries are sufficient for Canada. But if the Canadian boys have to look for their source of inspiration and instruction to the industrial centres of other countries, the best of them will sooner or later be attracted there; and even though they remain in Canada, they cannot help but feel that the professional side of their business is only a reflection of that of other countries, and the prestige of the Canadian industry and the pride they should have in it is to that extent lessened. This does not argue against Canadians seeking membership in the technical societies of other countries. On the contrary, there is much to be gained by this practice and the most progressive operators invariably follow it, just as the most progressive are habitual readers of the leading technical and trade periodicals bearing upon the science, practice and affairs of their industry, irrespective of the country of publication. But it is most important that Canada should possess similar institutions and publications of her own—institutions and publications calculated to make known the fact that at the steel centres of this country may be seen as up-to-date and efficient methods and equipment for producing this commodity as exist anywhere in the world, and that the experts in charge are equally skilled. Also that Canadian industry engaged in the working-up of steel and other metals are turning out a product that is equal, and in many cases, superior to that of their foreign competitors, notwithstanding that many of the latter may be working on a larger scale.

STEAM POWER

STEAM BOATS ON THE ST LAWRENCE

David Stevenson, *Sketch of the Civil Engineering of North America* (London, 1838), pp. 88-9.

Vessels bound for Montreal are generally towed up the river from Quebec by large and powerful steam-boats, belonging to the "St Lawrence Steamboat Tow Company." The company's charge for towing a vessel of 20 feet beam and 9 feet draught of water, from Quebec to Montreal, is L.33:6:8, and for a vessel of 28 feet beam and 15 feet draught of water (the largest size that ever penetrates so high as Montreal), the charge is L.83, 4s. Vessels of intermediate sizes are charged proportionally.

The art of towing vessels by steam-tugs is practised very extensively, and has been brought to great perfection both on the Mississippi, as formerly noticed, and on the St. Lawrence. In both of these rivers the narrowness of the navigable channels, and the great distance at which the ports are removed from the sea, render some other means than sails, for propelling the vessels navigating them, absolutely necessary. The most powerful tow-boat on the St Lawrence when I visited the country was the "John Bull." By this vessel I passed from Quebec to Montreal, a distance of 180 miles, in forty hours, being at the rate of four and a half miles an hour, against a current averaging about three miles an hour. Upon this occasion she had no fewer than five vessels in tow; one of these drew twelve and a half, another ten and a half, two of them drew nine, and the fifth about seven feet of water. The vessels were all towed by separate warps, and were ranged astern of each other in two lines, three of them being made fast to the larboard, and two to the starboard side of our vessel. The management of a steamer with so great a fleet of vessels in tow, in the intricate navigation and strong current of the St Lawrence, requires no small degree of caution and skill on the part of the captain, who on this occasion had his whole charge most perfectly under command: when it was necessary to stop the steamer's progress for the purpose of taking in fuel or goods, he dropped the vessels astern, and picked them up again on resuming his course with the greatest dexterity. Captain Vaughan, who commands the "John Bull," informed me, that it is by no means uncommon, at certain seasons of the year, to have six vessels in tow, and from 1200 to 1500 passengers on board of his vessel at the same time. He tows every vessel by a separate line, and generally keeps them all astern in preference to taking any of them alongside of the steamer, an arrangement which, in the St Lawrence, where the navigable channel is in many places very contracted, and often impeded by large rafts of timber, would be very apt to occasion accidents.

EARLY STEAM ENGINE BUILDING IN TORONTO

Colonial Advocate, July 4, 1833.

STEAM ENGINES

The various purposes to which these useful and powerful pieces of mechanism may be applied are so obvious that any recommendation we could bestow upon them would be perfectly superfluous. The generation of steam for various manufacturing purposes appears to be increasingly appreciated in the vicinity of this town. So much has this subject excited our capitalists, that a laudable competition has been entered into, not only amongst those who are engaged in the building of the numerous steamboats with which our navigable waters are daily becoming more splendidly supplied, for the convenience and comfort of the traveller and the accomodation of commercial interests, by facilitating our numerous exports and imports,—but also for the purposes of domestic manufactures.

For instance, there are now two excellent Cupola Furnaces propelled by Steam Engines in this town, which were but a few months ago propelled by horse power, in which castings of every description are made with the greatest expedition, inferior to none in America.

There are, also, two Steam Engine manufactories in successful operation in the town, viz. Sheldon, Dutcher & Co.'s and Charles Perry's; the latter of which we lately visited and was particularly struck with the superiority of the workmanship of a Steam Engine now preparing for Messrs. Worts and Gooderham's Windmill near this town. It strikes us very forcibly that we never saw anything of the kind wear the appearance of a more superior finish. From Mr. Perry's superior Steam Engine Factory we took a turn down to a Steam Saw Mill, recently erected near the Windmill for the purpose of examining its Engine recently manufactured by Mr. Perry, and to say the least of it we are decidedly of opinion that very few such pieces of Workmanship are to be met with in North America.

The rage for Steam Saw Mills may be said to have commenced in right earnest in this neighborhood. Mr. Bickett has lately erected one in the pine woods east of the Don in this immediate vicinity, the Engine of which was manufactured by Mr. Perry.

We should not be at all surprised if the Steam Engine should supercede water power for the use of mills, not being subject to the casualties of broken dams, stoppages by drought and frost, to say nothing of the unhealthiness of large ponds of stagnant water generating pestilential miasma and causing thereby an unhealthy state of atmospheric air throughout the surrounding neighbourhoods where such mills are situated, and the total waste of perhaps 50 to 100 acres of excellent meadow lands. And besides all this the mill-wright can calculate his machinery with the most unerring exactness, (without being subject to the inconveniences occasioned by the fluctuation of the water, being sometimes high and sometimes low,) where there is a given power to be constantly applied as a propelling power.

It is certainly paying a compliment far below Mr. Perry's merit, to say that he is every way deserving of public patronage,—the fact is, he manufactures a superior article which needs only to be seen and put in motion to be admired.

We intend to visit Messrs. Sheldon, Dutcher & Co.'s works before our next publication.

Colonial Advocate, July 11, 1833.

"LOOK HERE.—We perceive you are looking for the fulfilment of our promise, and HERE IT IS. We took an opportunity of exercising our editorial scrutiny upon the works of Sheldon, Dutcher & Co. and was highly gratified with the treat with which we served ourself.

To do justice to enterprise wherever we find it, is a duty we owe to the various individuals who embark their capital in such useful undertakings as are at once serviceable in themselves & tend in a very superior degree to the promotion of the prosperity of a country. For it is a fact which every day's experience proves, that well informed travellers form their statistical sketches and opinions more upon what they observe of the various manufactories of a town or country, than upon almost any other circumstance.

It is therefore but an act of justice to Messrs. Sheldon, Dutcher & Co. to say that they have the most extensive iron manufactory of any in York or its vicinity. We found them busily engaged in manufacturing the two engines destined to propel the Steam Boat Cobourg. They are constructing upon the low pressure principle, and are to be of sixty horse power each. Such parts of the machinery as we saw completed, appeared to be executed with neatness; but many parts were but just cast and some not even that. The Engine by which their works are propelled and which is the first of their manufactory appears to work with neatness, elegance and ease and is on the whole not a bad specimen. We certainly was not fully aware of the extent of their works until we lately explored them. Goodness, what a hammering and tinkering they keep;—why it is almost deafening. We counted five blacksmith's forges all in active operation, one forge where tin, copper and sheet-iron was manufacturing into the various utensils appertaining to cooking stoves; and besides all this, castings were going on, by the use of the Cupola Furnace, at no small rate. Bless us, what a brilliant sight to see great kettles full of iron reduced to red porridge turned into various moulds,—the stubborn metals thus yielding to the superior force of art and taking such shape as the workman pleases to prescribe for it. All this can be seen at the works of Sheldon, Dutcher & Co. We sincerely hope they may receive such a share of public patronage as will enable them to realize a handsome profit, as the just reward of their laudable enterprise.

We have gratified ourselves so much by our late excursions and besides, have furnished ourselves with such excellent opportunities of indulging our egotistical propensity of bragging of what we have seen, that we intend to continue our rambles of discovery through the town.

PIONEER ENGINE BUILDING IN LONDON

Elijah Leonard, *A Memoir* (London, Ontario, 1894), pp. 14-15.

Up to the time of leaving St. Thomas, I used charcoal for melting purposes, which I purchased from farmers in the vicinity, but was obliged to use anthracite coal soon after starting in London. I generally purchased my coal from G. R. Wilson & Co., of Buffalo, where most of my supplies then came from. These were carried in small schooners to Port Stanley, and thence drawn by teams the twenty-seven miles to London. About this time Mr. VanNorman's bog ore beds were giving out, and he could not supply me with all I wanted, and I was forced to purchase pig iron from Montreal. One of the first houses I did business with was Young, Law & Co. Others were, Mulholland & Baker, Frothingham & Workman. In the year 1842 or 1843 I went to Cleveland, O., with the late Mr. Charles Hope, who was taking over a schooner load of lumber for sale. I, of course, visited all the shops and foundries, and in one of them, the Cuyahoga Works, saw a steam engine cylinder and some parts unfinished. This took my fancy, as I had for some time known that my two horses were not of sufficient strength to do the work. The power was unsteady and unreliable, and a change must come very soon. The upshot of our visit was that they took the lumber (Mr. Hope being unable to sell to advantage) in trade for the engine, and I agreed to pay Mr. Hope. This was the first steam engine, as far as I knew, started in Western Canada, and it did continuous and good service until 1866, when it was destroyed by fire. This cylinder was originally intended for a horizontal engine, but I bolted its head on a bed-plate (first framing a stout oak foundation) and erected two upright standards alongside, to which was fastened the guides. The crosshead was joined by a forked connecting rod to a crank pin and shaft immediately below the cylinder. The crank shaft had on it two pulleys, one to drive the machine shop and one to drive the foundry. The fly-wheel was not bored out but "staked" on the shaft by six or eight keys, fitted to as many flat places on the shaft. This required a first-class mechanic. The cylinder was about eight inches diameter and twenty-four inches stroke. I well remember when we started it for the first time, not only did my fellow-townsmen turn out in good numbers, but some came from St. Thomas to see this wonderful piece of machinery start off. They nearly filled my little shop. We carried the steam from boiler to engine in cast iron pipes and the steam was admitted by an ordinary stop cock to the engine. The plug of this cock had not been properly secured, and when the steam pressure got up a few pounds it blew out with considerable noise, immediately filling the room with steam. Oh, such a scattering of spectators! Windows and doors were not large enough to let my friends out. They were awfully frightened, and tumbled over each other in their excitement. I knew pretty well what was the matter, and crawled under the steam and screwed the plug into its place. The engine went off nicely, but I never could get some of my friends nearer than the door afterwards. We attached a proper starting valve to the engine and a governor also, which was put up-stairs immediately above the engine. It regulated the admission of steam with a forked lever and butterfly valve. This engine continued to do all my work until I removed up to York street in 1865, and was put beyond repair by fire which destroyed the whole premises on the night of May 24th the following year. It was a sad sight to me to see one of my earliest enterprises laid so low. Only the immense brick chimney and the engine on its stout oak uprights remained, like two grim skeletons of what once was a hive of industry and a great source of pride to me.

WORKSHOPS OF THE GREAT WESTERN RAILWAY IN HAMILTON

Canadian Illustrated News (February 14, 1863), 163.

ONE of the many notable features which shew the industrial progress of Canada in the last few years, is the workshops of the Great Western Railway, of which our engraving is a faithful representation, showing as well as the workshops the company's grain elevator and large flour warehouse.

The men have not yet reached the prime of life, who, when boys, rushed from their school rooms to bathe in the very spot where that tall chimney now stands—emitting its rolling clouds of murky smoke—or to paddle their plank boats where that huge elevator receives and discharges its thousands of bushels of grain per hour, for it was then a secluded spot with which neither conventional nor police regulations interfered. But the spirit of improvement has made sad work of the old bathing ground. The limits of *terra firma* have been extended some 700 feet into the bay; and on this 'made ground' the workshops are erected, some twenty buildings in all, embracing an area of over forty acres. They are by no means remarkable for beauty of architecture nor symmetry of arrangement; but then they were not built to please the eye.

WORKSHOPS OF THE GREAT WESTERN RAILWAY IN HAMILTON

The first buildings erected are solid stone structures, which may last for ages for aught one can see to the contrary. The business of the Company however increased too rapidly, the demand for increased shop room became too urgent to await the slow process of the mason, in most of the recent erections, therefore, the carpenter has supplied his place.

If the beauty of architecture is wanting, a walk through the extensive works will reveal, in a marked degree, the beauty of utility—the only beauty specially sought for in their construction. The erecting shop is on the ground floor of the large building, in the foreground to the left. This is the receptacle for the work of all the various shops which constitute the locomotive department, and where each part is assigned its proper place in the perfect machine. This too, is a kind of general hospital for the iron monsters, when maimed in some unlucky accident, or when suffering from any of the numerous ills which locomotive flesh is heir to. The iron horse is a strong jointed, wiry customer, but coursing along at from forty to sixty miles an hour, and pulling a load of some hundreds of tons, is no light work; moreover, in spite of his seeming robustness, he is delicately organized, if we but examine him closely. In spite of the highest skill, constant friction will deprive those valves of their trueness, and a sedimentary deposit will enrust the inside of that boiler, like the stomach of a dyspeptic, notwithstanding all precautions; in either case our strong friend becomes like the retreating Zouave at Fredericksburg, 'fearfully demoralized', and must be sent to the erecting shop to recruit. Here you will find locomotives in every conceivable condition, from the unfledged

WORKSHOPS OF THE GREAT WESTERN RAILWAY IN HAMILTON

boiler with its coat of red paint, looking like a mammoth lobster, to the complete engine scrupulously clean and bright, emitting steam from every allowable aperture, with a hissing sound, suggesting to the mind the idea of an impatient steed snorting to be gone.

In this shop are ponderous lathes for turning crank axles, driving wheels, &c.; also a large planing machine for axles, a Braemar press and a cylinder-boring machine. The shop has twelve tracks, each capable of holding two engines; all the tracks come to a point at the turntable a hundred and fifty yards distant.

Proceeding up a flight of stairs, we are in a room 165 feet long by 83 feet wide, containing over thirty machines of the various kinds used in locomotive building. Seventeen are lathes, four planers, four drilling machines, three shaping machines, and others. The utilitarian eye gazes with pleasure on those long ranges of shafting, extending the whole length of this large building, with innumerable pulleys, belts and wheels in ceaseless motions, and giving employment to over sixty operatives. Here we were shown a set of Whitworth's gauges for turning and boring, varying in size from a sixteenth of an inch to four inches; also a set for taking diameters and lengths, of the same dimensions. The importance of these in securing accuracy of workmanship can scarcely be overestimated. Immediately behind this building we come upon the stationary engine, sixty horsepower, high pressure—drives all the machinery of both locomotive and car departments. Like all true mechanics, Mr. Sharp has a high regard for his engine, and has lately had the room in which it works repaired, finished in a simple, inexpensive, yet exceedingly tasteful way. A few steps further brings us to the blacksmith shop, a low-set brick building; inside, a dark, sooty atmosphere, pierced by the glare of some twenty-six smithy fires, and ringing with the sound of sixty hammers. Here stands the Nasmyth Steam-hammer—shown in our engraving—looking quiet and peaceful enough;—but the obliging foreman steps up to the small handle on the right, gives it a twitch, and straightway the huge hammer seems instinct with life, now tapping gently and quickly as a lady's fingers on the keys of her piano, again thundering down with the strength of a hundred Samsons, making the building tremble to its very foundation.— The hammer and furnace together are great economisers; one scarcely supposes that those small scraps of iron scattered about, many of them weighing but a few ounces, were in process of becoming important parts of a locomotive engine, but so it is. The process is thus: the scraps are piled on boards two or three feet long. These are placed on the furnace. Soon the heat fuses the scraps into a lump, which is pulled out and placed under the hammer, which with a few vigorous thwacks kneads them together as a baker would his dough. They are then beaten into layers of about an inch thickness, and the requisite number welded together to form a crank, axle, or the parts of a driving wheel as the case may be.—Our

STEAM FORGING HAMMER, GREAT WESTERN RAILWAY WORKS

sketch of the hammer shows the forging of a large shaft, for the stationary engine, fourteen feet long and weighing sixteen hundred weight.

From this a door leads into the boilershop. 'The man who hath no music in his soul' may enter here with impunity; but he who has, would do well first to ascertain if there is any rivetting going on. If so, let him forbear, notwithstanding the attractions of the place, among which we note a large punching and shearing machine, which will clip you off a piece of boiler plate half an inch thick and ten inches wide, in a shorter time and with less manual labor than is required to cut as much cheese. A radial drilling machine, the peculiarity of which is that the drill may be brought to any point within a radius of eight feet. Some smaller drilling and shearing machines may also be noticed. In this shop the boilers of the engines and the iron-work of the 'tenders' are made and repaired. So also are those splendid iron girder bridges with which the Company are replacing their old wooden structures. Three of these have already been completed and placed in their positions. A fourth is about to be commenced.

Finishing our inspection of the Locomotive Works, we pass to the Car Department, and enter the Machine Shop, a corner of which, is shown in our engraving, over the roof of the Erecting Shop. There we are sensible of a marvellous change from what we have hitherto witnessed.—In the Locomotive Department everything moves with a solemn, stately regularity, as if it were an undignified thing to be in a hurry. Here, to the contrary, each piece of machinery is rushing and screeching like an embodied fury, not only as if Rome had been built in a day, but as if the whole universe were waiting for that particular board which it is ripping into shreds, or that moulding, which it is fashioning so finely. There are in the Province, many larger collections of wood machinery than this, but there can be few more admirably adapted for the work required. Here, we saw a new branch of manufacture,—a substitute for cotton-waste. The high price of this article, set Mr. Sharp's ingenuity at work to lessen the expense; the result was, the construction of a plane with double irons, that, in front, having several rows of small teeth, which, driven through pine or basswood, divides the fibre of the wood, which is peeled off by the other iron, like an ordinary shaving. The stuff, when thrown together, has very much the appearance of curled hair. For packing axle-boxes and cleaning, it has been found a complete success, and can be manufactured, even by hard labor, at less than one-sixth the price of cotton-waste. The immense saving which this will effect, may be understood, when we say that the quantity of waste used, is over 18,000 pounds per annum, and its price is now from 25 to 30 cents per lb.

TARIFFS AND TECHNOLOGY

PROTECTION: THE CANADIAN MANUFACTURER'S ANSWER TO THE PROBLEM OF TECHNOLOGICAL DEVELOPMENT

Letters to the People of Canada, on Canadian Manufactures (Montreal, 1858), pp. 1-5.

IMPORTANT LETTER FROM JACOB DE WITT, ESQ.,
PRESIDENT OF THE BANQUE DU PEUPLE.
MONTREAL, July 26, 1858.
TO WILLIAM LYON MACKENZIE, ESQ., M.P.,
Editor of the Weekly Message.

You remember that we were very anxious to have Reciprocity with the United States. Why? Because we wanted their market for the produce of our Forests, Farms, and Seas; and why did we want their market? Because it was better than our own. Why was it so? Because they encourage their mechanics, *and we do not.*

But free traders affirm that the consumer paid the duties. If the Americans paid the duties on our lumber, &c., what would we care for Reciprocity? Let them pay their duties, and we will let their produce come to us free. The facts were that when our people exported our produce to the United States (before the Reciprocity Treaty), we, the *producers*, put our hands into our pockets, took out our money, *put it into the United States Treasury, and never saw it again.*

The great variety of important inventions and discoveries of new machinery, moved by Horse, Steam, and Water power, have so multiplied the power of production, and reduced the expense of manufacturing, that whenever there is any considerable competition, duties are almost invariably paid by the producers, to procure a market.

I think the case is different as to who pays the duties, the producer or consumer, in reference to many articles of the first necessity which we do not produce to any great amount, such as Salt, Tea, Coffee, Raw Sugar, Molasses, and other similar goods. Duties on these articles are in almost every case added to the first cost and charges, and are paid by the Canadian consumer. I think a wise policy would require them to be admitted free from duties, or nearly so.

I believe that all classes should (in proportion to their means) contribute to the expense of the State.

A reason why Salt, Tea, Raw Sugar, Coffee, and Molasses should be admitted free, is, that they are articles of the first necessity of life, and the labouring man consumes as much as the man of fortune. It is oppression and cruelty, that the labourer who works hard for his 50 or 100 cents per day, should pay as much duty as the man who is worth millions. I maintain that no duties should be exacted on those articles; but if the Government insist on adding duties on these things, then, by all means, let the duties be levied on the ad valorem principle (on the value), and not on the specific. It is not fair that my servant-man should pay as much as I do for these articles, or that he who buys a cheap article should pay the same tax as he who buys a costly one.

A great object is to afford EMPLOYMENT TO OUR OWN PEOPLE, and to those who emigrate from the British Isles and wish to live under the British crown. *Why should people be obliged to leave Canada for the United States to earn a living there, and we send our money to pay them there for their goods?*

'Tis said there is plenty of land. Let the people go and clear up the forest. Do you think a man who has spent half of his life learning a trade will go to the wilderness to perish there? No, you cannot drive him there; but you may drive him out of the country, to enrich another land by his skill, capital, and labor.

Shall we depopulate Canada by driving our young women from their parents' care and counsel, and the instruction of their clergy, to manu-facture abroad the goods and merchandize we want for our consumption at home?

In passing through the New England States we shall find their water-power all employed. Their running streams are not allowed to go to waste over their rocky beds; the water is *caught, tamed, and made industrious, diffusing wealth and prosperity all around*. Even their small rivulets are dammed up to catch the water formed by the melting snow and the showers. The streams that flow while the people sleep or worship on the sabbath are made to perform some profitable work. I have seen machinery moved by one water wheel, the NETT profit of which was estimated to be equal to the nett profit on fifty well-cultivated farms, adding to the popu-lation and the wealth of all around.

With such prudent examples before us, it seems *a disgrace to the people of Canada* that they do not employ more of their unlimited water-power, when it might be made to produce so much wealth and prosperity. Why do we sleep so long?

It is mainly owing to the manufactures of New England that their poor, hard land is worth and will sell for more cash than our rich lands here, and all over the Western World.

It has been said that the Tariff is to favor the manufacturer at the ex-pense of the public. Now I maintain, that a wise apportioned Tariff is necessary to induce capitalists to invest their funds in taming our water-power and in building up Manufactures which are for the common good, because they can invest their money in other ways where their funds would be quite as productive and with less risk.

A large proportion of our people are Agriculturists; how shall we best promote their interests? Shall we add competitors with them in the market for the sale of their produce, or shall we induce customers to buy and consume their produce?

Shall we provide them a *domestic* in addition to their foreign *market* for every thing which they can raise, by encouraging the manufacture of such articles as can be made with advantage in the country, and which will increase the value of every acre of land?

If all are farmers, who will be purchasers and customers?

Let us reflect on the great advantage to the farmer to have a home market. Is it a benefit to have the butcher from the neighboring town come to his door every week and enquire for fat animals, and give the farmer his price in cash for them? Much better than for the farmer to leave his farm and drive his animals to market, where the cattle arrive in bad plight, when the owner is obliged to take just what he can get (what he would not take if the cattle were at home) rather than be at the expense of taking them back to his farm.

Which system will bring the greatest profit, and most increase the value of his farm?

By encouraging the tanner, your neighbour, he can give you from four to six dollars for your ox hide. If you have not the tanner, you may be obliged, like the South American, to sell your ox hide for the same number of shillings.

I would like to ask the proprietor of every newspaper printed in Canada, how many more subscribers each would probably get if our goods were manufactured in our country than in a foreign land, and how much better the proprietor would be paid than he is at present? Would our manufacturers or foreign manufacturers afford the best support to the press?

Suppose those valuable mines at Marmora were worked so as to require a large city there, how greatly that would increase an editor's paying subscribers, in comparison with the subscription, if the same iron were made in another country!

Now, suppose that 100,000 tons of iron and iron goods were made at the Marmora Iron Works, would it not add to the common wealth of the country, and diffuse it among the people, instead of sending the capital out of Canada, to pay for it elsewhere?

Suppose we estimate, that by manufacturing such goods as we could with advantage in Canada, the paying subscribers to each journal would be increased ten per cent. Would not that be an advantage to their proprietors, and relieve many an aching brow? At the bankers I would enquire if they would not prefer to circulate their bills among our mechanics, than send the gold out of the country to pay for the very goods which, by employing our water-power, could be quite as well made at home?

Most people admit that we may make our pine logs into Deals, Boards, Scantling, &c. I ask, Why stay here? Why not let your sawmills, lathes, &c., go on, work up the timber into doors, sashes, furniture, &c.? Are they afraid it will be too valuable, make us too rich? Why sell our paper rags for a dollar, which, when made into printing-paper, would be worth four dollars? A pound is better than a dollar; but the greatest difficulty is, where shall we get the three dollars in cash to send away to pay others for doing what we can just as well do ourselves? But the greatest loss is depriving the country of the cash, so much wanted at home.

Why should we not work up our farm-wool into cloth, instead of sending the money abroad, thereby draining the country of cash to pay foreign labourers? By encouraging our own manufacturers by a *wisely apportioned Tariff, we shall increase our trade and the public revenue.* By making the cheaper goods, you enable the operatives to buy and pay for the more expensive. If you employ a female in making cheap cotton cloth, you enable her to buy and pay for a silk dress: without the employment she would be idle, or more dependent on her father or brother's labor for a cotton dress worth sixpence per yard, where, with employment, she supports herself, buys and pays for rich goods. In manufacturing the cheap goods, although we derive no foreign trade or revenue on those particular articles, yet the wealth created and diffused among the people by that means, retains capital in our country, whereby the trade and revenue are increased. See the immense trade between the United States and Great Britain. By manufacturing the cheaper articles, they are able to import the more expensive. This shows the effect of their high tariff.

A FURNITURE FACTORY

Canadian Illustrated News (January 17, 1863), 112.

THE Bowmanville cabinet factory is situated in the town of Bowmanville, county of Durham, and was started by the present proprietors about eighteen months since, and already ranks as one of the best in the Province. All kinds of cabinet furniture are made at the establishment, from the cheaper to the higher class.

The firm have been honored by making a large quantity of furniture for the residence of N. G. Reynolds, Esq., Trafalgar Castle, Whitby. As also the counters and fittings to the Ontario Banks in Toronto.

Their principle business however, is in the manufacture of cane-seat chairs, which have hitherto been imported in large quantities, from the United States; they make a greater variety of this class of goods than is made elsewhere in Canada, and fully compete with the American manufactures; their prices for this class of goods are as low as they are sold for in the United States, thereby saving the import duty of 20 per cent to the dealers who buy from this firm. There is on an average, seventy hands employed in this factory, a portion of whom are girls, who have been introduced to plait the cane in the chair seats and backs. The girls work at their own houses, the work being sent out to them, and brought back when finished.

The proprietors themselves being practical working men, the works are carried on under their own immediate supervision, and the system of labour is such that all the hands employed work to advantage. In the chair department each man has his part to do; a chair having to pass through six different hands before being completed. In the three story building the wood work is done, the first floor being devoted to cutting out the stuff, &c., here are found planors, turning lathes, saws of various kinds, &c.

CABINET FACTORY OF G.P. WALTER, BOWMANVILLE

On the second floor the cabinet work is made. The third floor is used solely for making cane seat chairs; here a great variety of machinery is employed to great advantage, all of which is of the best description. All chairs before leaving this room are stamped with the name of the firm.

The machinery is driven by steam power, the rooms, dry house, glue pots, &c., being heated by the exhaust steam from the engine.

The two story building is used for finishing and chair painting. The other buildings are used as store-house-office, &c., &c.

By special arrangement with the Grand Trunk Railway Company, they are enabled to send their goods at a low rate of freight.

As we like to see our Canadian Manufactures encouraged we would recommend any furniture dealer about purchasing goods to try G. P. Walter & Co.

MANUFACTURERS, MACHINES, AND THE NATIONAL POLICY

Canada, *Sessional Papers*, No. 35 (1885), 95-101.

Philip Palmer, manager of the Mispeck Mills, supplies the following:— "From 1879 to 1883, inclusive, had about 68 hands. Of this number, 20 were men over 16 years—12 for cotton and 8 for woollen—average wages, $8.50 per week. There were also employed 26 women—8 for cotton and 18 for woollen—averaging $5 per week. Of boys there were 14—10 on cotton and 4 on woollen—averaging $3.50 per week. Of girls there were 8, all employed on cotton, averaging $2.00 per week. The average hands during these four years was from 40 to 50. The National Policy gave an impetus to work in the Mispeck factory; and, indeed, but for the stimulus given by the Policy, the millgate would never again have been raised. The work to which the mill is devoted, is principally the manufacture of cotton warps. Woollen yarns are also manufactured. There are in the factory 1,200 spindles and 12 looms for making cotton and woollen cloth, though weaving, under the present management, has not been indulged in; operations have been confined to spinning cotton and woollen yarns. We have spent between $5,000 and $6,000 on machinery and improvements. The mill is driven by water, a turbine wheel being used. The dye-house connected with this factory, has facilities for dyeing yarns and any class of goods in first-class style. The dye-works branch of the factory is now in full operation, having all it can do. Business, owing to over-production everywhere, is somewhat depressed. As it does not pay just now to manufacture largely; spinning operations, in this factory, have been curtailed till the overstocked markets are relieved and stocks reduced. So soon as this period is reached, operations will be resumed. It is nonsense to say that without the National Policy factories such as ours could be continued in operation, or that the Policy is hurtful, in any sense, to the business." . . .

J. C. Risteen & Co.'s sash, door and blind factory and planing mill is another of the many proofs that energy and perseverance, combined with skill in workmanship and good business capacity, can, when properly exerted in a fair field, attain a high degree of success. Starting some twelve years ago in Fredericton, in a small way, Mr. Risteen, by steady application, made good progress year by year, the character of his work and its moderate cost proving a ready passport to general esteem. The efficiency of the factory, enhanced year by year since its commencement, and especially during the past few years, is of such a character as to justify the remark that it is one whose equipment is without a peer in the Province. It is not so much the number of men in this establishment, and, indeed, in many others, that indicates the extent of work done; it is the number and excellence of the labor-saving appliances which tell the tale. Risteen's factory has much to boast of in the way of machinery, and in opportunity for expansion there is no lack. There are several workshops on the premises—one 40 x 50 feet, one 76 x 56 feet, and one 26 x 36 feet (all two stories in height). Besides these, there are several lumber sheds and other needful buildings. The power by which the machinery is driven is centred in an engine of 30 horse capacity. In reference to the National Policy, Mr. Risteen remarked as follows:—"The National Policy directly affects my business only to a trifling extent, except so far as relates to St. Stephen. In my trade relations with that town it has been quite beneficial. The National Policy indirectly affects my business favorably, for in the increase of prosperity generally it cannot otherwise than be a considerable sharer. In the furniture branch of the business the benefits are, directly and otherwise, greater than in the other branches."

McFarlane, Thompson & Anderson's foundry started 13 years ago under the auspices of the present firm, since which time it has gone on from one degree of success to another, until now the number of its hands are more than doubled, and its machine and other facilities have been enlarged in like proportion. In the foundry department all kinds of stoves are manufactured, and in the machinery and agricultural implement departments good workmen under careful direction attend to the wants of customers. Mowing machines are a specialty, and in this line the works are credited with much excellence. Says the senior member of the firm in reference to the tariff:—"Don't know that the National Policy hurts us much in a general way. In one respect, however, it does operate to our prejudice. Our market to buy is in the United States. The tariff forces us to go to Ontario, where we obtain malleable castings, but at much larger first cost and much higher freight charge than formerly paid to foundries

in the Republic. Then, again, in dealing with the States we have opportunity for exchange of products, such as lumber, etc.; in trading with
Ontario there is no chance for this. Our steel cutters we get from St.
Catharines, Ont., the only place which produces them in the Dominion,
but at higher prices than formerly. . . .

The cotton mill is the crowning glory of Alexander Gibson's enterprising life. It is an immense and yet a symmetrical structure. No attempt
has been made to adorn it with architectural embellishments, and yet it is
not without a certain degree of real beauty. The location of the mill, on
the eastern side of the river, midway between the river and a high bluff,
on the crest of which Mr. Gibson has already erected several brick houses
for his work people, and intends to erect many more, is an admirable one.
The plain on which it stands slopes gradually towards the river, giving
good opportunity for drainage. The main building is 418 feet long, 100 feet
wide and four stories high, and faces the river to the west. Near the northern end and extending back in an easterly direction, is a wing, intended
for use as a picker house, 328 feet long, 98 feet wide and two stories high.
Two smaller buildings occupy positions in the rear of the main building
and attached thereto—one 85 x 40 feet and the other 55 x 40 feet—a
belt-race forming the connecting link. A tower in the centre of the main
building is 128 feet in height or 50 feet above the eaves. The chimney,
which stands in the rear of the mill and directly opposite the tower, is
circular in form, 20 feet in diameter at the base and tapering towards the
top, and 155 feet in height.

In the work of construction it is apparent that due attention has been
paid to economy, though not at the expense of thoroughness. The stone
for the foundation walls was obtained from a quarry not far distant from
the mill. Fine beds of clay and sands near the mill furnished the material
for the 5,000,000 bricks which, it is said, have been laid away in the
superstructure; and the bricks were made with the aid of five machines
purchased by Mr. Gibson. The deals for the main flooring, the birch for the
upper flooring and the pine boards for the ceilings, were all manufactured
in Mr. Gibson's saw mill and planed in his planing mill. Apart from the
posts and beams, which are Southern pine, the iron work, the cement, lime
and machinery, all the materials which have entered into the construction
of the mill, are home product. The labor, so much of it, of course, as neces-
sitated specially skilled work, had to be procured from abroad.

The girders which cross the mill, 11 feet apart, are constructed of pitch
pine, 12 x 16 inches. The flooring is composed of 3-inch spruce deals, and
is spiked to the girders and covered with planed birch boards 1¼ inches
thick. The ceilings consist of tongued and grooved pine boards. Light is
supplied by 518 mullion windows, each holding 36 panes of glass. The
walls are whitened with a wash of lime and calcimine material, which

helps to make lighter and still more cheerful a place already very pleasant. The building is heated throughout with steam, and the sprinklers or automatic fire extinguishers form a part of the provision for safety in every flat. The stairways and elevators at both ends of the main building are enclosed with brick walls, and the doors sheathed with tin, and in due time a proper system of fire escapes will also be provided.

Water is supplied to the mill and to the residences of the workpeople through pipes from a stream in the high ground a short distance from the mill, which has been dammed so as to give force enough to supply a tank in the tower which connects with the sprinkler.

The machinery of the mill will be driven by two engines of 650-horse power each, the maker being Harris, of Providence, R. I. The boilers, ten in number, were made in St. John, and have been in position some time.

Mr. Gibson, it is generally conceded, has the cheapest mill structure on the continent, and some go so far as to say the "best one" too. The mill, including the basement, which is as good as any other flat in the structure, has, in the opinion of those eminent architects, Messrs. Lockwood, Greene & Co.—the best authority on such matters in the United States—capacity for 60,000 spindles and some 1,100 or so looms. Mr. Gibson considers that the mill is capable of employing 1,300 persons. The mill will not, at the outset—it is the intention to make a start in January—be run at full capacity; only a fraction of its capacity will be brought into play, and some 200 persons will receive employment, at an average wage of about 80 cents per day.

At present only five of the workpeople's brick houses are completed; but in a short time the remainder of the 100 or more, which it is Mr. Gibson's intention to erect, will be completed. Instead of the large boarding house system for operatives, Mr. Gibson hopes to be able so to arrange matters as to have each family accommodate a certain number of the young people who will enter the employ, and thus inaugurate a family boarding system which he hopes will, in every way, be superior to the general boarding house plan in vogue in other places.

The Miramichi Valley Railway passes along the western bank of the river, in full view of and but a short distance from the bridge which spans the river near the mill. This will bring the workpeople within easy reach of Fredericton, the political capital of New Brunswick, which is but a trifle over two miles distant, and will soon be in a position to be reached over a bridge spanning the St. John River.

The tabular statements attached will give some idea of the number of men engaged in the construction of this vast cotton mill, and still occupied in fitting it up for active operations.

The total cost of the mill structure, with its equipment, all ready for a start, will probably reach $1,000,000.

The whole number of persons now at work in the mill, engaged in various capacities, may, at a low estimate, be figured at 116 persons, whose weekly wages will reach, at a moderate computation, $1,238 per week.

During the entire period of construction it is estimated that there were 400 men engaged in various kinds of work. At the moderate average figure of $9 per week, this would make the weekly wages of the whole force, for the period named, amount to no less than $3,600.

Mr. Alex. Gibson's saw mill, another enterprise, and one scarcely secondary in importance to the cotton mill, when considered in all its branches, was the first to tax the energies of the proprietor, and still remains in active operation. In this mill 120 men have for long years received employment, and in the store half a dozen more are kept busy. In the stream driving operations for the supply of logs to this and other mills, 500 men are required to bend their energies, and in the procuring of logs 800 more are called upon to exercise their skill and strength. The weekly wages of this vast body of people employed for a large portion of the year, to say nothing of the considerable number who receive employment at the port of shipment, amounts to the large sum of $11,286.

Mr. Gibson, during the interview I had with him, never once referred, either in terms of praise or words of blame, to the National Policy. He neither denounced nor endorsed it. He neither, by word or sign, indicated that it had either added a dollar to the cost of his lumber operations, or diminished by the value of a cent, the profit on his lumber sales. He did not deplore the fact of his large personal investment in a cotton factory, nor seem in any wise apprehensive of the success of his venture. He did not blame the National Policy for the world's over-production in almost every department of industry, nor rail at it because of any undue stimulus given to the cotton industry. In fact, he left the Policy severely alone. Silent on that subject, he was free in his expressions of hopefulness as to the country's future, even going to the length of pointing out how the Dominion and Jamaica would be mutually advantaged by a union, which would result in the free interchange of the products of the respective countries. Later, however, in reply to the pointed question, as to what he thought of the National Policy, and "whether, and in what respects, the National Policy bore hardly upon the industries in which he was engaged," I received the following comprehensive, and at the same time, suggestive reply:

"In reference to the National Policy, I may say that it is about time Canadians knew how to do something."

Developing Natural Resources 6
on a National Scale

Traditionally, Canada's industrial efforts have been devoted to the extraction of natural resources. Fishing, the fur trade, its replacement the timber trade, and products of the soil, whether vegetable or mineral, provided the main source of the country's income. Excepting the fur trade, all those industries became more intensive and extensive during the course of the nineteenth century. The extension of transportation systems expanded the reach of those engaged in resource exploitation. Railroads, for instance, were directly responsible for the development of Canadian mining, although they were not originally planned for that purpose.

The timber trade was, and continues to be, one of the great staple industries of Canada. Unlike the other staples, by the middle of the nineteenth century it was already subjected to intensive mechanization. Since most wood was exported in its crudest form, either as squared timber for shipment to Britain or as rough sawed lumber to the U.S., mechanization emphasized techniques for cutting, sawing, and transporting timber.

The exploitation of timber also produced strong regional differences in method. In eastern Canada the Shield provided an excellent system of lake and river transportation. Logs were harvested in the winter and driven downstream in the spring. In the east, water power also supplied the energy for industrial enterprises.

On the west coast the pattern was different. Millions of square miles of forest lay within a few miles of the sea. Trees were felled by crews of cutters, then snaked down to the water by cable systems powered by a donkey engine at the shore. The logs were then made into rafts and towed to saw mills by steam tugs.

The history of Canadian mining technology reveals a process of complex interactions. To begin with, whether it was coal, iron, or practically any other mineral, mines were opened or closed in response to the demand of foreign markets. The technology tended to be imported from the country that imported the products of the mine, but it usually required modification to fit Canadian conditions. Finally, the remote location of mineral deposits also meant that their exploitation waited on the railroad. Practically the only simple issue was that the country's mineral wealth was enormous.

Aside from western gold strikes at mid-century, the most significant exploitation of the country's mineral wealth came at the beginning of the twentieth century. Canadians made one of the most important discoveries in their history when they found nickel-copper deposits in the Sudbury basin of northern Ontario. Development of a process to extract the nickel turned a by-product into a major industry. Gold mining also stimulated a complicated technology. While placer-mining methods—with the aid of an Ottawa-inspired technique—could be relatively simple, processing precious metals called for the design of specialized smelters and concentrators. In the development of its mineral resources, Canada generated a body of technical expertise the equal of any in the world.

Hydro-electricity, another major natural resource, seemed to open the door to a new future for Canada. Industry, in particular, had long suffered from the fact that coal supplies were remote from potential centres of manufacture. Electricity promised a new source of industrial power, an opportunity, as T.C. Keefer pointed out, to escape Canada's traditional role of 'hewers of wood'.

Producing electrical power and transmitting it economically to the point of use were matters of important social and political consequence when public ownership was at issue. As the selections illustrate, Ontario's 'Great Experiment' also generated sharply opposing viewpoints. The application of electricity to transportation was an additional use that attracted Canadians, although it involved complex economic questions.

Resources influenced technology in a dual fashion. In the first instance, their exploitation led to a constant process of adaptation. In each industry a set of techniques was evolved to fit the Canadian situation. Visions of wealth from natural resources also stimulated ideas for developing related technologies. Water power in the form of hydro-electricity, for example, led Canadians to think of an expanded manufacturing capacity and of new methods of transportation.

For centuries, Canada seemed an inexhaustible source of raw material. But with the intensification of the extractive industries, it was apparent that supplies were not limitless. By the end of the nineteenth century, Canadians became resource-conscious. They turned their attention to conservation and home industry, to methods that would provide for the most efficient utilization and regeneration of the sources of their great national wealth.

A WEALTH OF WOOD

TIMBER RAFTS

David Stevenson, *Sketch of the Civil Engineering of North America* (London, 1838), pp. 177-80.

The fine timber which the country produces is much employed in all the public works, and, while it serves in some degree to compensate for the want of stone, it also affords great advantages for ship-building and carpentry, which have been brought to high perfection in America. The lumber trade, as it is called in America, that is to say, the trade in wood, is carried on to a greater or less extent on almost all the American rivers; but on the Mississippi and the St Lawrence it affords employment to a vast number of persons. The chief raftsmen, under whose direction the timber expeditions are conducted, are generally persons of very great intelligence, and often of considerable wealth. . . .

The rafts into which the timber is formed, previous to being floated down the large rivers, are strongly put together. They are furnished with masts and sails, and are steered by means of long oars, which project in front as well as behind them. Wooden houses are built on them for the accommodation of the crew and their families. I have counted upwards of thirty persons working the steering oars of a raft on the St Lawrence; from this some idea may be formed of the number of their inhabitants.

The most hazardous part of the lumberer's business is that of bringing the rafts of wood down the large rivers. If not managed with great skill, they are apt to go to pieces in descending the rapids; and it not unfrequently happens, that the whole labour of one, and sometimes two years, is in this way lost in a moment. An old raftsman, with whom I had some conversation on board of one of the steamers on the St Lawrence, informed me that each of the rafts brought down that river contains from L.3000 to L.5000 worth of timber, and that he, on one occasion, lost L.2500 by one raft, which grounded in descending a rapid, and broke up. The safest size for a raft, he said, was from 40,000 to 50,000 square feet of surface; and rafts of that size require about five men to manage them. Some rafts are made, however, which have an area of no less than 300,000 square feet. Rafts are brought to Quebec in great numbers from distances varying from one to twelve hundred miles; and it often happens that six months are occupied in making the passage. They are broken up at Quebec, where the timber is cut up for exportation into planks, deals, or battens, at the numerous saw-mills with which the banks of the St Lawrence are studded for many miles, in the neighbourhood of the town.

Sometimes the timber is shipped in the form of logs. The timber-rafts of the Rhine are, perhaps, the only ones in Europe that can be compared to those of the American rivers; but none of those which I have seen on the Rhine were nearly so large as the rafts on the St Lawrence, although some of them were navigated by a greater number of hands, a precaution rendered necessary perhaps, by the more intricate navigation of the river.

MAKING WITHS

T.C. Keefer, 'Rafting on the Ottawa', *The Canadian Illustrated News* (June 27, 1863), 81, 78-9.

In winter the scene is perfect—the milk-white floor, and the dark green ceiling upheld by thousands of copper colored columns—receding in beautiful perspective until lost in an imperfect and variegated horizon—afford a spectacle of woodland magnificence which even the Ottawa cannot surpass.

The lumberman lays out a main road from the stream into which he hauls, through the heart of the grove, and if this is scattered branch roads are required. A cheaper class of men, generally the 'greenhorns,' are employed as road cutters. Three men and a cook form a 'gang;'—two cut down the tree, line and score it, that is, split off the outer slabs so as to make it four-sided—and the third, the hewer, who is an artist in his way, smooths it with the broad-axe true and even as if planed.

. . . Then 'withs,' an inch and a half to three inches thick, having been twisted as if they were hempen cables, are taken one by one, the end of one passed under each square log and over the traverse, and racked on top in an immoveable knot by the leverege of a hardwood pole which is three or four inches thick. When the 'with' is thus tightened, the pole is cut off by the quick snap of the axe, leaving three feet, which by other turns of the 'withs' remain locked immoveably in each other. Three men are employed in fixing each of the withs, one to press open the logs with a lever, the other two do the binding. Our artist found more at that work and sketched them, but they were playing not working; the master raftsman being absent. The best withs are the 'blue beech,' grown on the dry margin of swampy land; root grown shoots of 'oak,' 'rock elm,' 'yellow birch,' 'ironwood,' or something obstinately tenacious. White birch is, they tell us, 'no good at all.'

The 'with-twister,' worked by horse-power as seen printed from the engraving opposite, is quite new in the lumber business.—The one figured here was partly invented by Mr. Gilchrist, the chief raftsman under Mr.

RAFT BUILDING, AND 'WITH' TWISTING MACHINE, ON LAKE ONTARIO, 1863

James Patton; but as he informed me, it could hardly have been made without the help and ingenuity of Mr. John Leitch, a working blacksmith of John street, Hamilton; 'He and his two sons,' said the raftsman, 'stayed up at nights and did the work, and did it well. Larger shops would not have done that. We got the castings at Gartshore's at Dundas; excellent foundry that; but without John Leitch the machine would not have been perfected in time, if at all. We might have got our rafts finished by employing double the number of men in with-twisting; as it is, our rafts, 70,000 cubic feet in one, went to market at Quebec in May; and the other two—about 300,000 feet are ready to start for Quebec at the middle of June.'

WOODS AND FORESTS

A Few Words on Canada, and Her Productions in the Great Exhibition (London, 1851), pp. 6-7.

All who are acquainted with the commerce of Canada are aware that her timber exportations form a very important item in it; and this will afford no matter of surprise when the variety of her forest growth is considered. Birch, oak, black walnut, hard and soft maple, ash, red rock elm, pine, bird's-eye maple, spruce, basswood, butternut, white oak, ironwood, tamarack, and others, are found in various places growing in luxurious abundance; but the white and the red pine are what the Canadians chiefly export. The valley of the Ottawa is one of the great sources of these two species, whence it is brought down the river, a distance of 660 miles, to the shipping port of Quebec, in enormous rafts, some of which cover a superficial space of 80,000 feet. In Mr. Warburton's interesting and valuable work, "Hochelaga, or England in the New World," we find the following description of one of these huge floating fields:— "For 100 miles up the great river the scene is the same, monotonous, if you will, but monotonous in beauty; the shores all along thickly dotted with the white cottages of the simple inhabitants. A short distance above Cape Rouge we met a large raft of white pine, one of the strange sights of the St. Lawrence. It was about three acres of timber, bound together by clamps of wood into a solid stage; on this were erected five or six wooden houses, the dwellings of the raftsmen. The wind was in their favour, and they had raised in front a great number of broad, thin boards, with the flat sides turned to the breeze, so as to form an immense sail. These floating islands are guided by long oars; they drop down with the stream till they meet with the tide, then anchor when it turns, till the tide again comes to their aid. They have travelled from many hundred miles in the interior; by the banks of the far-distant Ottawa those pines were felled; in the depth of winter the remote forests ring with the woodman's axe; the trees are lopped of their branches, squared, and dragged by horses over the deep snow to the rivers, where, upon the ice, the rafts are formed. When the thaw in the spring opens up the mountain streams, the stout lumberers collect the remains of their winter stock with their well-worn instruments, and on these rafts boldly trust themselves to the swollen waters." The largest white pine trees of the Ottawa are used for masts, and are of sufficient diameter to yield planks five feet in breadth, free from sap. The largest red pine tree will give logs of about 18 inches square and 40 feet long. White oak is another of the important commercial woods of Canada: it grows principally in the western division of the country, and is much used both there and elsewhere for ship-building. A large plank, 26 inches in breadth, of this wood is in the Exhibition.

From the same part of the province of Canada is chiefly derived the black walnut, the use of which for ornamental furniture may be seen in the various manufactured articles contributed to the Exhibition. It also forms a considerable material in the interior decoration of houses, and, as it grows in immense quantities, the inhabitants can afford to export it freely, which they do, generally to the United States.

The curled maple, bearing so strong a resemblance to satin-wood, and the bird's-eye maple, both well adapted for ornamental purposes, are abundant; the soft or sugar maple is not much used by the manufacturer, the proprietors of the land reserving it for its yield of the matter from which it has acquired its name. Hard maple is made up into the best articles of common furniture, and, with the black and red beech, it is extensively imported into the United States, where, as in Canada, it is used for similar purposes. These three kinds of wood and beech constitute the staple domestic fuel of the Canadians; the latter wood affords a peculiar acid, for the manufacture of which several establishments have recently been erected in the country. The presence of all the woods here enumerated is considered an undoubted sign of the soil being good and fruitful; as is also that of the bass, or whitewood tree, growing most extensively in both parts of the province. This kind is much used for the panels of carriages of every description, as well as for the interior of cabinetwork, and for some of the commoner domestic articles. The butternut tree is a sign of good dry land; it forms one of the best materials for veneering cabinetwork, as it is not liable to warp or crack. White spruce is almost exclusively applied to building purposes; it forms a considerable branch of export trade, large quantities of it as well of white pine being sent to Europe and the United States. Samples of the hickory-wood may be seen in the various agricultural and mechanical implements in the

Exhibition; its toughness adapting it, in a peculiar degree, for the handles of axes and tools of all kinds, for grain-cradles, &c.; it is of sufficient importance to be made an article of export to Great Britain.

This brief allusion to the principal trees that make up the vast forests of Canada will suffice to show their great importance to the settler in that country; and it is with this view that the Canadian authorities have been induced to contribute the various specimens that are placed in the Exhibition.

The total value of the timber imported from Canada in the year 1849 was £1,327,537. 15s. 4d. Of this vast sum upwards of one million's worth came to Great Britain, and the far larger portion of the remainder was sent to the United States.

MAKING MATCHES

The Lumber Trade of the Ottawa Valley (Ottawa, 1871), pp. 35-9.

E. B. EDDY

carries on the largest business in the manufacture of the products from our forests, on this continent, converting the timber of his enormous estates into every description of useful article from saw logs and lumber to wooden ware and lucifer matches.

The business was first established in 1854 when Mr. Eddy commenced his operations in this section of the country, by manufacturing matches; and such are the resources of the valley of the Ottawa, and the immense advantages of the water power of the Chaudiere, that he, with the characteristic energy of his race, has been enabled to build up a business on a gigantic scale, the productions of which are of vast utility to the people of this continent.

The saw Mills are fitted with gang and circular saws of all kinds and sizes, and the whole establishment gives employment to from seventeen to eighteen hundred persons, many of whom are girls employed in the manufacture of matches....

The force employed in driving the mills, is derived from the unlimited water power of the Ottawa, assisted by mechanical agencies of modern invention, and is equal to about 600 horse power.

THE MATCH FACTORY

Consists of a range of buildings containing, two machine rooms, two dipping rooms, two large packing rooms, a warehouse and shipping office, besides engine house, drying rooms, &c.

In the machine rooms, the wood is cut up by two different machines. The one, which is employed in making the best matches of seasoned wood, cuts up the blocks, already prepared, by means of fifteen small knives, which divide the wood into pieces the exact size of the match and then pass them through grooves into the separate divisions in the racks placed ready for their reception, at the rate of 4000 per minute from each machine.

These racks are pressed so as to place the small pieces of wood firmly in their position, and are taken to the dipping room. Each machine employs one man and one boy.

The dipping room for this class of match is divided into two compartments, in the first is a chaldron of molten sulphur, into which the racks are passed, each piece of wood receiving a certain quantity of sulphur. The racks are then taken to the other room and dipped into the final preparation of phosphorus &c., and then placed in iron safes built into the walls all around the room to dry, which takes about two hours, when they are ready for packing.

In the other machine room wood is cut up on another principle by a machine which contains 9 knives, and cuts the match into double the required length, at the rate of 340 strokes a minute, making 9 at each stroke, or 18 matches, equal to over six thousand a minute.

These sticks being of green wood are then placed in open boxes, and taken to a drying room heated by steam pipes. When dried they are rolled up in circular form between bands of wadding by machines which distribute each separate piece of wood into equidistant parts. The rolls are then taken to the dipping room, where they are dipped on each end in the preparations of sulphur and phosphorous and hung up on racks to dry.

They are then cut in two, by another machine and are ready for packing.

The packing rooms are divided into several compartments, and occupied entirely by girls, who are employed in packing the matches first in the small paper wrappers, (which they prepare from material supplied them, in their homes) and then into boxes of ¼ gross each which are taken to the warehouse and shipping room.

This factory gives employment to about 50 men and boys and about 90 girls.

RUNNING A TIMBER SLIDE

Memoirs of Robert Dollar (1927), pp. 8-9.

I worked my way up slowly until, in 1866, when I was twenty-two years of age, I was put in charge of a camp of forty men, and in the spring of the year I ran the logs down the Du Moines River to the Ottawa River, where they were boomed and taken by several stages over the rapids and

falls, and after a great deal of hard work and trouble we got them to Ottawa City. Up to this time no logs had been taken over the Chaudiere Falls. Under the direction of our manager I ran a quantity over these falls, but it did not prove a success.

We then tried to get the logs to the north side, past the town of Hull through the slide. This was successful and after a time we got them running well. To make up for so much lost time experimenting, I kept urging them to feed them in faster until my energy exceeded my good judgment, the result being that a jam occurred in the steep slide so that in a few minutes it choked full, and, before I could stop more coming, it completely stopped the water coming through the proper channel and it found a very improper one by going through the match factory of Mr. E. B. Eddy, flooding the floor, so that some hundred employees had to quit work. Mr. Eddy immediately appeared on the scene, and called me all the bad names he could think of.

At last I told him that we were only losing time and if he would let me alone I would try and stop the water going through the factory. I went at the job with all the energy I possessed while he sat on the bank and watched every move of myself and the men. It was very dangerous starting the logs, as when we got them started they would go like a shot out of a gun. We were successful and in an incredibly short time we got the logs started and the water ceased making a highway through the factory. When I finished, Mr. Eddy came up and said, "I take my hat off to you for the able and expeditious way you got those logs going." And after all the damage I had caused him he said, "I take back all I said to you on the start." The big, broad gauge man that he was; this made us fast friends as long as he lived.

THE WASTE OF TIMBER RESERVES

Robert Bell, *The Forests of Canada* (Ottawa, 1886).

The amount of timber which has been lost through forest fires in Canada is almost incredible, and can only be appreciated by those who have travelled much in our northern districts. The proportion of white and red pine which has been thus swept away in the Ottawa Valley and in the St. Maurice and Georgian Bay regions, is estimated by the lumbermen as many times greater than all that has been cut by the axe. Yet all this is insignificant in quantity compared with the pine, spruce, cedar, larch, balsam, etc., which has been destroyed by this means in the more northern latitudes all the way from the Gulf of St. Lawrence to Nelson River, and thence north-westward. It is true that the commercial value of this timber was not so great as that of the more southern pine regions which have also been partially ruined. The total quantities which have disappeared are almost incalculable, but even a rough estimate of the amount for each hundred or thousand square miles shows it to have been enormous, and of serious national consequence. The writer had traversed these great regions in many directions, and could testify to the widespread devastation which had taken place. Nearly every district was more or less burnt, the portions which had been overrun by fire usually exceeding those which remained green. These northern coniferous forests were more liable than others to be thus destroyed. In the summer weather, when their gummy tops and the mossy ground are alike dry, they burn with almost explosive rapidity. Small trees are thickly mingled with the larger ones, and they all stand so closely together that their compact branches touch each other, thus forming a sufficiently dense fuel to support a continuous sheet of flame on a grand scale. Before a high wind the fire sweeps on with a roaring noise, and at a rate which prevents the birds and beasts from escaping. Thus, in one day, the appearance which a large tract of country is to wear for a hundred years may be completely altered. After a time the burnt district becomes overgrown, first with shrubs and bushes, then with aspens and white birches, among which coniferous trees by-and-by appear; but finally at the end of a hundred and fifty years or more they regain possession of the burnt tract. This process of alternation of crops of timber appears to have been going on for centuries, but in modern times the fires must have been more numerous and frequent than formerly.

Along Moose River and the lower part of the Missinaibi, the original dark coniferous forest of these latitudes is replaced by the light green poplars and white birches, for more than a hundred miles, and this condition has existed since the memory of the oldest Indian of the district. Here and there may be seen a patch of large spruce—remnants of the original forest—and everywhere under the deciduous growth, the charred stumps of the old conifers may be found. On the east side of the southern part of Lake Winnipeg, and nearly all along Winnipeg River, the principal forests have been destroyed by fire, and replaced by aspen and white birch.

Forest fires are undoubtedly due occasionally to lightning, the author having once actually witnessed the origin of a fire in this way, and he had often been informed by the Indians that they had seen similar cases. But most of them are traceable to the carelessness of white men and demoralized Indians. In the partially inhabited regions, most of the forest fires originate by the settlers burning brush and log-heaps in clearing the land. It may be asked if we have no means of stopping this fearful destruction of the timber of the country. Laws on the subject do exist, but no adequate means appear to be provided for enforcing them. The author recommended a reform in this respect, before it be too late. Crown lands of real value for agriculture should be separated for the purpose of administration from those which are acknowledged to be useful only or principally for their timber, and settlement should be prohibited within the latter. Heretofore, the great consideration of Government was the peopling of the country, the timber being looked upon as of secondary importance, and it was willingly sacrificed in the interests of the settler, who came to regard it as his natural enemy. The time has come when we must change all this. In the absence of forest guardians and proper regulations, lumbermen have often to submit to a species of blackmail from discharged employees and pretending settlers in order to keep them off their limits. Indians sometimes burn the forests off each other's hunting-grounds from motives of revenge, but as a rule the fires which they start are from carelessness or indifference. When cautioned in a friendly way, they are willing to exercise greater care, and the beneficial effects of this course are already manifest in the region between Lake Winnipeg and Hudson Bay, where the author had remonstrated with them on the subject. He suggests that the annuities which they receive from Government be withheld as a punishment for burning the woods, or that a bounty be paid each year that no fires occur. In this way the Indian chiefs and headmen may be made the most efficient and earnest forest guardians we could possibly have.

Fires are not so liable to run in forests of full-grown white and red pines, such as those of southern Ontario, which have suffered comparatively little from this cause, but have now been mostly cut down and utilized by the lumbermen. Hardwood forests are seldom burnt to any great extent, except where the soil is shallow and becomes parched in summer, as, for instance, on the flat limestone rocks of Grand Manitoulin Island and the Indian peninsula of Lake Huron, through much of which fires have run, burning the vegetable mould and killing the roots, thus causing the trees to fall over even before they have decayed. Hence the term "fire-falls" applied in such cases.

If we had educated and intelligent conservators of forests in Canada, appointed by the Government, their duties, in addition to preventing the destruction of the timber by fire and otherwise, might be directed to promoting the growth of existing timber, encouraging transplanting, the introduction of foreign trees which might grow in this country, the dissemination of information on practical forestry, etc., investigating the causes of diseases among trees, directing the attention of foreign purchasers to our woods and pointing out to our lumbermen possible new markets for timber products and for varieties of woods not now utilized. That disease does sometimes cause great havoc among our forests is illustrated by the recent fact that the spruces in New Brunswick, the principal timber tree of that province, died over extensive areas, a few years ago, and the disease has now spread into the Gaspé peninsula. It is supposed to be due to a fungus which attacks the roots, but it is not certain that the fungus itself may not be induced by the pre-existence of some other disease. In the Province of Quebec the larches or tamaracs, have sometimes died from unexplained causes in extensive tracts. As soon as coniferous trees have become scorched by fire or show signs of failing vitality, their trunks are attacked by boring beetles, and they must be immediately cut down and immersed in water if the timber is to be saved. . . .

If the vast northern forests can be preserved from fire in the future, our supply of small timber is practically inexhaustible. When larger trees elsewhere shall have become scarce, much of it may some day be sawn into boards, scantling, joists, rafters, flooring, etc. Supplies of timber for railway-ties, telegraph-poles, mines, fencing, piling, small spars, cord-wood, charcoal, paper-making, etc., may be drawn from these immense districts for all time, since the greater part of the regions referred to are not likely to be required for agricultural purposes, and by a proper system of cutting, a new growth will spring up to replace the timber removed, and in its turn become available to keep up the supply. The practically interminable extent of these forests will allow ample time for the smaller trees, which may be left on any ground cut over, to come to maturity before it is again called upon to furnish its quota. Some of the woods of the more southern districts of Canada, which have had little value hitherto, except for fuel, only require to be better known to be utilized for many purposes.

The people of Canada have heretofore been accustomed to such an abundance of wood, and to the idea that trees stood in the way of progress of the country, that tree-planting has as yet made but little progress among us. A beginning has, however, been made in the last two years in the provinces of New Brunswick and Quebec, where "Arbor Days" have been proclaimed. In Ontario an Act was passed in 1883, and a fund set apart for the encouraging of tree-planting along highways. The time has arrived for more vigorous action by the general Government and the Local Legislatures looking to the improvement and preservation of the forests which still remain in Canada, and for the partial restoration of those which have been destroyed.

TIMBER ON THE WEST COAST

H.N. Whitford and R.D. Craig, *Forests of British Columbia* (Ottawa, 1918), pp. 168-9.

Up to about ten years ago, logging on the coast was confined to the timber close to the shore. Three miles was about the limit to which donkey engines could be successfully used. Since that time a number of logging railways have been built to reach the timber farther inshore. The use of railways in place of main skid-roads is increasing, since the former cost very little more to construct, except for the steel, which can be relaid, and are much more efficient. Twenty-one logging railways were in use on the coast in 1916.

River driving is practised in parts of the interior, where the logs are smaller than they are on the coast and where the rivers are not so swift. Very few of the rivers on the coast can be driven, however; they are usually swift and rough, and those large enough to transport the big logs are, as a rule, choked at the outlet with tideland flats and islands, which render driving difficult.

Nearly all of the logs taken out on the coast have to be towed to the mills. For this purpose they are made up into booms about 60 to 70 feet wide and 500 to 1,000 feet long. The outside boom-sticks are held together by chains and the boom is kept in shape by long 'swifters,' which are laid across the top of the boom and fastened at each end to the boom sticks. These booms do not stand very rough water, but, on the inside passage between Vancouver island and the mainland, the percentage of loss is small. Where rough water is to be encountered, cylindrical cribs, bound together by cables, are used with success, logs having been towed over 400 miles in safety. Though a few of the mills own their own tugs, the towing is generally done by special towing companies, who charge on a per thousand feet basis, according to a more or less fixed schedule of rates.

THE PULP INDUSTRY

D.L. McGibbon, *The Pulp Industry in Canada* (Montreal, 1912), pp. 4-8.

As you are all probably aware, pulp, whilst being a manufactured article from pulp wood, is still only a basis of raw material for the manufacture of paper. The two principal grades of pulp in use to-day are mechanical or ground wood pulp, and chemical or sulphite pulp. Mechanical or ground wood pulp is almost explained by its name, as the process of manufacture is very simple, consisting principally of grinding wood into pulp. Chemical or sulphite pulp is a very much more intricate process of manufacture, and consists in treating the wood by chemical process, and thus separating the fibres of the wood by the extraction of resinous material. In the manufacture of paper 70% to 75% of the pulp used is mechanical, and the balance, 25% to 30%, is chemical. Paper made altogether from mechanical pulp would not be satisfactory for newspaper or any other of the finer grades, as the fibres of the pulp are too short to give the paper sufficient strength, so that it is necessary to use a proportion of sulphite pulp, which by its process of manufacture retains the long fibres of the wood, and thus gives the strength to the paper.

The first consideration, therefore, to the manufacturer of pulp is his raw material and power. An enormous quantity of water power, on account of its cheapness, is necessary for the manufacture of mechanical pulp, and therefore it is usual for a pulp manufacturer to locate his mill at a point where there is good water power and where his source of supply of pulp wood is close at hand. A pulp manufacturer, having his water power assured and his source of supply of pulp wood for his raw material located, then figures on the quantity of raw material he will require for a season's operations. For the manufacture of a ton of mechanical pulp it takes a trifle over a cord of spruce wood, and for the manufacture of a ton of chemical pulp it takes almost two cords of spruce pulp wood. If, therefore, the pulp manufacturer has a capacity of so many tons of each kind of pulp per day, it is very easy for him to figure the exact amount of pulp wood he will require for the operation of his mills for a year. If he should have his own limits, his first step in procuring his pulp wood is to know exactly what his limits consist of and the amount of available spruce logs that are contained in same. As the Government regulate the size of a tree to be cut, he must therefore only figure on cutting trees in accordance with these regulations. In the case of the Laurentide Pulp Company who own such a large area of timber limits, we have found it more practicable to divide these limits into three districts, having a superintendent over each district. We have also found it much more practicable for each of these superintendents, by giving his whole time and attention to his district, to become thoroughly acquainted with all rivers, streams and lakes in same, and where the best points are to procure logs to advantage, rather than have one or two men for the entire limits, which by their large area would only permit them, to say the least, to have a superficial knowledge of it all.

Having, then, determined the quantity of pulp wood to get out in a season, and having your limits divided into districts, with a man thoroughly familiar with the conditions of each district, you determine the quantity you will get from each district. As a pulp manufacturer wants to ensure a uniform cost of his raw material for years, it is therefore bad policy for him to attempt to pick out the easiest spots to get pulp wood one year, and leave the harder and more expensive places for a following year. Under the circumstances it is necessary for him to average this up, taking some of the expensive wood each year so as not to leave it all for future operations. It is the policy of most pulp manufacturers to procure their pulp wood, or, at least, a large portion of it, by letting contracts to jobbers or contractors. This to my mind is a very cheap way to procure pulp wood, but from my experience the results of this method are but temporary. It has been the practice in the past to allot a certain territory to a contractor and give him a contract for a certain number of logs. As far as I can learn, the territory allotted to a jobber in the past has been much too large for the quantity of logs that his contract calls for. As a natural consequence this jobber, who has only one aim, viz.:—to make money out of his contract, picks out the easiest spots in his territory, and no matter whether there are some large fine spruce logs in his territory that should be cut, but which would cost him a trifle more to get out, he will leave these standing. The following year, therefore, when a contract is let in the same territory a higher price is demanded owing to the timber being scattered and only the hard places left to lumber in, and it usually ends up with the result that no contractor will go into this territory except at an exorbitant price, and it therefore falls to the lot of the pulp manufacturer to establish his own camps and get out the remaining available logs at a very high cost. This point I wish to emphasize more particularly, and that is, when a contract is let for a certain quantity of logs the area of territory should be limited, and so thoroughly explored that it can be cleared systematically of the logs that should be cut. As contractors for logs are more or less men of moderate means, and who, if a bad season sets in and a possible loss in fulfilling their contract stares them in the face, either fall far short of their contract or abandon it, it is therefore necessary for a pulp manufacturer, in order to be safe regarding his raw material, to establish some of his own camps which will get the logs out no matter what the set-backs are. It has been amply demonstrated that a camp, or camps, operated by a company cannot get logs out as cheaply as a jobber or contractor, at least in the Province of Quebec where the timber is scattered and the country very mountainous, but the result obtained by operating camps direct are in the long run very much more beneficial than from contractors. The Laurentide Pulp Co., as mentioned before, having such a large territory, and who require such an enormous quantity of pulp wood for the operation of their mills, have found it advisable to employ two inspectors, one for the jobbers or contractors and the other for its own camps. It is the duty of the former inspector to inspect regularly and frequently all jobbers' camps, and see that these jobbers do not waste the timber nor break the Government regulations. He also sees that all logs are stamped and properly culled, and when he finds anything out of the way, he reports it direct to the management of the Company. The inspector of the camps acts in a similar capacity, but reports on the general conditions of the camps in addition to the above.

Another bad feature of giving contracts to jobbers for logs is, that it is usual to give a contract for a certain quantity of logs to be of a uniform length. Suppose, for example, that a contract has been let for 50,000 spruce logs 13 feet in length, 7 inches at the small end and up. A contractor, if he cuts down a tree, will only make from this tree logs of 13 feet in length, and I have found from personal experience that a large proportion of these trees would permit of another log being cut from 8 to 10 feet in length, and still not be under 7 inches in diameter at the small end. This part of the tree is just as good for making pulp as anything else, but, as you know, the cost of handling and driving a small log is almost as great as a large log and if a manufacturer only considers his immediate circumstances, and his immediate cost of raw material, he will not bother with these ends of a tree, but, if he considers the fact that his raw material is worth money, and that by leaving these ends of the trees in the woods he is simply throwing away a part of his assets, and in addition to this is enhancing the danger of forest fires, he will, even at a slight extra cost, have them taken to his mills with the larger logs. In the case of a company operating its own camps this should be done in any case. In the case of the logs being cut for export to the United States, these ends of trees are not considered of any value.

MINING

PROTECTING A NATIVE CLAIM

British Columbia and Vancouver's Island (London, n.d.), pp. 26-9.

It appears from their reports that the auriferous character of the country is becoming daily more extensively developed, through the exertions of the native Indian tribes, who, having tasted the sweets of gold-finding, are devoting much of their time and attention to that pursuit.

They are, however, at present almost destitute of tools for moving the soil, and of washing implements for separating the gold from the earthy matrix, and have therefore to pick it out with knives, or to use their fingers for that purpose; a circumstance which in some measure accounts for the small products of gold up to the present time, the export being only about 300 ounces since the 6th of last October. . . .

The few white men who passed the winter at the diggings, chiefly retired servants of the Hudson's Bay Company, though well acquainted with Indian character, were obstructed by the natives in all their attempts to search for gold. They were on all occasions narrowly watched, and in every instance when they did succeed in removing the surface and excavating to the depth of the auriferous stratum, they were quietly hustled and crowded by the natives, who, having by that means obtained possession of the spot, then proceeded to reap the fruits of their labours.

Such conduct was unwarrantable and exceedingly trying to the temper of spirited men, but the savages were far too numerous for resistance, and they had to submit to their dictation. It is, however, worthy of remark, and a circumstance highly honourable to the character of those savages, that they have on all occasions scrupulously respected the persons and property of their white visitors, at the same time that they have expressed a determination to reserve the gold for their own benefit.

GOLD EVERYWHERE

British Columbia and Vancouver's Island (London, n.d.), p. 44.

The *Times* correspondent quotes the following as the experience of a man from San Francisco, well known there, connected with a business firm in that place, and whose statement is worthy of credit:—"We left San Francisco in April, in company with seven others, and ascended the Fraser River 275 miles. We prospected all along, coming up from Fort Hope to Sailors' Bar. We camped, and commenced mining Sailors' Bar, about twenty-five miles above Fort Yule, which has rich diggings, in some places paying as high as six bits to the pan (a bit may be set down at the value of one shilling sterling). When I arrived, miners were making as high as six ounces a day to the rocker. We mined along the banks of the river [the Fraser], and the average was from two to three ounces per day to the rockers. Miners are at work all along the banks of the river for twenty-five miles above Fort Yule; they average from two to four ounces a day. The country is very rich and very beautiful, but high and mountainous. There is plenty of timber and everything a miner can wish for, except game and provisions. There are plenty of salmon in the river, and brown bears in the woods, which are very good eating. Wherever we 'prospected' we found gold—at some places more, at others less; *but we found gold everywhere.* At the rapids or falls, twenty odd miles above Fort Yule, where the water fell nearly fifteen feet over the rocks, and prevented our ascending higher in the canoe, we prospected, and found gold very plenty. Near the falls, and from Sailors' Bar up, many miners were at work, all with rockers. Gold very fine—requiring blankets to be spread in the bottom of the rockers to save the finer particles. By the use of quicksilver twice as much gold could be saved, as some of it is as fine as flour."

MINING TECHNIQUES IN THE YUKON

William B. Haskell, *Two Years in the Klondike and Alaskan Gold-fields* (Hartford, 1898), pp. 203-9.

An old and skilled miner will sometimes shake out more gold in a day than a beginner can in a week from the same quantity of dirt. There is a trick about it that comes only by experience, and out of the same gravel a greenhorn may not get fifty cents' worth of gold where an experienced man would get a dollar. A good man can pan a ton of gravel a day, but it is hard, back-breaking work. There is the fascination, however, of ever watching the yellow color as the dirt washes away, and it will keep a man at work till he finds himself exhausted. It is the same fascination that is felt by the confirmed gambler, for every pan of dirt is a gamble. Dame Nature is dealing the cards. Will the player make a big stake, or will he lose? Having won it from Nature by hard work, he will very likely lose some of his winnings in an ordinary gambling game. He lives in an atmosphere of chance. What comes easy, goes easy.

After the pan is shaken and held in such a way as to gradually wash out the sand and gravel, care being taken near the end of the process to avoid letting out the finer and heavier particles which have settled to the bottom, all that will be left in the pan is whatever gold there may have been in the dirt, mixed with black sand, which is nothing but pulverized magnetic iron ore. Should the gold thus found be fine, the contents may be thrown into a tub of water containing a pound or so of mercury. The gold coming in contact with this forms an amalgam. When enough of this has been formed it may be fired or roasted. First it is squeezed through a buckskin bag to work out all the mercury possible, and what comes out is put back in the tub, while the contents of the bag is put in a retort, or, what is more probable in a mining camp, is put on a shovel and heated till the mercury has evaporated. The gold will remain in a lump, though with more or less mercury combined with it. This washing process must be continued after the layer of best paying dirt is reached, for in no other way can the pay-streak be followed.

When gold was first discovered in the Yukon valley the great drawback in successfully operating the rich placer mines was found to exist in the auriferous gravel being frozen into a solid, compact, adamantine mass, which the rays of the summer's sun could never melt, and with which the methods usually employed in washing out gold were totally ineffective. There seemed to be no end of the depth to which the frost penetrated the earth's surface, as the deepest shaft or prospect hole has yet to reach unfrozen gravel except in certain localities, and in such places no one has been able to account for the strange phenomenon. Various ways were tried by the miners of ten years ago to expedite the slow work of the sun in thawing out the congealed mass. Picks were found to be of no avail, as the heaviest blows would produce but little more impression than it would have done on a solid block of granite. Dynamite was experimented with, but a heavy shot resulted in blowing out only a "pot hole," and had no effect whatever in loosening the surrounding gravel. Hydraulics were proven equally futile, the stream from the giants serving only to bore a hole in the bank against which it was directed. In fact, the only manner by which the shallow or summer diggings could be worked at all was to strip or burn off the heavy coating of moss covering the earth, thus allowing the sun to reach the gravel beneath. This in a day would thaw to a depth of three or four inches, and after the frozen muck under the moss had been thawed out and thrown aside, the sun could then work on the gravel. As fast as it thawed it could be shoveled into the sluices, and another like amount would be workable the day following. But it was an unusual summer season that would permit of more than ninety days' work at the sluices, and claims that would not pay an ounce to the shovel were abandoned.

Then came the discovery of the Birch Creek mines, and the problem of profitably operating the mines in the winter time solved itself as a simple matter of necessity. With the pay-streak located from fifteen to twenty-five feet beneath the surface, it would have been impracticable and almost impossible to remove the barren earth lying above it. Prospecting had to be done by burning holes in the gravel. A huge pile of logs would be fired on the spot where it was proposed to sink and allowed to burn over night. In the morning a foot in depth, possibly, would be found to have been thawed out, and this was shoveled aside and a fresh fire kindled. By continuing this operation a number of days, the shaft would finally reach the pay-streak, and then it became a comparatively easy matter to ascertain the probable worth of the claim. If the gravel panned an ounce or two a day, more fires were built at the bottom of the shaft, and "drifting" was begun with the pay-streak, the latter being followed the same as in a quartz lode. The night is the time employed to "burn," the fires being heaped up with logs just before the day's work is finished. These last all night, and by morning, if the amount of fuel has been properly gauged, nothing remains but the dying embers and hot ashes; the smoke and gases have all escaped, and the work of shoveling the loosened gravel begins without delay. As the shaft sinks a windlass is erected over the opening, and as fast as the bucket is filled the contents are hauled to the surface and dumped in a convenient place for washing the following season.

When the drift has reached a short distance underground the bitterly cold weather of the winter has no terrors for the placer miner, and he prosecutes his work in comparative ease and comfort. As distance from the shaft is gained, a wooden track is laid on the floor of the tunnel, and a car pushed by hand is employed to convey the gold-bearing gravel from the ever-receding breast of the drift to the primitive hoisting works.

Who it was who first conceived the idea of drifting under the muck banks and thawing the frozen gravel by means of log fires would be difficult to determine, but whoever he may be, he deserves a monument as a perpetuation of his memory.

A BURNING QUESTION

William H. Ogilvie, *Early Days on the Yukon* (London, 1913), pp. 139-40.

Many questions of engineering were placed before me for consideration and practical solution. One important feature was brought forth at almost every meeting with any one; the question of bed-rock mining, as in more favoured regions farther south. The frost was considered by many an insuperable barrier, and it was pretty generally believed that bed-rock could not be reached by any practicable method. It was assumed that here, as elsewhere, the best pay would be found at the lowest depths, but how to get through twenty, thirty, and forty or more feet of frozen sand, clay, and gravel at reasonable expenditure of time and money was the question, and as it developed it *was a burning question*. All sorts of ideas were propounded and discussed, many impracticable from the paraphernalia required, and some impossible of execution; still, all helped the discussion along. As I had seen holes burned in the frozen crusts of the streets in Ottawa to reach defective gas and waterpipes, and I had several times had to use the process myself for other purposes, I suggested this as I had seen it applied, substituting, of course, the wood of the country for the coke used in the city. As some of the miners had already used the firing method to secure the bar gravels uncovered by the very low water of the winter months, I used this as an argument in favour of burning down. Whether my advocacy had much, or little, or anything at all to do with the inception of the method I cannot say, but it was tried, and a tremendous impetus was given to mining in the region. Bed-rock was reached, and a quality and quantity of gold found that had not been dreamed of before.

INVESTORS AND ENGINEERS

The Canadian Mining Review, vol. xvi (December, 1897), 335-6.

So long as London continues to be the financial centre of the whole world, promoters, shysters and sharks of all nationalities will flock there with the hope of selling nothing for something, and with the expectation of cheating capitalists; and it is equally true that the major part of the blame for losses incurred must rest on the investors and shareholders alone. . . . We have heard a great deal about the caution and prudence of the British capitalist and comparisons have been drawn, not entirely to his favor, with the enterprise and dash of the American capitalist. It would seem, however, that whenever a new mining country is discovered the cautious Britisher throws his caution over his shoulder, and believes the most extraordinary yarns brought to him from everywhere, and often vouched for by engineers of his own nationality.

During the last eighteen months there has been an influx into Canada (chiefly into British Columbia, but also into Ontario) of a large number of representatives of English capital, who, in very few cases, have been qualified for the duties they have had to perform. As we have repeatedly pointed out in these columns, most of the mistakes that English capitalists have made on the American continent, are directly attributable to lack of care in the selection of the men sent to represent them, to undue credulity (which is another word for lack of business prudence), and to the neglect of the ordinary precepts of mining. We can refer our readers in this respect to the many extracts and comments we have made upon the letters of Mr. Thomas Tonge, which have appeared in the London *Mining Journal* and other publications.

We are no pessimists as to Canada's mineral resources; on the contrary, we are firmly of the opinion that they are one of her chiefest sources of wealth, and we desire the introduction of British rather than American capital. But it is allowable, if not our duty, to point out to them the usually superior manner in which the American makes his mining investments. Perhaps the chief point of difference is in his selection of the engineer or agent, who is sent to make the examination or advise upon the purchase. The American usually prefers such a man as is familiar with the country and the district in which the proposition lies, and rarely sends a coal miner to examine a gold property or consults an expert in silver-lead smelting regarding the erection of his stamp-mill. But just as absurd selections are frequently made by our English friends. At present the particular recommendation for an English engineer who appears in Canada is the statement that he has been in South Africa, and frequently that experience is all he has had. It is unnecessary to say that experience with the South

African ores is of very little use in the larger field of British Columbia, which presents almost entirely smelting ores (either of silver-lead or of gold-copper character) occurring in rocks of the most diverse description, frequently of eruptive origin, and requiring a wider experience and a greater knowledge than is gained in the free-milling fields of those.

But perhaps the one cause which so far has contributed most to losses and mistakes with the English corporations in British Columbia, is the grasping haste which they have shown to acquire property, presumably in order to get a quotation at a premium. We have seen letters from the directorate of a London company in which complaint was made against their engineer that he had "turned down everything he had yet seen," and in which the individual to whom the letter was addressed was requested to "procure another engineer, one *who could get something* for the company."

We have heard some of the most successful mining men in the United States say words to the effect that they first looked to the *man*, and then afterwards to the *mine* offered, believing that their chances of failure were minimized if the character of the man upon whose advice they relied was unassailable. It has occurred to us that many of the English corporations now working, or intending to work, in Canada might do well to adopt this last suggestion, and to pin their faith less implicitly upon men whose only record is failure wherever they have been in charge.

A SURVEY OF CANADA'S MINERAL RESOURCES

G.M. Dawson, 'Canada as a Field for Mining Investment', *The Canadian Mining Review*, vol. xv, (1896), 214-16.

Canada has never yet become widely recognized as a country possessed of a great future in respect of its mineral wealth. In the official reports of exports from the Dominion, the produce of agriculture, fisheries, forests, animals and their produce, and even manufactured articles have all largely exceeded in value the total export of minerals. The value of minerals produced in Canada has, nevertheless, for some time, been steadily increasing each year, and in 1895 amounted to over $22,500,000. But this increase, satisfactory enough in itself, does not fully evidence the development which is now about to occur as the outcome of new and exceptional conditions. It is more particularly in the western province of the

Dominion, British Columbia, that epoch-making progress of this kind has begun; but its effect will not be confined to that province, for what is gained there must indirectly assist in bringing the necessary skill and capital to bear upon many minerals of the older provinces, the development of which has heretofore either languished or has been pursued with intermittent success, alternating with periods of stagnation. Such disappointments have too often been due to the practical worthlessness or insignificance of the deposits or undeveloped "prospects" foisted upon the public under the name of "mines" but in other cases really valuable properties have been over-capitalized or swamped by extravagant and incompetent management. In still other instances attempts have been made to work minerals which, although of value, do not yet admit of profitable exploitation under the local economic conditions, but which have absorbed considerable amounts of capital without at any time having afforded the least hope of becoming paying investments. Similar circumstances have, no doubt, attended the history of every mining region; but Canada has perhaps suffered exceptionally in this way in the past.

Returning after this digression to British Columbia, it may be interesting to trace in a few words the short history of mining in that province, which promises very soon to produce each year more from its mines than the aggregate yield of all the remaining provinces of Canada. "Placer", or alluvial gold, was discovered on the Thompson in 1857, and although coal had been found to exist on Vancouver Island many years previously, the country—then an isolated and remote colony—had remained practically a fur preserve of the Hudson's Bay Company, where the most important news, slowly conveyed by the annual "brigade", was the price of beaver skins in London. All this was at once changed by an influx of gold miners, pressing from point to point against great difficulties, of which many a thrilling tale remains to be told. In 1863, the "golden year" of Cariboo, nearly $4,000,000 in gold is estimated to have been produced, a result which, in proportion to the areas worked and the population actually engaged, was phenomenal. From this time the output decreased year by year as the comparatively limited known tracts became exhausted which were adopted for the somewhat crude methods of work possible in places very remote from efficient means of communication.

Meanwhile, the mining of the precious metals was proceeding by leaps and bounds in the Western States of the American Union, similar geographically and geologically, in position and character, to British Columbia, until there appeared to be some real basis for the assertion, often jestingly made, that Providence has stored all the metalliferous wealth of the continent to the south of the international boundary. To those familiar with the circumstances, there were other reasons for this slackness of development in the north, which need not here be detailed, but chief among them was the absence of the requisite facilities of transport, and thus concurrently with the completion of the western part of the Canadian Pacific Railway, a new era began, and in a very short time the local conditions have been largely reversed. In West and East Kootenay everywhere within reasonable distance of railway lines, mining camps began to spring up upon groups of rich deposits carrying silver and gold. The depreciation of silver, which became serious about the same time, has undoubtedly retarded the opening up of some of these deposits, but where they are rich enough to be very profitably worked with silver at fifty cents to the ounce, as is the case with a large proportion of the Kootenay ores, this is rather a sentimental than a real drawback, and one which has already been largely overcome. Other deposits producing gold, with copper as a by-product, have been affected only sympathetically.

The principal mining sub-districts so far established in West Kootenay are, nearly in order of their discovery, Nelson, Ainsworth, Slocan, and Trail. Nelson includes the Hall mines, yielding copper and silver, beside silver-lead ores, and some containing gold. Ainsworth and Slocan are characterized by silver-lead ores, with some yielding gold and other metals, particularly in the last-named sub-district. Trail, although later in claiming its place, has already surpassed the older "camps" in the matter of development and interest on the part of the mining world. Its deposits of auriferous pyrrhotites are probably unique; the veins as far as developed are of extraordinary dimensions and frequency, and several mines have even now reached the stage of paying handsome monthly dividends. The town of Rossland, in Trail district, is estimated to have a population exceeding 3,000, though but a few months old.

For these several mining centres, although so young, railways have already been built, mining machinery of all kinds has been introduced, several large smelters, both for reducing silver-lead ores and for matteing have been established, and from them the output is daily increasing. Perhaps a better idea of the amount of activity in prospecting and mining (although the latter is not more than in its initial stages) may be given by quoting a few figures. Thus, in 1895, over 3,000 new mineral claims were registered in West Kootenay alone. About fifty properties in all have become "shipping mines" on a greater or smaller scale, from which the aggregate output in 1895 is valued at about $2,100,000, comprising silver to the value of $739,000 and gold $679,500, followed by lead and copper representing smaller amounts. For the first six months of the present year the value of the output is estimated at over $2,200,000.

On the coast, from Alberni and other points, most satisfactory reports begin to come, although but little in the way of actual returns has yet been achieved. To the north, and as yet some 200 miles distant from any railway, Cariboo, which in early years proved to be so rich a find for the placer miner, has come to the front again as the site of extensive hydraulic mining operations, dealing on the large scale with comparatively low-grade auriferous gravels by methods already perfected by practice in California. The rapid and full-fed rivers of the district prevent the occurrence here of any questions of damage to cultivated lands from such mining operations while streams and lake reservoirs in the mountains provide ample supplies of water at every desired level. Many years ago, the writer maintained, with special reference to this district, that a development of the kind now taking place was certain to occur, relying upon the fact that in every such region the highly concentrated old stream-gravels, which were alone susceptible of profitable exploitation by comparatively simple methods, must be associated with much widely spread but less rich deposits; a forecast which is fully realized by the work now in progress.

Another interesting feature that may be mentioned in passing, is the amount of money now being carefully spent in placing extensive dredging plants of various types along a great part of the length of the Fraser River, which may be regarded as the great natural "ground-sluice" of the country, but of which the bed and deeper bars could never be reached or worked by the early miners. The quartz-veins of the Cariboo district as yet await development.

Little need be said of the coal mines in British Columbia in the present connection, for these, in the region of the coast and where already open to commerce have long passed the stage at which any difficulty was found in establishing confidence for their operation. They are in the hands of strong corporations, and their output is limited only by the dimensions of the profitable market, in which they compete, along the west coast, with the coals of Great Britain, New South Wales, and the State of Washington. The production now averages about a million tons annually. New fields, however, remain to be opened up when called for, even on the coast, particularly in the Queen Charlotte Islands. In the interior region, in the Crow's Nest Pass and the Nicola Valley, as well as in other districts still further from means of communication, important deposits of coal are known to exist. That of the Crow's Nest Pass has been shown by the Geological Survey to be an exceptionally valuable one, and about one hundred miles of railway only are required to connect it with the metalliferous mines of West Kootenay, where at present some considerable part of the fuel employed in smelting is Welsh coke, costing about fifteen dollars a ton. The coal mines on the line of the Canadian Pacific Railway, near Canmore, although politically included in the district of Alberta, also geographically belong to the Rocky Mountain region. They yield anthracite and steam-coal, of which the output is here again restricted only by the demand.

In writing thus first and at some length of British Columbia, I have placed in the front that region of Canada which affords now the greatest opportunities, and of which the product in metallic minerals may very probably for some time to come increase two-fold each year; but in doing so the resources of that part of the Dominion to the east of the Rocky Mountains must not be overlooked. The North-West Territory and Manitoba—speaking only of the southern moiety of that great interior region which has already been rendered easy of access by railways and roads—is pre-eminently a land for agriculture and stock-raising, but a great area is now known to be underlain by beds of coal, or of lignite-coal, often excellent fuels and everywhere available for local use. In a report on the southern part of what is now the District of Alberta, published more than ten years ago, the amount of coal contained in one of these beds in a known outcrop of sixty-six miles in length, and at an easily workable depth, was estimated at 330,000,000 tons. The mines at Lethbridge are situated upon one part of this particular deposit. The vast extent of these coal-fields of the North-West may be further evidenced by the fact that a rough estimate of their area between the 49th and 56th parallels amounts to 50,000 square miles, than which there is probably no larger tract in the world known to be characterized by a practically continuous spread of valuable mineral fuels.

Natural gas, in important quantities, has also been found in several borings sunk for other purposes, and although not as yet utilized the geological conditions indicate that a practically inexhaustible reservoir of this convenient fuel extends beneath a great area of country. Remarkable outcrops of "tar-sands", or sand impregnated with bituminous matter, found along the Athabasca River, support the belief that one of the most notable petroleum-bearing territories of the world there awaits development. Impressed by its probable importance, the Government has begun experimental boring operations, under the control of the Geological Survey, of which the results are awaited with great interest; and although it may not be assumed that the first or even the second boring must necessarily be successful, the eventual discovery of petroleum can scarcely be considered doubtful.

A PLEA FOR MINERAL DEVELOPMENT IN ONTARIO

Ontario Development of Mines, *Annual Report*, 1892 (Toronto, 1892), pp. 97-8.

As an agricultural country Ontario has practically reached its limit. If the Province is to advance in the future as in the past, or if it is not to retrograde even, the great Northwest must be turned to advantage. Its stores of timber have hitherto been a source of revenue, but fires and the work of the lumberman are steadily diminishing them. The only hope for rapid advance in the future lies in the development of the mineral resources, especially of the Huronian tract, which as far as explored have proved rich in ores. Iron ores of unsurpassed quality and in large amounts are found in the Province; copper ores occur in very large quantities; and the world's largest known source of nickel belongs to the Province, not to mention ores of silver and gold; so that Ontario may justly be described as one of the richest countries in the world in mineral resources.

Notwithstanding this, Ontario has been disappointingly slow in developing its mines, and what has been done has been the work not of Ontario men, but of Americans or Europeans, and has frequently been carried on in ways unsuited to our conditions. Every new mining region has its special conditions and difficulties, and the best methods of meeting them can be determined often only by costly experiments on a commercial scale. No mining region can reach the highest prosperity merely by shipping its ores to other countries, and it is safe to say that until Ontario ceases to sell its ores and low grade mattes and begins to smelt and refine its own iron, steel, nickel, and copper, no great advance is likely to be made. The establishment of smelting works of any kind on the right scale and wisely managed will give a market for many ores of too low grade for export, and will serve as a nucleus for a dozen other industries of great importance.

The starting of the manufacture of good quality steel, for instance, would probably be followed by the refining of at least part of our own nickel, to be used in making nickel steel, and that by the refining of the associated copper. I need not say that this would imply a demand for skilled and highly paid labor, would lead to the building up of great manufacturing centres through the cheapness of the main raw materials, and would afford the best possible markets for our farmers.

But the founding of such metallurgical establishments on the proper scale demands a large capital and great experience; and at the outset there would probably be little or no returns until the experimental stage was over. In many other countries this costly and discouraging initiatory period has been tided over by governmental aid until things had reached a self-supporting basis.

In a purely agricultural country like Ontario encouragement is particularly needed, since our people have not yet developed the skill and experience required for success in this direction; and the foreigners who might be expected to undertake the work are already interested in the success of rival establishments in the United States, England, or other countries.

Under all the circumstances it appears that our Government would be justified in aiding in whatever way seems wisest the establishment of smelting works in the Province, such aid of course to cease when no longer needed. Such a course has been adopted with advantage by many other countries. Norway and Saxony have even owned and worked important mines and smelting establishments with great benefit to the State.

In my opinion Ontario has reached an important turning point in its history. If no new departure is made our Province must stand still or even retrograde, while a wise utilization of our mineral resources will give the starting point for a growth of population and wealth which will keep Ontario in the front rank as compared with the rest of the world.

THE DISCOVERY OF NICKEL

Report of the Royal Ontario Nickel Commission (Toronto, 1917), pp. 20-37.

RECONNAISSANCES BY LOGAN AND SALTER

In a remarkably able and full report dated 31st March, 1857, and dealing with a great variety of subjects within the scope of his department, Hon. Joseph Cauchon, Commissioner of Crown Lands, treats of the wild lands of the Province of Canada, as constituting the home of future settlements, and endeavours to estimate the value for agricultural, mining and lumbering purposes of the territory north of Lake Huron. The materials for such an estimate were scanty. The principal sources of information drawn upon by the Commissioner are the report of Sir William Logan, Provincial Geologist, made in 1848, and the report by A. P. Salter, Provincial Land Surveyor, who in 1855, at the direction of the Commissioner, had ascended the various rivers emptying into Lake Huron from Sault Ste. Marie eastward, and furnished a general description of the tract....

THE CREIGHTON MINE FORESHADOWED

In 1856 Salter, who in the previous year had made the exploratory trip along the northern shores of lakes Huron and Superior already referred to, was again in the field for the purpose of running base, meridian and range lines preparatory to a general survey and subdivision of the territory lying between lake Nipissing and Sault Ste. Marie. Starting at a point on the Sturgeon river near its entrance into lake Nipissing, Salter ran a base line westward. On arriving at Whitefish lake he surveyed a meridian line due north twelve miles, which was continued the following year eighteen miles farther. In his report Salter remarks that the character of the country on the meridian line closely resembled that of the last section of the base line from the Wanapitei river to Whitefish lake, except that the valleys were broader and the soil generally lighter in character. He says:

> Between the fifth and eighth mile on this line I discovered considerable local attraction, the needle varying from 4 degrees to 14 degrees westerly. The existence of iron was plainly discernible on the rock.

Turning to the field notes of the survey, on file in the Department of Lands, Forests and Mines, it is found that the normal variation of the magnetic needle for the first five miles of the meridian line was about 3 degrees and 30 minutes west, but that at six miles 30 chains and 50 links, it deflected to 5 degrees 30 minutes west, and continued to show marked variations ranging to 14 degrees 10 minutes west at 7 miles 33 chains 50 links, and approaching the normal again only at 8 miles 17 chains 25 links. In the marginal column for remarks Salter makes the note, "Appearance of iron in trap."

Although not a geologist, Salter recognized the significance of this marked and extended attraction, and meeting Murray, who during the same season was continuing the geological explorations near lake Nipissing and on the north shore of lake Huron, upon which he had also been engaged during the two previous years, he mentioned the matter to Murray, and gave him particulars of the exact locality.

In reporting on his season's work Murray tells how he followed up Salter's hint:

> At the fifth mile a dingy green magnetic trap, with a large amount of iron pyrites, forms a ridge, and that rock, with syenite, continues in a succession of parallel ridges to the seventh mile, beyond which the country becomes low and marshy. These parallel ridges strike nearly east and west, and small brooks or marshes occupy the intermediate valleys.
>
> Previous to my visit to Whitefish lake, I had been informed by Mr. Salter that local attraction of the magnet had been observed by himself, while he was engaged in running the meridian line, and he expressed it to be his opinion that the presence of a large body of iron ore was the immediate cause. When, therefore, I came to the part indicated by Mr. Salter, I made a very careful examination not only in the direction of the meridian line, but for a considerable distance on each side of it, and the result of my

examination was that the local attraction, which I found exactly as described by Mr. Salter, was owing to the presence of an immense mass of magnetic trap.

The compass was found, while traversing these trap ridges, to be deflected from its true bearing upwards of ten degrees at several different parts, and in one place it showed a variation of fifteen degrees west of the true meridian, or about twelve degrees from the true magnetic north. Specimens of this trap have been given to Mr. Hunt for analysis, and the result of his investigation shows that it contains magnetic iron ore and magnetic iron pyrites generally disseminated through the rock, the former in very small grains; titaniferous iron was found associated with the magnetic ore, and a small quantity of nickel and copper with the pyrites.

Murray further states:

The magnetic trap discovered on Mr. Salter's meridian line north of Whitefish lake was observed to hold yellow sulphuret of copper occasionally; and Mr. Hunt's analysis of a hand specimen of the rock, weighing ten ounces, gave twenty grains of metalliferous material, of which eleven were magnetic, and consisted of magnetic iron ore, with a little titaniferous iron ore, and magnetic iron pyrites containing traces of nickel. The nine grains of non-magnetic mineral consisted of iron pyrites containing from two to three per cent. of copper and about one per cent. of nickel.

The location of this nickeliferous material is easily found. Salter's meridian line was retraced in 1883, and was made to form the west boundary of the townships of Waters and Snider. The point which is located 43 chains north of mile post VI on Salter's meridian is one and the same point as that which is located 43 chains north of the southwest corner of Snider on the west boundary of the township. It was here that Salter found unusual deflections of the compass and here noticed "the appearance of iron in trap." Here also, or near by, it certainly was that Murray discovered the "immense mass of magnetic trap," containing disseminated sulphides of nickel and copper. This locality is only 200 yards west of the great open pit of the Creighton mines. Unquestionably then, Murray walked over and examined the long gossan-stained ridge, at the foot of which in later years the greatest nickel mine in the world was discovered.

Salter and Murray duly reported to the government, which put their reports in print, and there they may be found to-day by those interested in the early history of the mining industry of Ontario. Doubtless the real significance of the discoveries these pioneers had made was not apparent to the public of their day, or even to themselves. Probably the financial results of the mining ventures on the north shore, virtually confined as these had been to the Bruce Mines copper group, were not of a kind to awaken lively hopes of large profits and quick returns. Nickel was not in great demand sixty years ago, even though its price was many times that of copper. A mineral deposit on Salter's principal meridian line, at least thirty miles north of the navigable waters of lake Huron, in a rough country entirely destitute of means of communication, was so inaccessible as to be of little immediate interest. At any rate, the mass of magnetic trap and the reports alike passed out of mind, and were only recalled when the Creighton mine was rediscovered; and this did not take place until the construction of the Canadian Pacific railway in the early eighties had brought to bear on the latest resources of the Sudbury region the vivifying influences of transportation and population.

FINDING THE MURRAY MINE

The building of the railway through this region in 1883 quickly led to the discovery that it was rich in minerals. The first deposit of nickel ore to be actually found was what afterwards came to be known as the Murray mine. The right of way for the railway was cleared for some distance west of Sudbury in 1883, and in August of that year a blacksmith on the construction gang named Thomas Flanagan observed an area on the right of way covered with gossan, and dug some holes in it which showed copper sulphide. When the "grade" reached the spot, a cutting in the rock was necessary, which exposed the deposit. A little later, the attention of John Loughrin, of Mattawa, afterwards for years member of the Legislature for Nipissing, who had a contract for making ties on that section of the line, was attracted by a deposit of "red mud" on the wagon road close by, and by the appearance of mineral in the rock cut. Doubtless others afterwards remembered that they, too, had noted the peculiar appearance of the place. This led to an application being made to the Department of Crown Lands by Thomas Murray on 25th February, 1884, for permission to purchase the lot, 11 in the fifth concession of the township of McKim. It was accordingly patented to himself, William Murray, Henry Abbott of Brockville, and John Loughrin, on the 1st of October, 1884, the price paid being the statutory one of one dollar an acre. The mine received its name from the Murray brothers, Thomas and William, then well-known merchants of Pembroke. The former was a member for several terms in the Legislature at Toronto, and also sat for Pontiac county, Que., in the House of Commons at Ottawa.

The patentees sold to H. H. Vivian and Company, of Swansea, Wales, who began mining operations in October, 1889, after having tested the quality and character of the Sudbury ores by smelting and refining them in their Swansea works. A smelter was erected and blown in, September, 1890; a second furnace was added a year later, and a third in 1892. These made a low grade matte, containing about 8 per cent. of nickel, which was bessemerized to a product carrying 35 or 40 per cent. nickel and 20 to 25 per cent. copper. Mining and smelting was carried on with more or less success until 1894, when the mine was permanently closed down. The property remained unworked until it was sold for $75,000 to J. R. Booth, M. J. O'Brien and associates, who prospected it by the diamond drill, and were successful in discovering a very large tonnage of ore previously unknown—now placed at eight or nine millions of tons. Messrs. Booth and O'Brien in turn sold to the British North American Nickel Corporation, Limited, which now owns and proposes to work the mine on an extensive scale.

The copper exposure in the C.P.R. right of way gave public notice of the discovery of mineral, and as soon as the snow had disappeared in the spring of 1884, prospectors were attracted to the locality, and took to the bush in the hope of finding other deposits.

Prospecting in the early stages of the Sudbury field was entirely a matter of searching for outcrops, and the prospectors, many of whom had little or no previous experience in the work, soon mastered such rudiments of geology as they found essential. Their favourite rock was "diorite"—now known in the Sudbury literature as norite—and the unfailing surface indication was a "burn" or gossan-covered area. Prospectors quickly established the rule that ore bodies were to be found at or near a "diorite" contact, and by their untiring labours during the first three or four years located most of the important deposits that have yet been found. The region was not mountainous, and the numerous waterways, made up of lakes, rivers and creeks, enabled the prospectors to penetrate with their canoes to almost any quarter and in almost any direction; but on the other hand, there was the disadvantage that the surface of the country was rough and broken, and covered with forest growth, green or already burnt. Rocky ground was plentiful, but the mantle of moss had sometimes to be removed before the formation could be inspected. Forest fires were of frequent occurrence, and the assistance they afforded by clearing the ground of timber and moss gave rise to the suspicion that in some cases the prospectors, if not actually guilty of setting out fire, were at any rate indifferent to its occurrence, and lukewarm in attempting to extinguish it. Other advantages the prospectors enjoyed were found in the greater part of the territory having been surveyed into townships, concessions and lots, thus permitting any finds to be easily and accurately located, and the presence of the railway, which facilitated travel and made supplies abundant and cheap....

THE CREIGHTON DEPOSIT RE-DISCOVERED

The success which had attended the efforts of the prospectors in 1884 naturally led to more extensive search in the following year, and in 1885 a number of important discoveries were made. Metcalf and McAllister were again on the lookout for copper properties, and Thomas Frood was associated with them as scout. The great Creighton deposit, whose influence on the magnetic needle had caused the aberrations noted by surveyor Salter and geologist Murray twenty-nine years before, was rediscovered, apparently by Henry Ranger. The latter states that after having finished the season of 1886 as prospector for Rinaldo McConnell, he set out on his own account and located the Creighton deposit that autumn, but that he was forestalled in his application to the Department by others. Metcalf and McAllister had applied to the Department 10th July, 1885, more than a year before, for several lots in the townships of Denison, Creighton and Snider, including the north half of lot 10 in the first concession of the last-named township, the Creighton lot, but there is nothing in the Departmental record to show that any discovery had been made, beyond the presumption raised by the application itself. This presumption is weakened by the unusual delay in securing title. In 1885 Samuel J. Ritchie, president of the newly-organized Canadian Copper Company, obtained a transfer of the rights of Metcalf and McAllister in the lands they had applied for, and on 24th January, 1887, patent issued to the Canadian Copper Company. Mr. Ritchie desired to know the exact situation of the outcrop with regard to the survey lines, and sent J. W. Evans and Thomas Baycroft to locate it. After tracing up the lines they found the post which marked the junction point of the townships of Waters, Graham, Creighton and Snider standing right on the hill of the Creighton mine. The deposit itself lay a short distance to the north and east.

Until the building of the Algoma Eastern railway, there was no means of transporting ore from the Creighton mine to the company's smelting works at Copper Cliff. In 1900, however, it began to produce and in steadily increasing quantities. Up to 31st March, 1916, the shipments had amounted to 4,753,433 tons. As is well known, the ore is of high quality, being especially rich in nickel. The average so far has been 4.44 per cent. nickel and 1.56 per cent. copper. The ore body is freer from rock matter than that of any other important mine, about 70 per cent. of the ore being sulphides.

The Creighton mine has been pronounced, and no doubt with truth, to be the greatest nickel mine in the world. At the present time it is supplying the larger part of the ore smelted in the furnaces of the Canadian Copper Company, and as the nickel output of this company is much greater than that of any other concern, the Creighton mine is actually furnishing the bulk of the nickel being used by the world. Some years ago borings by the diamond drill revealed the presence of reserves of ore at depth estimated at 10 millions of tons. The first workings were by the open pit method, but the mine is now worked by shafts and levels in the usual way.

GOLD MINING IN CENTRAL CANADA

A.H.A. Robinson, *Gold in Canada 1935* (Canada, Department of Mines), pp. 59-60. Reprinted by permission of the Department of Energy, Mines and Resources.

FLIN FLON MINE

The Flin Flon mine, of the Hudson Bay Mining and Smelting Company, Limited, situated on the Manitoba-Saskatchewan boundary, 91 miles by rail northwest of The Pas, Manitoba, is a copper-zinc mine, the ore from which carries also a small amount of gold that is recovered as a by-product. The rate at which gold is produced at Flin Flon depends, therefore, almost entirely on the rate at which copper and zinc can be profitably produced and sold. At present, it is by far the largest gold producer in Manitoba and, in the aggregate, the amount of gold contained in its known ore-bodies is estimated at about 1,332,000 ounces.

The Flin Flon deposit was staked in 1915, on a weathered gossan out-crop from which gold could be panned, but which was found on further investigation to be primarily a low-grade body of copper, zinc, and iron sulphides. In 1916 and 1917, the property was drilled by parties who held it under option, and the ore-body was thus delimited much as it is known to-day. At that time, however, the deposit was some 70 miles in an air-line from the nearest railway, and as, in addition, the treatment of the ore presented some metallurgical difficulties, there was considerable delay in getting financiers interested in its exploitation. In 1920, an option was taken by the Mining Corporation of Canada, Ltd., and underground development was started to check the results of the diamond-drilling. In 1925, the Mining Corporation succeeded in interesting H. P. Whitney of New York, following which exhaustive experiments were conducted to determine the best method of treating the ore. Early in 1927, a 50-ton pilot mill was built on the property and further extensive tests were made; and at the end of the year the Hudson Bay Mining and Smelting Company, Ltd. was formed to operate the mine.

In January, 1928, the Canadian National Railway started the con-struction of a branch line, which reached Flin Flon in October. Following the arrival of the railroad, a concentrating mill, an electrolytic zinc plant, a copper smelter, a cyanide plant, etc., were built at the mine. A hydro-electric plant equipped to generate 44,000 horse-power was built at Island Falls on the Churchill river and connected with the mine by a transmission line 58 miles in length. Before the end of 1930, there had been completed and put in operation at Flin Flon a plant estimated to be capable of treat-ing 3,000 tons of ore a day, and of producing 30,000,000 pounds of copper, 50,000,000 pounds of zinc, 60,000 ounces of gold, and 900,000 ounces of silver annually. Estimated ore reserves in the mine at this time amounted to some 18,000,000 tons, carrying 0·074 ounce of gold and 1·06 ounces of silver a ton, in addition to 1·71 per cent copper and 3·45 per cent zinc. It is believed that about one-third, or 6,000,000 tons, of these reserves can be won by open-pit mining.

THE ELECTRICAL AGE

THE SIGNIFICANCE OF ELECTRIC POWER

T. C. Keefer, 'Presidential Address', *Trans. Roy. Soc. Can.*, vol. II, (1899), 1-11.

Canada with a small population and insufficient capital has nevertheless held a foremost position in the products of the Forest and the Fisheries, as well as in the quality of those cereals and fruits which attain their highest development in a northern latitude. In live stock she has not suffered by comparison with any other portion of this continent, while in dairy products she is pre-eminent. If she has not, until recently, made much progress in mineral development, it has been more from want of money than of mines. If she has been long in attaining a position as a manufacturing country, it is accounted for by the fiscal and financial conditions of a sparsely settled country, the smallness of a home market, and the competition of greater capital and out-put, and therefore cheaper production elsewhere.

Amongst the many partially developed resources of Canada, perhaps there is none more widespread or more far reaching in future results than her unsurpassed Water Power. The value of this has been enormously enhanced, first by the expansion of the wood pulp manufacture, and the introduction of electro-chemical and metallurgical industries for which this country possesses the raw material; and, more recently, in the revolution which has been brought about by success in transmitting the energy of water falls from remote and inconvenient positions to those where the work is to be done.

Electrical transmission brings the power to the work, and when the prime mover is water, we have the cheapest power, and perhaps nearest approach to perpetual motion which it is possible to obtain;—one which is always "on tap," and, like gravity, maintained without cost and applied without delay.

An examination of any good map of our broad Dominion reveals, as its most striking feature, an extraordinary wealth and remarkably uninterrupted succession of lakes and rivers, suggestive of ample rainfall, the first great requisite in the occupation of any country.

The upper sections or sources of most of the Canadian rivers are chains of lakes, occupying in many instances the greater portion of the water course. These head waters are often upon nearly the same elevation and interlocked with the sources of other rivers flowing in opposite or different directions, and separated by narrow necks of land at a low "divide," rendering diversion from one to another possible, a feature which has in some places been utilized by lumbermen fearless of any legal injunction.

This terrace-like profile of the rivers and their frequent expansion into lakes, often dotted with islands, not only enhances the beauty of the scenery, but, for utilitarian purposes, constitutes a series of elevated natural mill ponds, containing latent power of unknown extent and value, awaiting that demand upon them which is now being made in consequence of the discovery that our second rate forest growth which has hitherto served chiefly to ornament their shores and islands, has become the most important, and can be ground into pulp and rolled into paper to meet the ever increasing demands of the newspaper, the bookmaker, and the innumerable forms into which wood pulp can be compressed for useful or ornamental purposes,—or as a substitute for wood or metal. . . .

Within the last ten years high voltage electricity has been firmly established with annually increasing power of extension, and this has brought Canada into the first rank of economical power producing countries. Water is thus represented by a power to which it can give birth, but which is superior to its own, in that, where ever transplanted, it can do nearly all the parent power could do, as well as give light, heat and greater speed: moreover it has given rise to industries only possible with abundant cheap electricity. What is more important to us is that such industries are those for which Canada possesses the raw material, but which, without water power, she could not engage in.

There are important industries in which we have for some time utilized water power—for which electricity is not indispensable—but which equally require large amounts of cheap power, and are capable of indefinite extension: but while these may not need the intense electric current necessary for electro-chemical industries, they will find electrical transmission of inestimable value in many situations; while, for lighting and heating purposes, water power is invaluable to all.

Heretofore we have cut our spruce into deals and exported it to Europe, and more recently into pulp wood and exported that to the United States; but, manufactured by our water power into paper, the raw material would yield this country ten times the value it is now exported for.

The extension of railways combined with electrical transmission, will promote the local manufacture of such wood products (including all valuable hard wood) as can bear transportation; thus giving the largest amount of local employment, as well as tonnage to the railway; and delivering us from the position of "hewers of wood" for other countries.

POWER FROM A NATIONAL HERITAGE

Hydro-electric Power Commission of Ontario, *Genesis of the Power Movement* (Toronto, n.d.), pp. 5-6.

THE object of this brief pamphlet is to show in a concise form, the origin and growth of the demand from the people of the Province of Ontario for cheaper electrical energy, for power, light, heating and other purposes.

This Province has been handicapped industrially, owing to the fact that it possesses no coal mines within its border. There are, of course, abundant coal deposits in the far East and far West of Canada, but the cost of transportation makes the use of this coal practically prohibitory in the Province of Ontario. We are, therefore, almost entirely dependent for our fuel supply upon the coal fields of Pennsylvania, controlled, as they are, by large and powerful corporations, who also practically own the highways over which this coal is transported. As a result, the people of this Province must always be subject to any laws which may be enacted respecting the export of coal, or strikes should they occur in their mines. For example, during the last great coal strike in the United States, both soft and hard coal increased in value to a practically prohibitory figure, and our factories were either compelled to shut down or pay a price beyond all reason. The fuel famine became so widespread that the City Council of Toronto found it necessary to vote the sum of $50,000 of the people's money for the purpose of supplying coal at actual cost in small quantities to the working people of that city.

The public had, however, been watching with interest the development of power on the American side of the Niagara Falls. It had been claimed that the "white coal" of the Falls could be economically transmitted to supply the needs of 1,600,000 people in the Province of Ontario, out of a total population of 2,000,000, and the trend of public opinion was that this great national heritage should be conserved in the interests of the people.

The first concrete step in line with this growing sentiment was the appointment of a Committee by the Toronto Board of Trade on the 25th of April, 1900, of which the late Mr. W. E. H. Massey was Chairman. Their investigation, naturally, had specific reference to the needs of

Toronto, and in the report submitted by that Committee it is significant to note the following words: "Our hope for cheaper power is to bring the current from one of the great Niagara generating plants." "The Toronto Electric Light Company have signified their intention of bringing power from Niagara Falls, and the question arises whether or not Toronto, as a city, should control this proposed Niagara power connection. . . ."

Public opinion, however, was gradually being aroused to the necessity of preserving this vast asset for the use of the people to whom it belonged, and in the early part of 1902 this found expression in several meetings of representatives of different cities in the Province, as well as those from the Canadian Manufacturers' Association and Boards of Trade.

ONTARIO HYDRO: THE GREAT EXPERIMENT

Reginald Pelham, *An Expensive Experiment, the Hydro-electric Power Commission of Ontario* (New York, 1913), pp. 73-80, 85-6.

So far as the utilization of a water power is found to be desirable, its value to the community will be represented by its greatest possible utilization. The power of falling water is a continuous supply of energy, but on the other hand, a large proportion of the purposes to which such energy can be applied are intermittent, and therefore, the power of the water can be utilized by such intermittent services only to a partial extent. It follows, therefore, that the natural and economic utilization of water powers is by such industries or processes as will, with the least possible loss in production and in transmission, utilize for the greatest period of time the continuous force of the water-fall. . . .

The purposes to which electrical energy are applied, such as electric lighting, manufacturing, power and railroad operation, are erratic, inter-mittent and variable, and do not therefore, constitute an economic use of the continuous power of the falling water. On the other hand, certain forms of industry and processes which have come into existence since the introduction of electricity, utilize the energy generated by a water power in a practically continuous manner, without the accompaniment of the loss of much of the available power during the course of the year's operations. . . .

As between the use of the falls [Niagara] by such an industry and the use of the power in an extensive and erratic utilization by transmission to long distances for lighting and manufacturing purposes, there cannot be any question that the public is the gainer by the more continuous use of the water power, the product of which then becomes a source of enrichment to the country, while the irregular and less productive purposes for which power is required can be served by other methods of power production better situated, and adapted to the irregularities of operation. . . .

These facts all demonstrate that the proposition to convert water power to electrical energy for the purpose of its conveyance to long distances for general commercial and public purposes, is economically unsound. The useful application of energy in this form is limited and results in an economic loss of a large proportion of available energy which could be more economically and advantageously utilized in the immediate vicinity of the falls, and by such purposes and industries as require the largest possible and most continuous use of power.

It has, however, been claimed in support of the Great Experiment of the Province of Ontario, that the distribution of energy in this form was desirable as a means of attracting the establishment of new general industries in the Province, and this point of view was evidently that which influenced the opinions and actions of the business community in furthering the movement which resulted in the establishment of the Hydro-Electric Power Commission.

At the time this discussion was in progress, it was not made clear to those who engaged in it, that energy, even at a low cost, is not a large inducement towards the establishment of industries of a general character in a locality, the selection of a situation being governed by the larger elements of suitable labor, the accessibility and price of raw materials, and transportation to and from the place of manufacture, together with other questions, such as taxation, tariff, and above all, proximity to the sources of demand for the product.

Unless therefore, a locality should prove specially advantageously situated in some or all of these respects, the element of cheap energy is not of material importance. . . .

While it is the fact that coal is not found within its soil, yet the Province is remarkably well situated as regards the transportation of coal from the great coal districts of the United States, and in course of time the east and west boundaries may be served by water and rail with great Canadian supplies of fuel.

In all cases where the transmission of electrical energy is to be or has been undertaken, the eventual value of the operation will be limited by the comparative cost of the real production of energy. As a concrete instance, the conditions in the City of London, may be referred to. This place is rather more than one hundred miles from Niagara Falls, involving a large expense in the transmission of electrical energy. It is located very advantageously as regards the supply of oil fuel, which is situated less than one-half the distance from Niagara; and it is also about an equal distance from the Detroit River at which point supplies of coal from more than one source are available, so that coal of excellent quality can be purchased in London at three dollars per ton.

The share of the capital cost of the line of transmission of the Hydro-Electric Power Commission involved in connecting the City of London to Niagara, has amounted to $256 per horsepower used. A good steam power plant could be constructed for less than one-third of this expense.

STEAM vs ELECTRICITY ON RAILWAYS

S. J. Dodd, *Electrification of Railways* (Ottawa, 1918), pp. 17-19.

"The question is a very important one, and very complicated. It is not now so much a problem in mechanical or electrical engineering as one in economics. The ordinary man who has seen the miracle wrought by the application of electricity to industrial plants, imagines that the same result can be obtained by its application to the railways. It must not be forgotten, however, that the miracle has been brought about by the tremendous improvement in, and the reduction in, the cost of transmission of power, rather than in the reduction in cost of its production.

"If the industrial plants could be located immediately at the power site, or at the pit mouth, the cost of transforming the power into electric energy would be saved. All plants cannot, however, be so located, and even in the limits of one shop, it is more advantageous and economical to transmit the power electrically than by shafts, pulleys and belts. In the steam locomotive, the power is produced immediately at the point at which it is to be used, so that the advantages of easy and cheap transmission are, in a great measure, lost.

"After this is said there still remain many decided advantages which the electric has over the steam locomotive. Therefore, there are many decided economic reasons for the adoption of electric traction on our railways, just as there are many and decided reasons against its adoption.

"Some of the reasons in favour of its adoption are quite evident. Coal in all the great central area of Canada is entirely lacking; water-powers are abundant, and, even under equal conditions, hydro-electric power is cheaper than steam.

"The cost of maintenance of the electric is only a fraction of that of the steam locomotive. The steam locomotive requires hours in the roundhouse after a long run before it can be again fit for road service, whereas the electric can be sent out again almost immediately after its arrival. The road can thus be operated with fewer units. Electric locomotives can be so connected that they may be operated in pairs under one crew without any loss of power; steam locomotives can not.

"On long ascending grades the electric locomotive with the strength of the power house at its back, retains its full power and freshness to the very summit. The steam locomotive can not. On long descending grades, the electric motor can return to the power line, power derived from the train's momentum. All this is lost in the case of the steam locomotive. As far as operating expenses due to power are concerned, the electric locomotive has every advantage, and is capable of effecting many and decided savings.

As far as capital charges and maintenance of roadway are concerned, the advantages are all with the steam locomotive. The cost of electric installation is heavy; therefore, the fixed charges are materially greater.

"On a large portion of the railway mileage in Canada, it would be necessary to develop new water-powers without any market other than the railway. The railway load fluctuates not only from month to month, but from hour to hour. It is almost a certainty that the power development would require to be three or four times as great as the average load; hence, comparatively expensive power. The maintenance of the roadway is materially increased, the danger from snow, especially in the mountains, where electric traction would be peculiarly advantageous, is much increased. The troubles arising from the failure of any part of the electric installation are widespread, and much more disastrous than the failure of a steam locomotive.

"Balancing the pros and cons, it is found that electric traction materially reduces the operating expenses, but materially increases the fixed charges. The saving in operating expenses is nearly directly in proportion to the number of trains per day: the greater the density of traffic, the greater the saving. The cost of installation is in a great measure independent of the density of the traffic, or the number of trains per day. On a road of a given standard, the cost of many of the items which go to make up the whole, is the same, whether the trains be few or many. The problem thus always resolves itself into this: With the number of trains per day on a given section of a road, will the undoubted savings and operating expenses be sufficient to offset the undoubted increase in fixed charges? Every division of the road is a separate and independent problem.

"Canada is a very large and sparsely settled country, with a greater railway mileage per capita than any other country in the world, hence the traffic per mile is very thin. The Canadian Pacific, I understand, has not, as yet, found a place where the traffic is sufficiently dense to justify the cost of installation of electric traction.

"Coal has increased greatly in cost and is difficult to obtain at any price. The scarcity is only temporary, but part, at least, of the increased cost is sure to be permanent. As labour and all supplies have increased in price, the operating expenses have risen rapidly. Therefore, from an operating point of view, electric traction has become more desirable. This is largely offset by the increased cost of money, making the fixed charges due to an electric installation decidedly greater. No road in Canada, excepting the Canadian Pacific, is in a position financially to contemplate large capital expenditures."

Engineers and Rational Technology

Canada provided a dramatic setting for engineering accomplishments. Extremes of climate, an immense and varied terrain, and the need to achieve large effects with limited means, gave any project an aura of grandeur. The engineer should have been the ideal hero for this particular scenario. He symbolized progress and the triumph of rationality; he commanded great enterprises and depended for success on the power of modern applied science. At the same time, the engineer seemed the essential spirit of individualism. Often as not he carried out his labours in frontier areas, where courage and skillful improvisation were daily requirements. It was a life style that emphasized hard work, fortitude, and single-mindedness. Dreams of wealth and fame were built on those foundations. Some men, the CPR's Sir William Van Horne, for instance, provided a handsome example of the rewards that flowed from large-scale technical achievement.

Few engineers ever reached Van Horne's eminence, however. They dealt in the rhetoric of individuality, but usually spent their lives in a corporate structure. That uncomfortable reality fundamentally shaped the ways in which engineers viewed themselves, their employers, and their place in society. Even in the earlier years of the nineteenth century, they found themselves in an occupational no-man's land. They did not feel easy about a close relationship with capital, but they rejected out of hand any means of expressing their interests that seemed like trade unionism. Engineers looked to local employment opportunities for the chance to rise in their careers, and as the basis for an engineering profession in Canada. But throughout the nineteenth-century, Britons and Americans were often hired to fill technical positions in Canada.

Engineers sought a resolution of their problems in professionalism. They lacked the prestige of their counterparts in medicine or the law, and hoped that the establishment of journals, societies, and schools would raise the status of engineering and thus its remuneration. Until the closing decades of the nineteenth century, engineers were too few in number and too widely scattered to form the critical mass necessary for viable organizations; early efforts such as the Canadian Institute were doomed to failure.

The establishment of the Canadian Society of Civil Engineers in 1887 revealed some of the factors that stimulated technical men to think of themselves as members of a profession. There were three general issues. First, engineers wanted to regulate the standards of practice, and to exclude from engineering work all those who did not meet those standards. In particular, engineers were irritated by the fact that they could not engage in surveying without belonging to surveyors' guilds while, without any parallel restrictions, surveyors could work as engineers. Second, they wanted protection against the employment of foreign engineers on Canadian projects. Finally, engineers hoped that the formation of a professional society would serve to mitigate unseemly competition for jobs, and lead to a better public appreciation of the dignity and importance of engineering.

But all engineers did not necessarily share the same professional concerns. Thomas C. Keefer, first president of the society, argued in favour of a prestigious organization, aloof from certification concerns. Alan Macdougall, who had also been instrumental in founding the society, took a different position. The society's first order of business, he felt, was to gain control of its own profession. Meanwhile, in the field of mining engineering, the line between entrepreneur and engineer was badly blurred, and as the editorial in the *Canadian Mining Review* plainly indicates, there was sharp opposition to a rigorous definition of engineering standards.

The question of professionalism touched other issues of importance to Canadian engineers. One was the matter of training. During the nineteenth century most Canadian engineers received their education in the office of an established practitioner, through on-the-job training, or by a combination of the two. England's Crystal Palace Exhibition in 1851 marked a turning point in attitudes about technical education, however. In the decade that followed, engineering courses were begun in the Maritime provinces, at McGill in Montreal, and in University College at the University of Toronto.

Consistent with Canada's need for transportation systems, civil engineering received the most emphasis at first. In time, educators recognized the necessity for instruction in other fields of engineering, particularly as a basis for industrial development. The 1871 report of a special commission on technical education in Ontario argued for a school of technology specifically in terms of an emerging international industrial competition. To some, the logical extension of that position was a federally supported technical institution.

Special training, and a desire for the prestige enjoyed by older professions, also raised the issue of social responsibility. In the opening years of the twentieth century, Canadian engineers became increasingly concerned with air and water pollution and with the conservation of natural resources. Their interest sprang partly from Theodore Roosevelt's 1908

Conference of Governors, which had generated wide publicity for conservation. But the movement also had implications for engineers and their professional societies. Conservation suggested the application of specialized techniques to solve major national problems. John Galbraith, Dean of the Faculty of Applied Science at the University of Toronto, used the occasion of his presidential address to the Canadian Society of Civil Engineers to argue the case for the engineer's importance in matters of broad interest. Galbraith's characterization of the engineer as an objective force in vital public issues was one the profession would continue to cherish.

Municipal engineering provided another opportunity for important public service, especially as cities increased in size. But public service also meant politics, and engineers had mixed feelings about playing in that game. When Vancouver fired its city engineer in a 1911 political controversy, the profession faced just such a dilemma. And when it finally decided not to intervene, engineers were left with an unresolved contradiction between their aims and their actions. In time, Canadians came to recognize more clearly the importance of engineering skills, but on the whole the profession failed in its efforts to convince the public that it had more to offer than technical expertise.

AMERICANS ON THE GREAT WESTERN

A. G. Bogue and Lillian R. Benson, eds, 'An Engineer on the Great Western: A Selection from the Personal Reminiscences of Silas Wright Burt', *Western Ontario History Nuggets* (London, 1952), pp. 9-10. Reprinted by permission of the University of Western Ontario.

I should here say something about the Great Western Railway, the first of any extent built in Canada. It ran from the Suspension Bridge at Niagara Falls to Windsor opposite Detroit, Michigan, and was thus a link between the roads from Albany to Buffalo at one end, and the Michigan Central at the other. These roads were both interested in the Canadian project which united them and they contributed to the funds for its construction which were completed by subscriptions in Canada and England. All the principal engineers were from the United States and the subordinate positions were filled by Canadians. The contractors were all "Yankees" except that a small interest in each contract was reserved for Canadians, who also sub-contracted largely. There was thus a chain of Yankee engineers and contractors on the whole line of the road, one hundred and twenty-nine miles long, at stations from ten to fifteen miles apart. And the visiting to and fro, and the feeling that we were compatriots in a strange land kept up an *esprit de corps* and hospitality such as I have never known equalled. . . . While the Canadians greeted us as the harbingers of prosperity for their country, they were strongly prejudiced against us as "Yankees", a term applied to all born in the United States. Greater intercourse and mutual interests have since then greatly abated this prejudice, but in 1852 it was very strong, and the insular bigotry of the Englishman in his estimate of foreigners was exaggerated by those colonists. Probably the aversion to "Yankees" had been heightened by the participation of many of them in the rebellions of 1837.

AN ALIEN ENGINEER

The Canadian Engineer, vol. vi, (April, 1899), 336.

St. Mary's, Ontario, had been discussing waterworks systems for two years, but little progress had been made until early last month. Committees of the town council and board of trade had collected some information from other towns, and a public meeting had been held at which some of these had been read. A civil engineer from the United States who happened to be passing through (it is reported in the local papers) stopped off for a few hours, drove round the town with the chief officials and was instructed to prepare plans for a water supply system for the town. The engineer in question is of unquestioned ability, and has constructed some very large works in the United States with a great deal of success, but it would seem almost unfair to Canadians that an alien engineer should be employed upon the mere offer of his services without considering the claims of the many successful members of the profession who have done good work in Canada and depend upon Canadians for the substantial recognition of that work which will enable them to remain in Canada and follow their chosen profession.

A SUCCESS STORY

Alexander Somerville, 'Memoir of Charles Legge, Esq., Civil Engineer, Montreal', *Canadian Illustrated News* (January 16, 1864), 100.

Charles Legge was born September 29th, 1829, at Gananoque, County of Leeds, Canada West, and received his early education under the Rev. Alexander McLean and other teachers at the village academy. In 1846 he entered the Queen's University at Kingston, and during the summer vacation engaged on a trigonometrical survey of the north shore of Lake Huron, which was conducted for the Canadian Government by Alexander Vidal, Esq., of Port Sarnia, returning in the same autumn to the University. A letter from Mr. Vidal certified thus: "His acquiescence to my wishes and sincere endeavours to assist me in my work, deserved and have obtained my warmest approbation, and have secured my high esteem." The Rev. James Williamson, LL.D., Professor of Mathematics and Civil Engineering in Queen's University, wrote of Mr. Legge, July, 1847: "I fervently trust our best hopes may be realized, and that our University may have cause to be proud of having numbered him among her sons."

From an early age Charles Legge was destined for the profession of a Civil Engineer in consequence of the predilection shown for mechanics, a quality of mind inherited from his father, who is yet living, and is a mechanician of the highest order. He was articled as an engineer pupil to Samuel Keefer, Esq., the present Deputy Commissioner of Public Works, then Chief Engineer of the Welland Canal.

On the appointment of that gentleman to the office of Chief Engineer of Public Works, the pupil followed his professional teacher from the Welland Canal to Montreal, and in succeeding years applied himself with great industry and zeal to acquiring a thorough knowledge of the mysteries of his future profession. He succeeded in this so well that in the year 1852, the Honourable John Young, then Chief Commissioner of Public Works, with a keen perception of the youthful Mr. Legge's talents and industry, appointed him superintending engineer of the St. Lawrence Canals, in which position he gave the greatest satisfaction. In the succeeding year he was promoted to the charge of the Junction Canal, then in course of construction. That was a position better suited for exercising the young engineer's talents than the one he last occupied. He remained directing the construction of the Junction Canal, and they who have minutely examined it from Iroquois Village to the highest lock on the St. Lawrence opposite Frazer's Island, six miles below Prescott, as I did, and noted the nature of the work at the Galouse Rapids, the stupendous locks, and the great water-power furnished from the canal to the Canada Starch Company, know how perfect the engineering has been. He remained there until, in compliance with the urgent request of his late chief, he resigned his position in the Government service, and joined Mr. Keefer on the Grand Trunk Railway, to which that gentleman had been appointed. There he was employed, in the location of the line between Kingston and Brockville.

On the completion of that work, and at the commencement of active field operations his valuable services were at once secured by Mr. Hodges on the part of the contractors who appointed him to the Cornwall District of the railway, where he remained until the opening of the line from Montreal to Kingston. At that time owing to the completion of the work a great reduction of the staff was made. Young Legge expected to go with the rest, when to his surprise and gratification he was telegraphed for to Montreal to receive the appointment of superintending engineer of the south half of the Victoria Bridge, then about being commenced.

The confidence displayed by Mr. Hodges in the appointment of this young Canadian engineer, at the time scarcely twenty-five years of age, to this highly important post was not misplaced; he knew his man and put that man in the right place. The work thus entrusted to him was driven on with the utmost rapidity, and unparalleled success. Nearly fifteen hundred men, embracing mechanics of all classes, were under his control, as well as the quarries of Lake Champlain and Mile End, nearly one hundred miles apart, both of which had to be frequently visited and the work there going on examined and measured.

Throughout the five busy years thus employed Mr. Legge commanded the unqualified confidence of Messrs. Ross and Hodges, as well as of every contractor, mechanic and labourer under his charge, as was evinced by the numerous costly gifts bestowed on him at the completion of the work by both employers and employed when bidding each other farewell.

Before the completion of the Victoria Bridge a project had been mooted by Messrs. Hodges and Ross for building a tubular bridge over the Niagara River, a short distance below the Falls. The great engineering difficulty in carrying out the scheme was the scaffold on which to erect the land piers. A design was submitted to the two eminent engineers by Mr. Legge and met with their most cordial approval. For boldness of design, strength, rigidity, and lightness, united with ease of construction it stands unrivalled, and if the young engineer had achieved but this alone, it would have placed him high among the clever men of his profession. The proprietors of the *Canadian Illustrated News* hope ere long to give their readers a view of this grand mechanical structure, which at no distant day will receive a material embodment.

The following copies of letters testify how highly the two chief engineers of the Victoria Bridge esteemed Mr. Legge.

From James Hodges, Esq., Principal Agent for the firm of Messrs. Peto and Betts, Contractors for building the Victoria Bridge—"Montreal, 12th January, 1860. Mr. Chas. Legge has been employed on the works of the Victoria Bridge as Assistant Engineer for nearly five years and by his unwearied perseverance and attention to his duties has always given me great satisfaction. I can with great confidence recommend him as a very practical man—competent to take charge of any engineering work."

Mr. Ross, chief Engineer to the Grand Trunk Railway Company, wrote thus:

"Mr. Charles Legge has been engaged for the last five years, as superintendent upon the works of the Victoria Bridge, in the construction of coffer dams, building the weirs, and erecting the tubes, in which capacity his attention to his duties, has rendered him a most efficient assistant, trustworthy and correct. His long practical experience will qualify him for the construction of engineering works of any extent."

The great work, however, with which Mr. Legge's name is destined to be most intimately linked, is the celebrated Hydraulic Docks at Montreal— a gigantic work truly, and one which when carried out will give Montreal facilities for manufacturing, with warehouse, railway and dock accommodation such as no other city in the world can equal or even approach, and will place her far in advance of all others in commercial prosperity. For many years past the leading merchants of the commercial metropolis, headed by the Honourable John Young, have been strenuously exercising themselves to obtain more extensive facilities for commercial and manufacturing objects, and in furtherance of this design have at various times employed a rather large number of eminent Canadian and American engineers to furnish plans by which this object could be achieved. Plans, Reports, and Estimates had therefore multiplied to a prodigious extent in the archives of the Board of Trade and Harbour Commissioners, but all of them possessing objectionable features, precluding the adoption of any.

Early in the year 1861, a large committee of wealthy and influential merchants was organized with the indefatigable Hon. John Young as chairman, with the view of another attempt being made. On this occasion native talent was called in. Mr. Young's old protégé in the Public Works Department, Mr. Legge, was appointed to draw up the plans. In the course of one week the entire scheme was developed on paper and the committee invited to examine the same. So clearly were the advantages of the whole plan made apparent, and so susceptible of being carried out for a moderate outlay in proportion to its vast extent, that the cautious, long-headed moneyed men at once resolved to form a company, obtain a charter and construct the work. The charter was accordingly obtained, and the company organized, when but for the "Trent Difficulty" with the prospect of immediate war with the neighbouring Republic, with the delicate relations which have since existed between the two countries, the work would have been commenced and now well on to completion.— When more peaceable times arrive the great work will be started. The extent of its influence on the prosperity of the country none can determine.

A preliminary report describing the nature, extent, and mode of accomplishing the work is before me, from which in some future issue of this paper extracts will be made—suffice it now to observe that by the most eminent American and foreign engineers, Mr. Legge's scheme of Hydraulic Docks stands unrivalled in ancient or modern times, whether as viewed on the whole as an Engineering conception, or analyzed into all its various mechanical details.

Mr. Legge has also prepared a Dock scheme for the Mill proprietors at the foot of the Lachine Canal, accompanied by elaborate plans and estimates with a very able report. The entire cost, I understand is about one million of dollars, but the land reclaimed and adapted for warehouses, each provided with a railway, cart, and ocean-ship connections, will sell for more than the entire cost, leaving the dock dues and railway rent as profit for the enterprise. A third rail across the Victoria Bridge will connect all the narrow gauge New England railways with these new warehouses, in addition to the Grand Trunk Railway.—Since these plans were prepared, the Montreal Harbour Commissioners have undertaken to execute the work and have already made considerable progress.

Many other extensive works have also owed their origin to this gentleman, to one of which we may refer hereafter, a magnificent park scheme at Montreal, on the site of the Priest's Farm.

Mr. Legge for some years past has been consulting engineer for several of the most extensive Hydraulic companies in the Province and is regarded as one of the first hydraulic authorities on the continent. He is yet a young man but has attained by his own unaided efforts a name of which he and his native country may justly be proud. Many grey headed veteran engineers would be pleased to have attained that position at the termination of their career, which he now occupies when scarcely beyond the threshold.

A COURSE IN CIVIL ENGINEERING

As quoted in Alfred G. Bailey, ed., *The University of New Brunswick Memorial Volume* (Fredericton: The University of New Brunswick, 1950), pp. 77-8. Reprinted by permission of the University of New Brunswick.

A course of instruction in Civil Engineering will be given at King's College by Mr. McMahon Cregan, who has been appointed to that duty by His Excellency the Visitor, and will commence on the fifteenth of February next, and continue until the end of April. It will be open to students of the College on payment of a fee of ten shillings and to all others on payment of a fee of two pounds, for the Course.

Persons desirous of joining the class are requested to communicate with the Registrar:—The course will embrace with other subjects, the following syllabus: "An explanation of the construction and uses of Logarithms, Sines, tangents, etc., Trigonometrical Formulae; Resolution of Plane Triangles; methods of Surveying with the Theodolite, Circumferenter, etc. Construction, use, and Adjustment of the Instruments used by Engineers, both for field and office work; levelling: Method of determining best route for Railway, etc.; Computation of the quantities of land, earthwork, etc., required for the execution of the works; Horsepower of Machinery, etc.; Method of "setting out" Railway curves and side widths; Calculation of gradients and theory of inclined planes; Superelevation of rails; Composition and resolution of Forces; Calculation of strains and pressures; strength of materials; theory and practice of timber and iron framing viaducts, bridges, etc.

Three lectures a week will be given in the College; and instruction in the field will also be given once a week, or as often as may be expedient.

SHOULD A YOUNG COUNTRY PROVIDE TECHNICAL EDUCATION?

J. George Hodgins, ed., *Documentary History of Education in Upper Canada*, vol. xxiii (Toronto, 1908), 15-16.

No one who has attentively studied the educational progress which we have made during the last ten years, or carefully watched the development of the material resources and manufacturing industries of this Province, but must have been painfully struck with the fact that, while we have liberally provided for the merely intellectual wants of our people, we have almost entirely neglected making any provision for training, and then turning to practical account that superior scientific and industrial skill among ourselves, which in other Countries contribute so largely and effectively to develop their Physical and Industrial resources. We have hitherto been content to receive our supply of such skilled Assistance from abroad; and we have left to European and American Institutions the duty of the development of Canadian talent and ability of such of our youths as have enterprise and means enough to go abroad to acquire that practical knowledge of the Industrial Arts, which we deny to them in their native land.

In this respect our American neighbours furnish a favourable contrast, and display their usual national sagacity. In their great industrial and manufacturing centres, they have established Institutions devoted to Industrial Science and Education. Nor have they been content with a meagre provision in this respect. In the small State of Massachusetts, (with a population in 1870 of 1,457,000), they have already established three such Institutions as the Government now propose to establish in this Province. In the neighbouring State of New York, they have no less than four Schools of Technology, (more or less extensive), one of which was established nearly fifty years ago. The result has been that in all of their great Civil, Military, Engineering and Industrial and Mining projects, they have always been able to command the best skill and talent among themselves; and that talent always receives a sufficient encouragement by being constantly employed, either in the service of the State, or in the great Railway, Mining, or Industrial, enterprises which are so largely developed and encouraged in the United States.

As to our own Country, some may doubtingly ask: what need is there that we, (a young Country), should provide for instruction in the Industrial and Mechanical Arts? To this we reply, that the almost unconscious development among ourselves of the Manufacturing interests of the Country has reached a magnitude and importance that it would be suicidal to those interests, (in these days of keen competition with our American neighbours), and injurious to their proper development, not to provide without delay for the production among ourselves of a class of skilled Machinists, Manufacturers, Engineers, Chemists and others. No one can visit any of the industrial centres which have sprung up in different parts of the Country and in our larger Towns, without being struck with their value and importance, and the number and variety of the skilled Labourers employed. Inquiry into the source of supply of this Industrial class reveals the fact, that, from the youngest Employé up to the Foreman of the Works, they are almost entirely indebted to the British Isles, to the United States and other Countries for that supply.

If you pursue your inquiries further, and ask what provision is made in the Schools of the Town, or other establishments in the County for instructing young Lads in the elements of Mechanics, Chemistry and Natural Philosophy, and thus preparing them in some degree for supplying the natural demand created in these Establishments? you will find that there has been little done of a practical nature in this direction; and that these subjects have been allowed to occupy a subordinate place in the Course of Study in the Public Schools. There are exceptions, of course, in some Schools, but not to any great extent. We are glad to find that this will be no longer the case; but that, influenced by a knowledge of the facts which we have stated, provision has been made in the New School Bill, for giving due prominence to these important subjects in all of our High Schools.

As a fitting sequel to this provision in the High Schools, for developing the taste and stimulating the desire of our youths to prepare themselves for industrial pursuits, is the proposal to establish a School of Technology. Such an Institution will supply a great desideratum; and, with the elementary training now proposed in our High Schools, will enable us to provide within ourselves for the supply which the Manufacturing Establishments that have grown up in the Country, so imperatively demand. A Boy, who in his School career shows a Mechanical turn, or Scientific taste, will no longer have to seek its higher development outside of our own Country, or, from want of means, leave it ungratified. He will now have provided, almost at his own door, an Institution which will be admirably fitted to give the freest scope to his talent and genius in this particular direction.

Rising up above this mere local view of the question, other broader and more comprehensive ones force themselves upon our attention. Are we not conscious of the extraordinary Scientific and Industrial progress of the present day? Do we not hope for, and predict under God's providence, a great future for this Country? Have we not in the assertion of our incipient nationality, entered the lists of industrial competition with the United States, and even with England and other Countries? And do we not, therefore, require to make, without delay some provision for training that class of our young men, who must in the future take the leading part in that competition? The wonderful progress of the Mechanic Arts, is within the memory of most of us. The marvellous revolution, caused by the practical application of Steam and Telegraphy, (those golden links of Science), to Locomotion, Commerce, Industry, and intercommunication, has so stimulated the inventive genius of man, that we now cease to be astonished at any new discovery; and only await each successive development of Science still more wonderful than the last, to calmly discuss its merits and advantages. In this active race of competition, our Province, (the leading one in the Dominion), cannot stand still. With all of our inventions, we have not yet been able to discover a royal road to learning; and our youth cannot, Minerva-like, spring fully armed into the arena of competitive Science and Skill. We must, therefore, provide liberally for their patient and practical instruction in every grade and department of knowledge, so that, with God's blessing, we shall not fall behind in the great race of national intelligence and progress.

THE CANADIAN INSTITUTE

The Canadian Journal: A Repository of Industry, Science, and Art, vol. I (1852-3), 3-4.

THE CANADIAN INSTITUTE, like many other Societies of a similar character, dates its origin from a small beginning. One or two individuals whom inclination led to seek for that intercourse between persons of a more practical and scientific turn of mind than is generally to be found in ordinary debating societies, and being themselves connected with the surveying and engineering professions, were induced to believe that the formation of a society consisting of gentlemen engaged in those pursuits, would draw together many kindred minds, and offer an opportunity of accumulating such knowledge as is necessary for the diversified practice of the professions, and of mutually benefiting each other by the interchange of individual observation and experience.

With the view of considering the establishment of such a Society, a few Surveyors, Engineers and Architects, residing in and near Toronto, met on the 20th June and 20th July, 1849, when a Prospectus of the proposed Society was adopted, and copies forwarded to members of the profession generally, throughout the province, soliciting their advice and cooperation.

Subjoined is a copy of the Prospectus in accordance with the principles of which the Society was first organized, on the 22nd of September, 1849.

PROSPECTUS.

To be composed—1st. Of Provincial Land Surveyors, Civil Engineers and Architects, practising in the Province, as Members.

2d. Of Members of the same profession not practising in the Province, as Corresponding Members.

3d. Of men distinguished in Science and Arts, residing in the Province, but not belonging to either of the above professions, as Honorary Members.

4th. Of Students under Articles, as Graduates.

The Officers of the Institute to consist of a President and Vice-Presidents, Council, Secretary, and two Auditors, to be elected annually.

The Treasurer to be a Chartered Bank in the City of Toronto. The Rooms of the Institute to be situated in the City of Toronto.

Libraries to be formed, and collections made of Maps, Drawings, Models, &c. A Museum to be established for the collection of Geological, Mineralogical, and other specimens.

Professional discussions to be held and papers read. Transactions to be published.

Standard Instruments to be kept for reference. Philosophical observations to be made and registered.

A Board of Arbitration to be established for the settlement of difficulties arising between members in the practice of their professions.

The Subscription of Members to be One Pound per annum. The Subscription of Graduates to be Ten Shillings per annum.

It will thus be seen that the proposed Society was strictly of a professional character. The foregoing Prospectus, with a suitable circular, was transmitted to nearly 500 persons throughout the Province; in reply, from twelve to fifteen letters only were received. The promoters were disheartened, the monthly meetings were but indifferently attended, although notices of such meetings were regularly issued, and by some of its members the society was entirely abandoned, at a time when their assistance was most needed. At last, the attendance at the monthly meetings dwindled down to two, and then the prospects of the young Institute were gloomy indeed. At that small meeting various schemes were talked of as to the ultimate chance of success, and it was then considered that by opening out the Society to those whose pursuits or studies were of a kindred character, and by holding regular weekly meetings for the reading and discussing of papers, the Society would gradually take a practical stand and proper footing. The experiment was tried, and weekly meetings were held regularly during the winter months, the attendance being occasionally good, although often dispiriting. Several interesting communications of professional and general interest were read, some of them eliciting spirited discussions. Many of the meetings were, however, occupied by discussions connected with proposed changes in the Constitution and Regulations of the Society, until at last on the 12th of April, 1851, it was determined that proper steps be taken for obtaining a Charter similar to the one the Society now enjoys. By this effort its hitherto strictly professional character was changed to one of a general description, and the way was paved for the Canadian Institute as it now exists.

A FREE FIELD AND NO FAVORS

'President's Address', *Transactions*, Canadian Society of Civil Engineers, vol. 1 (1887), 10-11.

I am unable to say when the first agitation for the formation of a Canadian Society of Civil Engineers began. I know it was a subject of discussion among Engineers, and I believe also of newspaper communications by Engineers, long before any concerted action was attempted. The Canadian Institute, incorporated in 1851, was formed "more particularly for promoting surveying, engineering and architecture."

I think the agitation dates from the formation of the Land Surveyors into a close corporation. Formerly, the surveys in connection with the right of way upon canals and railways were made by the Engineers engaged upon the work, as well as the topographical surveys connected therewith. Engineers out of employment were prohibited from practising as land surveyors, without first undergoing an apprenticeship, as well as passing an examination. On the other hand, Land Surveyors, whether competent or not, could practice as Civil Engineers. It was natural, therefore, that a feeling should grow up, that not only was a standard of qualification required, but that the profession should be put upon the same footing as Land Surveying, and be restricted to those who were qualified by law; but whenever this was proposed, the general sentiment was found to be against it. This is probably due to the knowledge that the great

Institution, organized at the Kendall Coffee house, in Fleet street, on the 2nd January, 1818, by William Maudslay, Joshua Field, Henry Robinson Palmer, James Jones, Charles Collinge and James Ashwell, of which Telford was the first President, and which is the mother of us all, had proved a magnificent success without protection; as well as to the reflection that the founders of the profession in Great Britain and the United States were born Engineers, and sought only a free field and asked no favors.

A PLEA FOR REGULATION

Alan Macdougall, 'A Plea for a Close Corporation', *Transactions*, Canadian Society of Civil Engineers, vol. VI (1892), 110-11.

The writer formed his opinions about the ultimate aim of all engineering societies, 15 years ago, he has not had occasion to change them; the unexpressed desire, one may almost say—will, of the profession is towards higher attainments in its members, and the recognition of them by a properly constituted professional body. Universities and colleges may grant degrees in arts, medicine or law, the holder of a degree obtains no professional advantage until he is admitted to professional standing by a corporate body, duly qualified and entitled to do so. The feeling has grown rapidly in the Dominion in the last five years that professional standing must be recognized, and a qualification obtained whereby a man's standing can be established. The architects of the Provinces of Quebec and Ontario have organized; in British Columbia a movement for organization is on foot; the Provincial Land Surveyors of the Province of Ontario have had increased power granted to them by legislation and they are now endeavouring to get a charter to enable them as a body to license their practitioners, instead of being licensed by the Government.

The formation of a close profession will not be injurious to the engineering interests, or to the public. It is not yet 25 years since the medical profession in the Province of Ontario, obtained a charter; no injury has arisen to the public from the formation of this into a profession: it would take only a few minutes to satisfy any sceptic that the movement has been of the greatest benefit to everybody. The several Provinces have each their law societies, they are all close corporations. Who ever heard of importing leading counsel from the United States to plead a cause in any Canadian court, who has suffered in any way from this arrangement? Can anyone say that the cause of justice is badly served because the members of the Canadian bar do not practice in the United States courts? Does public health suffer because American physicians do not have branch offices in Canada? Who can say that these distinctive cordons have provoked bad feeling between the respective professions in each of these two countries? On the contrary we know that the very best and friendly relations exist between these professions. The formation of these professions into such close corporations has been attended with the very best results to every one, of inestimable benefit in elevating the morale of the practitioners, the movement has resulted in incalculable benefit to the public.

ENGINEERING ARROGANCE

The Canadian Mining Review, vol. xvi (February, 1897), 37.

The lower house of the Nova Scotia Legislature has recently passed a measure entitled "An Act concerning Civil Engineers," which, for egotism, arrogance and blind pride reflects the highest credit upon its originators, a coterie of the institution known as the "Canadian Society of Civil Engineers."

Dwellers in the eastern part of Canada have known for a long time that this society contained most of the swelled heads of Eastern Canada, and that the really able practising engineers, though still allowing their names to remain on the membership list, did not go to the meetings nor contribute to the amazing erudition to be found amongst its transactions.

It has been equally well known that of recent years many of its members have been extremely dissatisfied with the administration of the society, and have felt that the rooms in Montreal were more of a shrine in which a few members could express their mutual admiration of each other, than a meeting place to which visiting engineers would wend their way. From the east and west, not only whispers but loud voices of members have been heard in remonstrance, and one member distinctly announced his intention to resign on the evening in January last when the Annual Feast was going on.

But the crowning audacity and conceit of the institution is shown in this bill in paragraph 4 of Sec. 1, in which these solons have declared that the statutory meaning of the expression "civil engineer" in Nova Scotia shall mean "anyone who acts or practices as an engineer in * * * * * electrical, mechanical, mining or other engineering works."

No doubt an institution whose utility as a society is dead, would like to have infused into its veins the vigorous blood of the mechanical, mining and electrical engineers of this province by the sea.

But we may be assured that this Nova Scotia bill is only the thin end of the wedge, and that the aims of the society are to have similar bills enacted all over the Dominion, so that the great and glorious "Civil Engineer" shall monopolize all practice.

But a further perusal of the bill shows its iniquity, and that these gentlemen of the Can. Soc. C. Eng. are not working for glory. Oh, no, they are after pelf! For it is further enacted in Sec. 2 that no person shall use the name nor practice in any of the engineering professions *unless he is a member of the* Canadian Society of Civil Engineers, and *pays therefor the sum of* $20 *per year* to the treasurer of this omnipotent institution! Herein is the gist of this bill which should have been entitled "A Bill to increase the revenues of the Canadian Society of Civil Engineers by coercion of all other engineers."

The provisions of this unique bill go on to say who may and who may not be admitted to the privilege of paying this private institution the sum of $20; to say that the council of this tremendous body of learning shall have power by committee to examine all candidates for admission; and to arbitrarily decide whether or not a man shall be permitted to practise his profession.

And these solons bring coercion into the Act also, for Sec. 10 inflicts a fine upon any engineer who may give an opinion in Nova Scotia unless he is a member of this society, and also puts a premium upon dishonest clients, inasmuch as it robs the engineer, who is not a member, of his legal right to recover for his services. (Sec. 9.)

The REVIEW does not hesitate to characterize this bill and this attempt of the Can. Soc. of Civil Engineers, as the most iniquitous and impertinent piece of legislation it has yet seen.

Canada has a society known as the Federated Canadian Mining Institute which numbers in its ranks almost all the practising mining and mechanical engineers of the Dominion who are cognizant of the needs and requirements of their professions, and who are vastly better able to say who shall and who shall not practise as mining and mechanical engineers than the Can. Soc. Civil Engineers ever has been or ever will be, and many of whom would smile at the idea that any committee of this omniscient society knew enough to examine them.

ENGINEERS AND THE PUBLIC INTEREST

'President's Address', *Transactions*, Canadian Society of Civil Engineers, vol. XXIII (1909), 111-13.

The profession, as a whole, should be represented in Canada by a single authoritative body, somewhat after the pattern of the Medical Council, or the Benchers of the Law Society in Ontario, to which should be entrusted the subjects of engineering education, qualifications for professional standing, professional ethics, etc.; in short, all questions of general professional interest. It is only by the hearty co-operation of the various classes of engineers that such a movement could succeed. The Canadian Society of Engineers, with its Council, would thus exercise functions which are necessary for the strengthening of the profession in its relations with the public, and which lie outside the province of the special engineering societies.

As a rule, the engineer does not come immediately into contact with the public. At the same time, there are questions of public interest in which he, in common with the chemist, the metallurgist, the biologist, the medical practitioner, the forester, and others, is regarded as an authority. The public expects the engineer to aid, by his advice, in the improvement of transportation, the prevention of railway accidents, the abatement of smoke, the preservation and improvement of public health, transmission of power, the irrigation of arid lands, the economical management and conservation of forests and mines, the improvement of agricultural soils, the conservation of river flow, etc., etc. Such questions are matters of municipal and governmental policy, and cannot be properly controlled by money-making corporations or individuals. Before a move can be made in these matters, a strong body of enlightened public opinion must be formed, and who should be better qualified for the task of stimulating and guiding this public opinion than the engineer? If he is too busy or too backward to undertake this duty of his own accord, what about the editor of the engineering newspaper? The latter is never hampered by modesty, and should write not only for his subscribers but for the public as well. He need not fear that his work will be lost; the lay press will print his good articles, and give him due credit for them.

Mr. Carnegie is reported to have made the statement that at the present rate of consumption, the supply of iron ore (presumably the more important and richer ores) of the United States would be exhausted in forty years, and the supply in England within seven years. He based this opinion on the best expert evidence he could obtain. If this statement be correct, what a prospect does it not open for the vast iron resources of Canada, and yet, at the same time, what a warning does it not convey to the government which controls these resources? In the United States the total production of pig iron up to the present is 350,000,000 tons, of which over one-half has been made within the last ten years. The production of the world in 1907 was 61,000,000 tons, of which the United States are to be credited with 26,000,000, Germany with 13,000,000, Great Britain with 10,000,000, and other countries with 11,000,000. Canada produced 600,000 tons, less than 1% of the total. In the United States the acid Bessemer process seems to have reached its maximum output, and in the future will rapidly diminish in importance, owing to the increasing scarcity of the requisite ores and its inability to use scrap. It is being rapidly superseded by the basic open hearth process, which can utilize ores containing a larger percentage of phosphorus, and also all kinds of scrap.

The future of electric processes in iron and steel production in Canada will depend more upon the cost of hydro-electric power than on any other factor. Closely connected with the conservation of the iron and timber resources of America is the great Portland cement industry, which has sprung into importance within the last twenty years. The Canadian production in 1907 amounted to 2,400,000 barrels, the United States production to 49,000,000 barrels. Concrete and ferro concrete will replace steel and wood in construction in ever-increasing quantities. As in the case of the electro-metallurgy of iron, the cost of hydro-electric power is a large item in the manufacture of cement.

The conservation and regulation of river-flow for water power alone, to say nothing of transportation and irrigation, is a necessity for the future industries of the country. The regularity and volume of river-flow in its turn is dependent upon the preservation of forest growth, especially in the mountainous and upland regions. Forest conservation, in fact, is one of the fundamental conditions of future prosperity. And so one might go on, and enumerate one after the other, various sources of wealth and well-being now extravagantly exploited which demand for their wise development the knowledge and skill of the engineer. It is to be hoped that the conferences initiated by President Roosevelt to consider the conservation of natural resources will bear fruit in pointing the way to practical solutions of these national problems. Canada has already made a good beginning, both in collecting information regarding our resources, and in passing legislation.

A VOTE FOR DISINTERESTEDNESS

'Report of Annual Meeting, 1911', *Transactions*, Canadian Society of Civil Engineers, vol. xxv (1911), 157-80.

There is a matter which Mr. Kennedy wishes to bring up.

Mr. Jas. C. Kennedy.—Mr. President and gentlemen, I have no resolution to offer, but I think a matter of some importance should be explained by some of us who have come from what I might call the "storm centre." It is with regard to the City Engineer of Vancouver. A wave of public criticism passed over Vancouver last autumn, and, as all municipal engineers well know, the criticisms of the public on the engineering of a city or a municipality are not generally very fair, not from the reason that the public intends to be unfair as a majority, but because they do not know the facts—they do not know the inner workings of the city engineer's department or what his instructions are. There has been ever since last autumn a great deal of criticism of the City Engineer's work at Vancouver by the public. It became the popular thing to cry down the City Engineer, and of course the candidates for election took up the cry, and were quite prepared to sacrifice the Engineer. Every City Engineer will understand this pretty well, I think. In this case it was carried to such an extent that the Vancouver Branch of the Canadian Society of Civil Engineers saw fit to step in and do what they could towards obtaining fair treatment of the City Engineer. Immediately after the elections, the City Engineer, who had remained silent, and was of course not in a position to reply to every public criticism, sent a letter to the newly-elected Council asking that, in justice to himself and to those who had supported him throughout the past year, an investigating board of engineers be appointed to enquire into the affairs of the City Engineer, and to report to the Council; or, if the city preferred to do so, they were asked to appoint an investigation committee under the Public Utilities Act. The Engineer stated plainly and in a manly way that, in the event of the finding of the committee being adverse to him, the Council could consider the communication that he had sent in as his resignation. The newly-elected Mayor appointed an investigation committee of his own to consider the affairs of the City Engineer's department, and to report, and I believe I am right in stating that that committee was hostile to the City Engineer, and, as far as we could discern, was selected on that ground, with the exception of one man. Within twenty-four hours they brought in a report to the effect that after making a thorough investigation of the affairs, they had decided to recommend to the Board of Works that steps be taken to procure a supervising engineer to take over the engineering of the city. That report was sent to the Board of Works. The Board of Works called a meeting a week ago last Monday evening at 7.30, and within thirty minutes had adopted the recommendation and passed it on to the Council, which sat at 8.30 the same evening. The engineers of Vancouver, the Branch of the Canadian Society, or as many as we could muster in the short time, appeared before the Council and asked for a fair investigation of the work of the City Engineer. We pointed out that he had asked for an investigation, and we considered it was only British fair-play that he should get it. There were four members of the City Council who spoke very favourably of the City Engineer, and condemned the unfair treatment that was being meted out to him. Our representations were ignored, and the recommendation of the committee was put through in spite of everything. Now, it has seemed to us that this is a very opportune time to bring this matter before this Society. I do not wish to propose any resolution, as I might perhaps be considered as biased, but if the gentlemen present see fit to endorse what the Branch has done out there, or to assist the City Engineer and protect him against this unfair treatment, I am sure the Branch at Vancouver will be exceedingly glad. . . .

MR. DUGGAN

I can fully understand the sympathy of the engineers from Vancouver with their associate, who they think has been unjustly dealt with, and I think it was quite proper for them as individuals to use their influence with the City Council on behalf of their associate, and also that the Society should be informed here of all the circumstances of the case. I think, however, the matter should rest there, and that we should take no action whatever with reference to it.

As a Society, we are simply an organization banded together to further our profession by presenting scientific and technical questions for the consideration and discussion of our brother engineers and for personal intercourse. While this is our primary object, we must of course consider public questions that bear on the welfare of the profession as a whole, and we have at times approached the Dominion and Provincial Governments with reference to proper legislation, but I do not think we have ever made representations as a Society to any other governing bodies, certainly not to any City Council. We have, as far as I know, kept strictly out of politics and out of all controversies with the public. I do not think the Society is competent to deal with this question under its Constitution; there is certainly no precedent for doing so, and I think any resolution looking to representation to the Vancouver City Council would be entirely out of place.

MR. J. C. KENNEDY

I would like to ask Mr. Duggan if he thinks that when the Canadian Society of Civil Engineers, or a Branch of it, see plainly an injustice done to one of its members, it should not take any action to defend him and to see that he gets justice done to him. I might have pointed out before that the engineer's reputation is at stake there, and there is no charge against the man—not a solitary charge. The committee that was appointed was composed almost entirely of members who had never been on the Council before, and it was impossible for them to know what the conditions of the department were, or to obtain the facts without a longer consideration. It is true that it was popular for the public to condemn the man, but they did not know what they were doing. The fact of the matter is, the city is going ahead at a phenomenal rate, and it is a very difficult thing for any man to keep pace with it, and leave the streets—that is where the complaint came—leave the streets in such a condition that they would not inconvenience a good many people. It is so easy to find fault with a man for something of that kind, whether he is to blame or not. Not one member of the Board of Works, under whose direction he worked for the last year, had a word of fault to find with him, and the only member of the old Board that was left on the new Council defended him, and I will be disappointed if this Society does not see its way clear to take some action in a case of this kind. Of course, I do not think they should take action without knowing something of the facts—without satisfying themselves of the facts; but if these are the facts that have been stated, surely we ought to do something for a member who is ill-treated in this way and his character damaged. They are advertising—or at least they are seeking for a man to take his place, and they have not notified him that his services are not satisfactory or that they propose to dispense with them. . . .

The Committee has carefully considered this rather complex question, and has come to the conclusion that we really should not interfere with it. It is, in the first place, contrary to our precedents. The several cases of the kind which have previously come up have not been quite so formal as this, but the Society has always felt it impracticable to take any action as such would be contrary to the spirit of our Constitution and the whole attitude of the Society. That is to say, we are a scientific body and not a trade union. And then in discussing the matter more fully with the Vancouver members who are familiar with the matter, and from reading the newspaper accounts, we felt that it was a controverted question, and although there was nothing in the world against the character of our professional brother, Mr. Clement, yet there were questions as to his efficiency, and after all it settles down to the question as to whether we have a right to interfere between an engineer and his employers; whether they are not justified in saying, rightly or wrongly, that they do not want a certain employee. It appears Mr. Clement is not dismissed, but that they are considering whether they shall make a different arrangement and perhaps have some other engineer over him. In view of all these circumstances, we came to the conclusion that we could not recommend any interference on the part of this Society. One other consideration is that it was urged that Mr. Clement had not been fairly treated inasmuch as he had no opportunity of replying at the investigation, and no opportunity to be heard. In so far as we are concerned, the Council of Vancouver has also not been heard, and to treat the matter fairly, we should put the parties to the dispute in the same position. We have therefore felt that it is impracticable for the Society to deal with the matter at all, however strongly we may personally feel, as to any unfair treatment of Mr. Clement. I suppose we have all been subject to some such condition and had to fight through it as best we could.

8 | Technology and the City

There is a long and important relationship between urbanization and technology. Whether in the city-states of the ancient world or in the metropolitan centres of the modern era, advanced technology has always been identified with the city. Emerging Canadian municipalities marked their own progress in the same way—waterworks, public transit, and street lighting were measures in the march of civilization.

While Canadians generally believed that urban development and progress were synonymous terms, it is also true that poor construction techniques and inadequate sewerage facilities made most cities ideal breeding grounds for fire and disease. A melancholy series of cholera and typhoid epidemics made people aware of the need for urban sanitary facilities. Yet because these epidemics were especially rampant among the poor, it was easy to assume that the vicious habits of the lower orders were the primary cause of illness. Alfred Brunel, city engineer of Toronto, cast his argument for sanitary improvements in a form calculated to appeal to middle-class ratepayers. The editor of the *Canada Lancet*, a medical periodical, fastened the blame on municipal leaders for their failure to adopt a rational program of city sanitation. Nonetheless, dumping raw sewage into the nearest water supply was still a convenient and apparently inexpensive method of disposal. As Samuel Keefer pointed out, there was still 'plenty of important work' to do in the field of sanitary engineering.

Since the Halifax fire of 1750, which nearly destroyed the whole town, almost every Canadian community has experienced major fire disaster. Large numbers of wooden structures, often carelessly built and closely spaced, inadequate water systems and fire-fighting equipment, the slow emergence of building codes, materials testing, or other systematic measures to prevent fires—all these factors contributed to the high incidence of urban fire loss in Canada. During the years from 1912-1915, the country suffered a per capita loss of life and property from fire greater than any other nation in the world. The conservation movement of the early twentieth century provided an opportunity to deal with the problem at a national level. Cities represented a resource just as valuable as minerals or forests. One of the best analyses of the cause and prevention of fires, *Fire Waste in Canada*, was published by the Commission of Conservation.

Despite the obvious hazards of city life, most Canadians saw the answer in more technology, not less. An adequate water supply was one of the major jewels in the diadem of municipal facilities. It offered health to the citizenry, provided protection against fire, and served as an important ingredient of economic prosperity. The design for a water system and the manufacture of steam engines and associated apparatus also presented opportunities to demonstrate the level of Canadian technology. Hamilton's water works were justly celebrated as a cooperative triumph of domestic engineering talent, manufacturing skill, and political foresight. In near-by Toronto, the Water Works Committee was less fortunate in its choice of a locally made steam pumping engine.

The response to change was not always positive, even before the current resistance to urban development. City-dwellers also recognized that municipal facilities defined the limits of growth. But they perceived those boundaries as obstacles to be overcome. Electricity promised better lighting. City engineers came to play an increasingly important role in extending municipal facilities. And industrial research seemed the answer to the problem of fire destruction.

PROTECTION FROM DISEASE AND FIRE

SANITATION AND SOBRIETY

Alfred Brunel, *Report of the City Engineer on Improvements and Works of Repair, for the Year 1860* (Toronto, 1859), pp. 16-18.

If any evidence, beyond that afforded by ordinary observation, aided by common sense, were necessary to show the importance of works such as are named at the commencement of this section, it might be found in the results of the sanitary improvements made in the cities, towns and villages of Britain, during the last ten years, as published in the Reports of the *Registrar General.* Upon the data obtained from the returns made in compliance with the act of Parliament in that behalf, it has been established beyond a doubt, that a most important improvement has been effected in the health of the inhabitants of those places where the proper sanitary regulations have been made, resulting in a remarkable prolongation of human life. In the town of Ely, the death rate has been reduced since the commencement of the sanitary improvements there, from 26 in 1,000 to 17 in 1,000. In Liverpool, it was reduced by similar works, from 39 in 1,000 in 1847, to 29 in 1857, and further to 27 in 1,000 in 1858. In Bradford, it has been reduced from 28½ in 1,000 to 22. In Gloucester, from 27 in 1,000 to 24; and in Croydon;—which being a small town of only 10,600 inhabitants, is perhaps the most remarkable instance of all,—the rate has been reduced from 28·16 to 15·75 in 1,000;—while in 19 towns containing an aggregate population of 468,000, which have been drained and cleaned under the General Board of Health, the average rate has been reduced from 28 in 1,000 to 21. Showing an annual saving of 3,200 lives.

With such a result before us it is abundantly worth our while to enquire whether we cannot make some advance in the same direction, and whether we have not an ample field for our labour.

It is true the subject is not a very inviting one, for "sanitary philosophers are but scavengers;" they have only to clear away the filth that impede the course of nature, to provide the people with the means of obeying the scriptural injunction to "wash and be clean" and to enforce the proper use of them; this was sufficient of old, and—applied to localities—it is so still.

It may be said that in the outskirts of this city the ground is so sparsely occupied that the effluvium arising from cess pools, stagnant water, and other filth, becomes too much diluted to be injurious; this is only partially true, for if the area is great in proportion to the number of inhabitants, so is the surface from which the miasma emanates, which being evaporated from decaying vegetable matter, stagnant water, and undrained ground, is as deleterious to health as any thing can be, save the emanations from the cess pools themselves.

(The application of sanitary regulations here equally necessary.)
Apart from such sources of miasma, however, there are within the city limits, districts, densely enough populated, where the filth may fairly be said to vie with the filthiest localities of the older cities of Britain; where the evils resulting from inefficient drainage or rather from the absence of all attempts at drainage—augmented as they are by the greater severity of the climate, and by the less substantial character of the tenements, are quite as great as any that have been combatted by the sanitary science of the mother country. In these districts we have a wide field for improving the condition and adding to the comforts of those whom circumstances compel to inhabit these unhealthy localities, and at the same time to re-move the health-destroying impurities from the vicinity of others, who, though able to inhabit more substantial tenements, are nevertheless, ex-posed to the effects of the malaria bred in the neighbourhood.

If then it is true, that there is no incentive to intemperance so strong as that created by the *"air poisons"* generated by filth; and no home so seductive as that which is clean, no homeward path so certain to be regularly trod as that which is free from material pollution; if the final path *from* the grog shop to the HOME can be most certainly constructed by sanitary improvement; or if—as has been said on high authority, and as I steadfastly believe—"no missionary is so successful as cleanliness;" then in addition to the reasonable hope of being able to join advan-tageously in those efforts which have been elsewhere successful in the pro-longation of human life, and the prevention of disease, we have the stimulus of both philanthropy and religion to urge us forward in the prosecution of the works hereinafter recommended.

(Economy promoted by sanitary improvements.)
Nor is the pursuit of economy adverse to the carrying on of works of sanitary improvement. If undrained houses, damp cellars, festering filth, back lanes covered with decaying garbage, and cess-pools overflowing with human fæces, are parents of disease, they are also parents of unthrift, for what is so costly as disease? Who can reckon up the value of the days lost in consequence of sickness? or the depreciated value of labour per-formed by the sickly denizens of unhealthy localities? A robust population is necessarily more thrifty, because infinitely more energetic and self-reliant than a sickly one; and one day's work per annum, saved from the sick-bed, more than pays the operatives share of the cost of such improve-ments, while the enhanced productiveness of robust labour, infinitely more than compensates the employer for *his* contribution towards them.

Again, to create greater comforts and render more desirable for residences, the central portion of the City, is to reduce the temptation to seek suburban residences, as well by the wealthier as by the middle classes, and consequently to reduce the necessity of extending the ephemeral improvements of plank sidewalks, "grading," and "*channelling*," over wide areas, which though apparently of little first cost individually, are a continuous expense, and therefore infinitely more burdensome to the rate-payers than more perfect and durable works covering less space.

It is true that while the money paid in rates is so palpable as to be seldom paid without reluctance, the money saved requires faith to discern; yet having before us the experience of those nineteen towns previously referred to, and the *three thousand* lives annually saved; and this further knowledge, that sanitary improvements instead of increasing have invariably diminished the rates, and taking into account, moreover, that a city notoriously healthy and offering superior inducements as to cleanliness and comfort, is sure to be most attractive to those who are seeking permanent residences; we cannot doubt but pecuniary advantages must result.

THE HEALTH OF TOWNS AND CITIES

'Health of Towns and Cities', *The Canada Lancet*, vol. v (June 1, 1873), 323-5.

Within the last few years sanitary interests have grown almost to the proportion of a distinct science. . . . No one at all familiar with the causes of disease and the modes of prevention, can pass through even our most favored rural districts, to say nothing of towns and cities; without being impressed with the great need of legislative enactments, by which the health and lives of the people may be protected, and their welfare and happiness promoted. Some of our city fathers, however, seem to labour under the delusion that in some way or other, owing to climate, abundance of food, plenty of water supply and natural drainage—we are to escape from many of the perils that older countries suffer from. . . .

Our towns and cities, are for the most part, the growth of comparatively few years, and they are in the most favorable condition for improvement. They readily admit of thorough drainage and sewerage, and pure water can in most cases be readily supplied; and these, together with the constant (not spasmodic) removal of all filth, are the great desiderata.

These are matters, however, that are usually unattended to, until the approach of cholera, or some other fearful epidemic arouses us from our slumbers, and then frantic efforts are put forth, and loads of money expended in cleansing the city, when it is, in all probability, too late. If on the other hand, such measures were regularly and systematically attended to, and all regulations for the cleanliness of the city faithfully carried out, neither the much dreaded cholera, nor any other form of epidemic could obtain a foothold amongst us.

SEWAGE DISPOSAL IN HAMILTON

Sixth Annual Report of the Provincial Board of Health of Ontario, Being for the Year 1887 (Toronto, 1888), lxiii.

REPORT OF COMMITTEE ON SEWAGE, DRAINAGE, AND WATER SUPPLY
re FERGUSON AVENUE SEWER NUISANCE IN BAY AT HAMILTON, MAY, 1887.

TORONTO, 10th May, 1887.

To the Chairman and Members of the Provincial Board of Health.

GENTLEMEN,—Your committee appointed to investigate the nuisance alleged to arise from the outfall of the Ferguson Avenue sewer, in Hamilton, beg leave to report as follows:—

Your committee visited the locality of the mouth of the Ferguson Avenue sewer, and found that the nuisance complained of is caused by the sewerage being driven back on the adjoining shores and depositing there its more solid portions. We found men engaged in carting away the deposits and were shown pits in which large quantities of it lie buried.

This sewer carries the sewage of about 15,000 people. Nuisances arising from its outfall cause great annoyance to persons residing in the neighbourhood.

Your committee are of opinion that, looking at the matter purely from a sanitary point of view, the preferable method of dealing with the sewage is by chemical precipitation; the sewage to be compressed by means of Johnson's filter presses. We have no data to go upon in connection with works of the kind on this continent; and the computations of cost vary considerably in different places in England. Mr. Samuel W. Gray, City Engineer, of Providence, R.I., made very extensive and careful enquiries during a tour of investigation, and as a result states that the annual cost per head of population in England varies from 24 to 36 cents, and considers that a safe basis to go upon for America would be to compute the cost at about double of that in England. During the past few months, however, further experiments tend to bring the cost down to a lower figure.

If, from financial reasons, the city of Hamilton should not adopt this method of disposal, resort might be had to the plan of carrying the sewage out to a sufficient distance from the shores to prevent the accumulation of floating matter on the latter, and into a sufficient depth of water to obtain such a dilution of the sewage as will prevent its being in any sense a nuisance.

The depth of water should not be less than from 15 to 20 feet, and the distance from the shore not less than 2,000 feet. Should it be found that the head of water required to keep free from deposit a pipe of this length is not available pumping would have to be resorted to.

Provision would have to be made for allowing flood water (that produced by heavy rain storms)—to flow into the bay at the shore line.

All of which is respectfully submitted.

W. OLDRIGHT.

D. GALBRAITH.

SANITARY ENGINEERING

Samuel Keefer, 'President's Address', *Transactions*, Canadian Society of Civil Engineers, vol. III (1889), 49-51.

It has now come to be pretty well understood as an established fact in sanitary science, that imperfect drainage of houses, badly constructed sewers, polluted drinking water, and filthy streets, are direct causes of disease and death, as to the same causes, scarlet fever, measles, diphtheria, typhus and typhoid fevers may be referred.

In the city of London, two centuries ago, the mortality was 80 per 1000, and it was not until the beginning of the present century that the birth rate exceeded the death rate. According to the "Bills of Mortality" there has been a steady decline in the death rate ever since, until now by a more strict attention to sanitation, London has become one of the healthiest cities in the world.

Mr. Edwin Chadwick, a leader of sanitary reforms in England, has lately stated in Brighton, that it is not long since the death rate of London was 24 per 1000, and now it is but 14 or 15 per 1000; and he maintained that had the sanitary reforms been carried out according to the plans prepared, it might have been reduced to 12 per 1000. . . .

It is to be deplored that we have no such progress, no corresponding results, to point to in Canada.

About a year ago there was published in the *Montreal Star* (14 Jan., 1888) a list of twenty towns and cities in Canada, shewing the populations and deaths, and the death rate per 1000. These twenty towns and cities had then an aggregate population of 653,047—the deaths 16,586, and the average death rate 25·40 per 1000.

As we have no "Bills of Mortality," nor any vital statistics with which to compare these figures, it wil be sufficient for my present purpose to assume them as approximately correct at the time they were made.

Then comparing the twenty modern towns and cities enumerated with the ancient historical and densely populated city of London, in which there are as many people now living as there are in all Canada, it might reasonably be expected that the mortality in these Canadian localities could, by strict sanitation, be reduced to a par with that of London, in which case fully six thousand lives might annually be saved to the country in these places alone. But when we take these several places in detail we find some startling revelations. The lowest rate of mortality is found in the inland towns and cities of Ontario. These towns are Belleville, Guelph, Chatham, Galt, Peterborough, ranging from 16·50 to 19·75 per 1000. The cities are London, Kingston, Hamilton, Toronto, ranging from 18·31 to 21·50 per 1000. Halifax shews 20·52, Ottawa 28·70, Montreal 27·99, Quebec 33·57, Three Rivers 32·10, Sherbrooke 27·37, St. Hyacinthe, 41·83, and, saddest of all, Sorel 44·88 per 1000!

There is cause for serious reflection in these figures, shewing what a heavy responsibility rests with the Boards of Health in all larger cities and towns. I have gone into these details in order to prove to the Sanitary Engineer that there is in Canada plenty of important work for him to do.

There is no branch of the engineering profession in which a man can do more good to his fellow man than in protecting and promoting the health and comfort of those who have their homes in towns and cities where he can apply his beneficent art to save life, and preserve the health of the living. It will be his pleasing duty to provide pure water, pure air, clean streets, and a perfect system of drainage, that shall carry off all surface water before it has time to become stagnant, and all waste from houses and yards before noxious gases are allowed to generate, and to convey the same with all possible dispatch to the proper outfall, there to be disposed of as circumstances shall dictate.

FIRE IN THE CITY

CONSERVATION AND FIRE LOSS

J. Grove Smith, *Fire Waste in Canada* (Ottawa, 1918), pp. 17-18.

Of the material resources chiefly affected by fire, forests furnish the most conspicuous example. The standing timber of portions of Canada is fast approaching exhaustion. Hon. Senator W. C. Edwards, addressing the eighth annual meeting of the Commission of Conservation, drew attention to the fact that the importance of Canada as a lumbering country and the extent of her forest resources have been much over-estimated. Referring particularly to eastern Canada, he stated that, within a few years, lumbering will be so reduced that it will be of much less importance. In this connection it was pointed out and especially emphasized that the great enemy of Canadian forests has been fire. This latter statement is true in regard to other than forest fires. No fewer than 20,700 buildings of frame construction were destroyed by fire in Canada during the last four years, with a total loss of over $14,000,000. Approximately $8,000,000 of lumber value was burned in buildings of other than frame construction. Lumber yard fires contributed another $6,500,000 and the destruction of wood products in process of manufacture, $3,725,000. These figures merely represent readily ascertainable values and are doubtless incomplete. They demonstrate, however, that fire is largely responsible for the depletion of our lumber supply, even apart from forest conflagrations.

As the supplies of timber become further exhausted it is evident that Canada must substitute some other form of building material. The supplies of stone, gravel, clay, cement and lime are practically inexhaustible. While the use of these materials has heretofore been restricted by competition with the cheaper and more easily fabricated wood products, improved methods of manufacture and wider markets are rapidly diminishing the difference in cost. Careful investigation by the Government as to the structural qualities of the more permanent materials would undoubtedly enlarge their use, and thus have an important influence on the preservation of our diminishing timber supplies. There is the strongest justification for such immediate action. If it be the duty of the state to promote the public welfare by the prevention of forest waste, the broadest application of the principles of conservation should extend to the protection of created values. In the last analysis the loss by fire of a city dwelling is even more important to the people of Canada than the loss by fire of timber in the public domain. Both the building and the timber are assets of the nation. If they are destroyed, these assets are wiped out. No system of taxation will serve to restore them, whether the tax be collected by constituted authorities under the law or by private interests as premiums on policies of insurance. Re-forestation costs money, which must be levied through taxation in some form. Replacing buildings destroyed by fire costs money, a large proportion of which, by means of insurance, is assessed against property which has not been burned. In both cases, the cost is borne by the people of Canada as a whole and is, therefore, a matter of public concern.

A DESTRUCTIVE FIRE

J. Grove Smith, *Fire Waste in Canada* (Ottawa, 1918), p. 285.

THREE RIVERS, P.Q., 1908—At noon on June 22nd, fire, presumably started by children lighting matches, was discovered in a small wooden stable at the rear of a business block. The stable burned rapidly and ignited several adjoining outbuildings. Within an hour of the outbreak, fanned by a moderate breeze, the fire had developed into a conflagration which swept toward the river through the heart of the city. Brigades from Grand'mère, Shawinigan, Montreal and Quebec, were of great assistance in fighting the conflagration to prevent it spreading north and south and also from backing up into the residential district to the west against the wind, which had considerably freshened during the afternoon. Within the limits of the conflagration everything was entirely consumed, but on the edges several wooden structures escaped, while solid brick or stone buildings adjoining them were burned. The fire burned an area 1500 by about 1000 feet, comprising about 30 acres. The city waterworks drew water direct from the St. Maurice river. The pumps had a total capacity of 4,500,000 gallons. The ordinary pressure on the mains was 125 lbs., an unusually high pressure, but when several streams were drawn it fell very rapidly. There was abundance of water and large pumping capacity, but the mains were too small, and the pumps could not force it through them to give an adequate pressure where it was so badly wanted. The defects in the waterworks and fire extinguishing appliances had been repeatedly pointed out to the civic authorities, who were always going to lay new and larger mains, to improve their appliances and to install a new fire alarm service. Fires were infrequent in Three Rivers, however, the improvements were postponed, the fire brigade became lax about drills, and what, in 999 cases would have been a small stable fire became this thousandth time, a conflagration. The property loss was estimated at considerably over $2,000,000, with insurance losses amounting to $1,132,400.

THE NEED FOR RESEARCH

J. Grove Smith, *Fire Waste in Canada* (Ottawa, 1918), p. 178.

Equally important as the setting of definite structural standards in Canada is the provision of adequate facilities for obtaining unbiassed conclusions as to the qualities of materials. Under existing conditions, architects, builders and municipal officials have necessarily to accept the bare statements of the manufacturers as to the relative value of the majority of new materials and devices. When formulating municipal building laws, those in charge of the work are persistently besieged by representatives of various products, each with convincing testimony that his particular material should be given preference, or, at least, recognition. In the confusion caused by a multiplicity of conflicting data, requirements are more often framed and interpreted to favour good salesmanship than in accordance with experience.

Owing to the difficulty of conducting adequate tests of materials in Canada, it is rarely possible to include requirements respecting quality in building specifications. To mention a particular brand of cement or plaster, for instance, might exclude the best on the market and to simply specify 'plaster' might admit the poorest. Often an effort is made to duplicate material once found satisfactory by prescribing a specific brand and adding the words 'or equal'—a recourse which is absurd, since, without definite standards or adequate testing facilities, comparison is impracticable.

The disadvantage under which architects, engineers, builders and municipal authorities labour, in the absence of a central authoritative testing laboratory or bureau, has been emphasized by many of the leading architects in Canada.

MUNICIPAL IMPROVEMENTS

THE HAMILTON WATER WORKS

'Hamilton and its Water Works', *Canadian Illustrated News*, (September 26, 1863), 222.

At the southern end of the Beach, which divides Burlington Bay from the Lake, Hamilton has established the first link in its Water Works—a large basin having been dredged out, into which the water from Lake Ontario percolates through the sand, thus forming a natural filter.

The water passes from this into the pumping well at the engine-house, where it is forced by two powerful engines to the reservoir on the side of the hill about two miles east of the city and the capacity of which is sufficient to provide, at least, a fortnight's supply of water, should any accident occur to prevent pumping and from it is distributed throughout the city. The whole system, we believe, is as complete as any on this continent. The engines are certainly a credit to Canadian workmanship, and are the most powerful and highly finished of the kind in the Province. They have worked like a charm, and nothing has arisen to cause any outlay on them since the first stroke. The pipes were manufactured by D. Y. Stewart & Co., of Glasgow, and after all were laid by the contractors, Messrs. Hendrie & Co., not half-a-dozen leaky joints were found.

The hydrants were made in Hamilton after the most approved model, and have worked well—doing good service when unfortunately required during fires.

The Engine House was built by Mr. Geo. Worthington, of this city, and is pronounced by good judges a piece of the best hydraulic masonry to be seen anywhere.

The reservoir was constructed by Mr. A. P. McDonald, and is a most substantial work. This is a favorite spot to wander about: the view from it is magnificent. To the left, the city with its spires is seen—in front, our beautiful Bay, and to the right, Lake Ontario.

The almost inestimable value of this great work to the city can scarcely as yet be appreciated by our citizens. The old sources of supply—wells— are still used by many; but when our population shall become somewhat larger, it will be seen that this source would be totally inadequate. A large supply of good water is a blessing to a city upon which no price can be put; and this water, passing through a natural filter, is, perhaps, superior to that supplied to any city on the continent.

The reservoir is 185 feet above the level of Lake Ontario. Its capacity is about 6,000,000 gallons.

The water is now used in about 1,100 houses; but the revenue, as yet, pays but little more than working expenses.

It reflects not a little credit to the Water Commissioners, that work of such magnitude—costing $786,479 34, was carried to completion without a single legal difficulty with any one of the contractors, and it equally bespeaks the ability of Mr. Keefer, that the expenditure was within the estimates. Mr. Keefer not only rendered eminent services as the engineer; but he showed ability in another department, namely, finance, and received the thanks of the Commissioners for the successful completion of financial arrangements, which enabled the Commissioners to proceed with the works, where otherwise they might have had to suspend operations,— however, there was not an idle hour in the prosecution of the works.

The present Principal of the Commercial College, Toronto, J. E. Day, Esq., was secretary to the Commissioners, and performed his duties in a most commendable manner.

The Mechanical Engineer who, on behalf of the Commissioners, super-intended the manufacture and erection of the engines, receiving every piece of iron that was used, was Mr. Charles Robb, now mining Engineer in Montreal. He also very handsomely rendered much assistance gra-tuitously, in making designs for the several fountains in the city which were erected by subscription.

His Royal Highness, the Prince of Wales, was pleased to inaugurate the Works, on the occasion of his visit to this country.

One of the early promoters and best friends of the Water Works scheme, was Wm. Davidson, Esq., whose name is to be found associated with all the early negociations on the subject.

None connected with the work, however, deserve a more honorable mention than Adam Brown, Esq., the Chairman of the Commissioners. To the discharge of the duties of his position Mr. Br. Brown brought the full power of that vigorous and enthusiastic mind which is ever foremost in matters of public interest.

Though his arduous labors have been highly appreciated by his fellow citizens, their full value will not perhaps appear until the Water Works become a financial success.

The engines by which the water is pumped from the filtering basin to the receiving reservoir deserve more than a passing notice. They were manufactured by John Gartshore, Esq., Hall St., Dundas. They are of about 200 horse power each, and each engine has both a high-pressure and a low-pressure cylinder, the diameter of the former being 42 inches, with a a stroke of eight feet, and of the latter, diameter 36 inches, stroke six feet. The fly-wheels weigh 25 tons each; the two receiving air vessels, six feet in diameter, 16 tons each; and the two walking beams, 30 feet between the centres, 15 tons each. The great beam or entablature, weighing 12 tons, in one solid casting, is, we believe, the largest casting ever made in Canada. A peculiarity observable in the parallel motion of these engines is that the three centers are worked by one radius rod. The power is supplied by four Cornish Boilers, 30 feet long and six feet in diameter, having one flue through each. They weigh about nine tons each; and consume about 3,200 lbs. of coal per day, working one engine. The pumping capacity of each engine is nearly 100,000 gallons per hour.

In visiting the establishment of Mr. Gartshore, where this magnificent work was constructed, we were forcibly struck by the signs of life pervading the great establishment, covering an area of four acres of ground. It was commenced in 1838 by Mr. Gartshore and the late James B. Ewart, Esq. For some time it occupied a position second to the Niagara works, but it has now become the first foundry in the province. Then a casting of 4,000 lbs. was a curiosity—now the capacity of the moulding shop is sufficient to produce a casting such as the entablature of the Water Works mentioned above, weighing twelve tons, or even larger. About 150 hands are employed; and work to the value of over $100,000 is yearly turned out.

At present the establishment is chiefly occupied in the manufacture of dry-sand castings, such as locomotive cylinders; and steam castings, such as coal oil stills, up to 10 feet in diameter, agricultural implements, and every kind of machinery. The casting of car wheels from American iron has been commenced; and pipes of the same iron cast here are used for the oil wells now being sunk at Bothwell.

The boiler shop constitutes quite a feature of the establishment. It is fitted up with punches, drills, shearing machines, &c.—indeed, the whole establishment is provided with machinery of the latest pattern, and best calculated to save manual labor.

Both steam and water are employed as motive power—two engines of 25 horse power each supplying the former; the latter is of about 40 horse power.

We were shown a large spur mortise wheel which also acts as a fly wheel, made for Wright's Cotton Mill, Dundas. It is 15 feet in diameter, and weighs 8,000 lbs., being the largest mortise wheel ever cast in Canada.

THE ENGINE THAT COULDN'T

Charles Martin, *To the Citizens of Toronto Relative to that Huge Experiment, the Canadian Engine* (Toronto, 1886), pp. 3-5.

To his worship the Mayor, and the Corporation of the City of Toronto.

MR MAYOR & GENTLEMEN:—

The time has arrived when that huge experiment, to resuscitate an obsolete principle, called the CANADIAN ENGINE, which the claptrap cry of *Home Manufacture* induced your predecessors to allow to be carried out at the expense of the taxpayers, should be disposed of, which, if we may judge of it by its record, a record obtained by very careful *nursing*, yet upwards of forty mishaps, more or less serious having occurred during its short existence, it should have a short, shrift, instant removal, and the sureties be called upon to recoup the City's heavy outlay.

The Council of that day are alone to blame for leaving us this unpleasant legacy to deal with. Not having in the City employ a Mechanical Engineer, they should have submitted this absurd scheme to such an one whose professional standing and practical experience was such that his opinion could have been relied upon. It would not have taken him long (and there would have been no difficulty in guessing correctly what his opinion would have been) instead of being guided by the opinions of Messrs. Tully & Sproatt—very estimable gentlemen and deservedly respected, but what do they know about pumping engines?—and disregarding the logical reasoning of Messrs. Kennedy and Fensom, the People's representative experts.

This mongrel machine (I feel Mr. Mayor and Gentlemen that no name can be too expressive after the abuse that has been lavished upon those opposed to its introduction from their practical knowledge of its merits, and others from their disinterested and conscientious belief of its unfitness.) This mongrel machine began its career after several minor mishaps, by its being discovered by its promoters that they had committed a great blunder as to the size of the pumps, (which I may here remark, are of most defective design and faulty construction, say nothing of their absurd valves, the delivery being only one-third the area of the piston instead of being one-third larger area.) The pumps were too small—their diameter must be increased. This they do by taking out the brass lining, and thus further intensify their previous error as they do not increase the area of delivery, and by putting a solid ring on the pistons make them non-elastic. After more tinkering, the builders and promoters declare they are ready for a forty-eight hours' test, in order to prove that they can fulfil the term of their contract. The farce was gone through without the City having a single representative capable of conducting such, on their behalf. Honestly the engines never pumped more than 9,000,000 gallons, or did a duty exceeding 50,000,000 foot-pounds, per 100 pounds of coal. Mr. Sproatt deducts 1 per cent. for slip, arising from clumsy wooden valves that rise 1½ inches over a contracted delivery, not more than one-fourth the area required, nor does he test the pistons. If he had, 20 per cent. deduction would have been little enough. On account of the contracted delivery, the pressure is equal to a head of 267 feet. (I suppose they thought they must not take more.) Why should they benefit by defective construction? Why give them credit for more than the head allowed No. 2 Worthington—239 feet? Both are precisely under the same circumstances. The specification says ordinary coal. Why allow what they claim,—that it only evaporated eight pounds of water instead of ten? Every improper advantage has been taken to foist upon us this worse-than-useless machine. By fair computation it has never pumped nine million gallons in 24 hours, nor is it possible to make it pump the quantity that can be pumped easily by the No. 2 Worthington, and it cannot be relied upon for 24 hours without a breakdown.

Mr. J. H. Venables sent in a report dated May 9th last, showing the work performed by the Canadian Engines since Nov. 12th. It would be taxing our credulity too much to believe one word of it. It states that it run 110 days of 24 hours at a stretch. Of this period 14 days consumed 39,000 lbs. of coal per day; 35 days consumed 38,000 lbs. of coal per day; 34 days consumed 37,800 lbs. of coal per day.

Could any one credit that any body of men could shovel an exact quantity of 38 to 39,000 pounds of coal day after day? Impossible.

The W. W. Com. wanted a report and they got one.

The numerous break-downs that have occurred Mr. Hamilton can best furnish you with particulars of. Suffice it to say that at one time or other every part of the machine has failed; and yet the promoters of this machine have had the effrontery to say that these break-downs are the usual incidents of new machinery. Rubbish !

STREET RAILWAYS

H. Y. Hind, et al., *Eighty Years' Progress in British North America* (Toronto, 1863), pp. 255-6.

The first street railway company in Canada was organized the 29th of May, 1861, for the city of Toronto; and the materials being prepared, the Yonge street line was commenced on the 26th of August, and opened to the public on the 11th of September in the same year. The Queen street line was also commenced on the 16th of October, and opened the 2d of December. This company claim six miles of single track, eleven cars, and seventy horses;—which, with stables, car-houses, &c., are put down at a cost of $175,000 in stock and bonds. The cash outlay has probably been something under half of these figures.

The Montreal street railway was likewise commenced in September, 1861, and opened in the following November. The total length of track is six miles and a quarter; the cost of which, including eight cars, brick stable, forty stalls, and car-house, was $89,263.13; of which $42,500 was paid the contractor in stock. The company have besides, four one-horse cars convertible into close sleighs, three covered sleighs, five open sleighs, and sixty-three horses, with harness and other equipments, costing, together, $10,164.52:—making the total cost almost $100,000.

The street railway is an institution for the benefit of those who ride at the expense of those who drive; and is a flagrant violation of the rights of the minority, if not of the majority. The rights of a single owner are considered sufficient to prevent the closing or alienation of a highway; gas and water companies are only permitted temporarily to obstruct a street; but the horse railway is a permanent obstruction—practically dividing a wide street into two narrow ones, and a narrow one into two lanes.

These railways are a great relief to commercial cities, where the business centre is ever extending, and pushing the population into the suburbs;—and they therefore much increase the value of suburban property;—but it is questionable whether they will be found profitable as investments in Canada. It will be only occasionally that they can be worked in winter—and then only in Western Canada, so that during this period their permanent way is of no value; and the traffic by sleighs, always open to competition, will be barely sufficient to cover expenses.

Where, however, they do not pay as investments they are often warranted, provided the traffic is sufficient to cover the working expenses, if laid down in connection with, and by the owners of real estate, in the suburbs. Still there should be some limit to the extent to which the streets of a town may be cut up for such partial and selfish purposes; as there is a tendency to obstruct streets with them where there is no plea of necessity, but chiefly to secure the franchise for the future. If proper discrimination were used, a few leading arteries could be laid down, in streets which are not thoroughfares, without much inconvenience to the public, and with nearly equal advantage to those who use them—a precaution which has not been taken either in Toronto or Montreal.

PIONEER ELECTRIC LIGHTING IN MONTREAL

John Smillie, 'Pioneer Electric Lighting in Montreal', *Canadian Electrical News* (January, 1894), 8-9.

In the year 1881 electric arc lighting was creating quite an agitation among those who were interested in the betterment of street lighting and the lighting of large halls for public assemblies all over the northern part of the continent of America. The city of Montreal was not behind the rest of the country in watching for the success of the new light, and no wonder, for it would have been hard to have found a city that was worse served with gas, than the city of Montreal at that time.

I cannot say whether the Brush arc machine placed in the Custom House to light up the wharves, or the crude attempts of the Craig people, who had one going at the Exhibition, and also on one or more of the Richelieu and Ontario Navigation Company's boats at that time, were the first to go into operation here, but the successful plant was the Brush, which went very well from the start.

The next plant to be put in was at the Quebec, Montreal and Occidental Railway Works at Hochelaga, and the St. Lawrence Hall, by the United States Electric Light Co., for a local company of which the late Mr. Senecal was president. The plants at Hochelaga and at St. Lawrence Hall were being put up at the same time, but the one at Hochelaga was in advance of the one at the Hall, and was therefore finished first; and it was at that station the first public exhibition of electric incandescent lighting was made in Canada. I believe it was in July, 1881, when the formal starting of the incandescent plant took place, and it was made the occasion of a grand luncheon given at the Hochelaga works, at which no less a personage was present than his Grace the late Duke of Sutherland, who upon that occasion predicted a great future for incandescent lighting. Who would be bold enough to say that his prediction had not been fulfilled at the present time? and further, who would be rash enough to say we had reached the limit of improvement in incandescent lighting? none at least I am sure of those at this meeting. . . .

You will see by the lamp and switch before you, the method we adopted for connection; it was no uncommon thing for a wire to short circuit by making contact with the gas lamp, and in a moment we had the covering on fire for as much as 30 feet at times. This wire was double covered cotton, dipped in paraffine, and when it caught fire it made quite a blaze and smell. Indeed it required the closest watching, and even then we had two or three insipid fires which vigilance alone prevented from being of a dangerous character.

One of those fires, I will describe, which will be enough to show to you what troubles were in store for the unfortunate who had to look after an electric plant in those early days of electric lighting. In the refreshment room of the St. Lawrence Hall hotel we fitted up an old lamp; its form was a stem with three rings, one very large and the other two below, each about 12 inches smaller than the one above; on those rings we hung about 25 lamps, and the wire came through the ceiling and down the stem, and branches were taken to lamps of the small size wire, the return wires being clustered and carried up between the floors, then a large size wire carried down to main gas pipe and grounded. One of those small return wires made contact with positive wire and short circuited, and when it got very hot, it bent down, unable when hot to support its own weight; unfortunately lying directly under it was a ¾ inch composition lead pipe (gas); the heat very soon melted it, and you know what would follow. I was in the refreshment room at the time, and the lights gave a bad flicker. The room above had been left with carpet loose, also part of flooring, so that we might easily get at the wire. When the room was reached and flooring lifted there was a ¾ inch gas pipe burning and lead melting, and the wire at almost a white heat. It was quite a long distance to where the engine was; the gas main was in another building, and the joists and flooring on fire. Gentlemen, it was one of those dilemmas that a man does not want to be placed in very often in his lifetime. I had the gas shut off as quickly as possible, then the belt off the incandescent machine, then fire in the woodwork put out. The damage done amounted to very little, but it would have been bad enough had we not caught it in time.

As a matter of fact all our pipes were charged more or less with electricity. The drinking fountain in the office at times was so charged that when you took hold of the pull to draw water, you would get such a shock that you felt disinclined to try it any more. The surprise to me to-day is, that we did not succeed in burning down the hotel.

We had this plant going for two years, and the incandescent machine is in good working order yet. I had no trouble with this machine; it ran smoothly and had no repairs done to it whatever; it had a separate machine for exciting its magnets. The workmanship on this machine was first-class. The mechanism for increasing or diminishing the current was of a complex character; this I will not attempt to explain at this time.

At the junior conservative ball held in St. Lawrence Hall in 1882, at which Lady Macdonald was Lady Patroness, we had placed upon the banquet tables a number of fish bowls, some with different coloured waters in them, and others with clear water, and gold and silver fish therein. We had incandescent lamps placed in them, and when the guests sat down to the tables, we switched on the current, and I can assure you it had a very beautiful effect. We had to keep ice constantly in the water to keep it from over-heating. I mention this circumstance because it was considered quite novel at that time.

The engine we used was an old slide valve, with cut-off valve; it was 11 inches by 22 inches; we carried 60 lbs. steam pressure. We allowed four incandescent lamps per h. p., this gave us 14¼ h. p. for incandescent machine, and about 6¼ h. p. for arc machine, or 20½ h. p., not speaking of friction of engine or shafting. Our average run per day was 5 hours and the consumption was 925 lbs. of Scotch coal, or in other words 8.6 lbs. per hour per h. p.

This, gentlemen was what we did in the year 1881.

The Conservation Movement of the early twentieth century marked the first time that a serious effort was made to apply scientific and technical expertise to industry. For years, Canadians had taken for granted their soil, the forests, and water. But cheap and easily available natural resources encouraged waste; forests disappeared, the soil was exhausted and eroded, and streams were polluted. Gradually Canadians became aware of their losses. Between 1873 and 1909 thirteen Royal Commissions were appointed to enquire into matters related in one way or another to conservation, and in 1909 the first conservation act was passed.

Conservation aimed at a balance between development and preservation. It stressed the rational management of natural resources, for both present and future generations. It was, for example, not concerned with the efficient extraction of timber so much as it set itself the problem of guaranteeing a supply. To accomplish that end required a novel kind of technology. Conservationists had to link up a number of distinct specialties, such as fire control, the study of soils, climatology, and plant pathology.

This tentative courtship between science and resource management was rapidly overshadowed by the first World War. Canada came into the conflict with a strong sense of industrial unpreparedness. In particular, manufacturers felt themselves helpless spectators in a technological revolution that rendered their factories, their labour force, and their products uncompetitive in the international marketplace. Germany, as critics like George Bryce often pointed out, organized its educational system to provide industry with skilled chemists and technicians.

Mobilizing for war required massive government intervention. Canada was called upon to feed her allies, provide them with steel, munitions, and later with airplanes. Old industries had to be expanded and new ones created. Wartime urgency accelerated the normally slow process of innovation. The experience of the Shell Board showed that the nation had the ability to establish whole new manufacturing activities in a matter of months. In the nickel-steel industry the war indicated the importance of processing raw materials at home.

Of all the lessons to come out of the war, the importance of science and technology was in some ways the most critical. It became apparent, for instance, that countries geared for war production would inevitably find themselves engaged in a fierce peacetime competition. And just as in war, advanced technology might well determine the victor. In some minds, therefore, the problem of converting industry to peacetime production could only be solved by a national effort of the same order that had gone into planning for war. Perhaps the most important outcome of this line of thinking was the National Research Council, a result of the war-spawned Honorary Advisory Council for Scientific and Industrial Research.

The war also suggested the future importance of the automobile and airplane. Each was a rare sight before 1914, but by the 1920s both seemed destined for a significant role in Canada's affairs. Aviation provides a nice example of the characteristic way in which Canadians have visualized and employed new technologies. Initially techniques and technicians were imported and government played a major role in providing plant and equipment. But as the relation of flight to natural resource exploitation became increasingly apparent, an industry emerged with its own momentum. The modest nature of aviation developments in Canada, however, concealed some highly original and successful efforts in adapting the new technique to the needs and conditions of this country. And as with all transportation improvements, Canadians were ultimately led to see aviation as a critical factor in the nation's future.

In the post-war years the automobile also became a necessity for many parts of the country. Its immediate application to freight movement, however, posed a threat to that great symbol of national achievement, the Canadian railway, and reflected an early discontent with rail passenger service, too. The automobile raised perplexing political questions. If the railway was British in its origins, for Canadians the automobile was American. It either had to be imported from the U.S. or produced here from American patents. But it was clearly a form of transportation of great significance, and as politicians rushed to deal with it, of great rhetorical potential.

Even if new techniques such as industrial chemistry, aviation, and the manufacture of automobiles became national concerns and suggested the formulation of national policies, the ability of the federal government to marshal the country's technical abilities in the Great War was not matched during the Great Depression. Wheat production climbed to record levels during the 1920s, but agriculture, the most important Canadian industry, was in economic trouble even before the depression struck. Political power, moreover, had shifted to the provinces, who were even less able to devise crisis strategies.

Paradoxically, while agricultural science brought increased wheat yields, a decline in farm income sent country youth to the cities in increasing numbers. The bumper crops so vital during the war glutted markets during the 1920s. And the machinery bought to harvest foodstuffs for the army left the farmer burdened with debt during the post-war depressions.

While some farmers identified rapacious implement manufacturers as the source of their problems, most sought a solution in the application of more technology. Simultaneously, the high cost of capital equipment stimulated co-operative experiments. As in wartime, there were lessons from the lean years, too. The farmer was forced to become a managerial expert, a technologist whose weapons were considerably more sophisticated than a team of horses and a plough.

CONSERVATION

CONFLICTING VIEWS ON WATER POLLUTION

'Report of the Commission Appointed to Enquire into the Condition of Navigable Streams', *Sessional Papers*, No. 29 (1873), 6-13.

In November, 1871, a Bill, intituled, "An Act for the better protection of navigable Streams and Rivers," was introduced into the House of Commons by Richard J. Cartwright, Esq., M.P. for the County of—————. After the preamble the following enactments were contained:—

Section 1. That from and after the first day of July, 1872, no owner, tenant, &c., &c., of any saw mill shall throw, or cause to be thrown, or permit to be thrown, any saw-dust, edgings, or rubbish of any description into any navigable stream or river, either above or below the point at which such stream or river ceases to be navigable.

Section 2 declared the penalty for violating the preceeding section, for the first offence, a fine of not less than twenty dollars, and for the second and each subsequent offence, a fine of not less than fifty dollars for each offence, and by this section also was declared the manner in which the fines were to be summarily recovered.

The third Section made it the duty of the several fishery officers to examine and report upon the state of the navigable streams and rivers, and to prosecute all parties contravening the terms of this Act.

By the fourth Section, it was provided, that in cases where it was clearly shewn to the satisfaction of the Minister of Marine and Fisheries, that no injury is accruing, or likely to accrue to the navigation of any stream or river, he might, by proclamation in the official *Gazette*, exempt from the operations of the Act, the whole, or any part, of such stream or river, lying above the point where it ceases to be navigable.

The introduction of this Bill was immediately followed by a strong petition to the House of Commons . . . , signed by Gilmour & Co., and seventeen others, chiefly connected with the mills upon the Ottawa, and its tributaries. In accordance with the arrangement which we laid down for making our report . . . we now proceed to give a resumé of the allegations in the petition, viz:—

That petitioners represent a very large capital, invested at the Chaudiere and elsewhere on the Ottawa and its tributaries; employing at least 8,000 men, and 3,000 teams; producing a very large addition to the exports of Canada, amounting to four hundred millions feet of lumber, and four millions of dollars of value annually.

That the proposed legislation, with regard to the navigable streams and rivers, will most injuriously affect those interests, as it is *impossible* to *prevent saw-dust* from mills, driven by water, falling into the water, and consequently the enforcement of the Bill would compel them to close their mills, and remove to other localities where steam power can be used.

That they fully recognize the importance of maintaining the navigation of the Ottawa River, but that they are in a position to prove, as well from the result of actual investigation of the River Ottawa, as from the experience of similar operations, of fifty years past on the Hudson and Penobscot Rivers, that *navigation* is not *injured* by the falling into them of *saw-dust*, which is yearly carried off by the spring freshets. . . .

The first of the papers in the above list . . . , is a report, the date not given, made to Mr. Bronson, by Professor Green, treating the subject in a purely Engineering point of view, he puts the questions: —

1st. What are the causes which induce the formation of bars in navigable or other Rivers?

2nd. What materials usually compose such bars?

3rd. What are the specific gravities of these materials?

4th. What velocities of current are necessary to take up and transport these materials to the point of final deposit? After these, a fifth is indirectly added. What is the specific gravity of pine saw-dust, and the velocity of current necessary to take it up and transport it?

To these questions, clearly and logically put, Mr Green gives, in their succession, indisputable answers, so far as his theoretic calculations and experiments extend. The entire report, which is very voluminous, exhibits great research, and intimate acquaintance with the best scientific authorities, both native and foreign, upon the subject on which he writes. This report is concluded thus:—

"In view of my experimental results, together with the facts observed "by the U. S. Engineers upon the Hudson River, and in view of the ex-"perience of lumbermen and navigators upon the Hudson and Penobscot "Rivers, I have formed the following opinions," viz.:—

That saturated pine saw-dust will not be permanently deposited in water where the velocity of the current exceeds 0.25 of a foot per second, or one-sixth of a mile per hour.

That water-logged chips may be deposited when the velocity of the current is less than 1.00 feet per second, or two-thirds of a mile per hour.

That saw-dust may accumulate in eddies and in still water, or where the velocity of the current is permanently less than 0.20 to 0.25 of a foot per second.

That bars of *saw-dust* and sand combined will not be formed under any circumstances, for the reason that when the velocity of the current is diminished so as to permit the deposit of sand, it is still more than twice as great as is necessary to hold and transport saturated saw-dust; and hence,

That saw-dust will not accumulate or be permanently deposited in rivers "where sand bars occur, unless there exist expansions of the river be-"low such sand bars, sufficient to make a cross section, more than "double that at the side of the bar.

That if in low water saw-dust should accumulate in small quantities, *the "accelerated current of the first freshet would take it up and sweep it "down stream*; and finally,

That it is extremely improbable that the minimum freshet velocity in the "Ottawa River, ever falls below 0.25 of a foot per second, there is no "reason to anticipate the formation of permanent or troublesome bars, "or accumulation of saw-dust in that river.

"This opinion may be modified or strengthened when more definite "and precise information shall have been obtained in relation to the mag-"nitude of the Ottawa River, its water shed and other characteristics.

I am, &c.,

D. M. GREENE,

Civil Engineer.

We now come to report our own examinations and observations made during our inspection of the Ottawa, comparing, as we go on, the results and the conclusions we have formed from them, and shewing where they corroborate or conflict with the various opinions contained in the foregoing.

From Lachine to the foot of the Carillon Rapids we proceeded up the

Ottawa in the steamer *Prince of Wales*. From the head of the Grenville Rapids we were conveyed up the river in the steamer *Queen Victoria*. On nearing such wharves as we stopped at we found a good deal of sawdust disturbed by the wheels.

From the very extensive saw mills at Hawkesbury it may be said that nearly the whole of the bark, slabs, edgings, sawdust, etc., is discharged into the river; this waste, together with what is brought down from the other mills above Grenville, is soon caught in the rough, rocky bottomed rapids below, and form, in sundry parts of them, large jams, which the succeeding freshet or flood carries away. On coming up the river, we observed large quantities of it strewn along the south shore, below the rapids, and saw very little floating sawdust.

In the large bays and eddies above these rapids are very extensive shoals, standing over the surface of the water at the time we passed; from the distance we were at they appeared to be composed of pure sand; we did not examine them, however, as their position is out of the line of channel, and we were anxious to get to the portions of the river where the chief obstructions were alleged to exist.

From Grenville to Ottawa we did not meet with any obstruction whatever. On nearing the city we saw sawdust floating, but not in large quantities.

On arriving in Ottawa, in order to facilitate us in our examination, we engaged the services of the steamer *Fairy*, which we found well adapted to our purpose, and the intimate acquaintance with the river possessed by Captain Nichols, who accompanied us, enabled him to bring us to the several points where it was expected we could find obstructions in the channel.

We found the bay at the entrance to the Rideau Canal to be so fully obstructed and blocked up with logs, square timber, etc., that it was with very much difficulty and by pushing aside the booms and logs, that we could get to the lock. We lost so much time in accomplishing this that we had to postpone making our soundings and bearings.

Early the following morning we steamed down to McKay's Bay. Here we found an enormous mass of *sawdust* accumulated, where previous to it, there had been 40 feet of water. This pile was several feet over the surface of the river when we examined it. The end of a bar of sawdust, which runs out from the main mass down stream, lies from 40 to 50 yards within a line drawn from the upper to the lower points of the bay, and is consequently out of the direct course vessels take when going up or down the river. This bank or island of sawdust goes down deep pretty rapidly towards the river, to the shore it gradually shoals in, and at present the beach there, that had been a convenient place for repairing vessels, booming lumber, etc., is now rendered useless. This great mass has been for several years accumulating, but in a greatly increased ratio within the last four or five years, during which same period the production of saw-dust at the Chaudiere has been almost three fold. The extreme height of flood over low summer water at the site of this mass has been as much as twenty-two feet. Notwithstanding the greatly increased pressure by which it is thereby operated on, as well as its being subjected, more or less, to the influence of the torrent of water then pouring over the Chaudiere, so short a distance above it, the holding of its position, undisturbed by such great forces, is a *convincing proof of the tenacity with which* sawdust *will keep its place* after being some *time deposited*. Further proof of which may be found also at the mouths of several of the rivers below Quebec, where considerable deposits of sawdust, carried down from the mills above, remain in a *slimy state on the beach to this day, undisturbed by the roughness of the water in storms, or by the rapid current of the tides daily.*

FERNOW DESCRIBES HIS TASK

'The Chair of Forestry at Toronto University', *Canada Lumberman and Woodworker* (May, 1907), p. 14.

Editor CANADA LUMBERMAN:

Dear Sir,—In response to your inquiry, I may say that I can at present speak only of my immediate task, namely, the organization of a College of Forestry. The object of this newly to be established Faculty is, of course, in the first place to impart technical information to students who propose to take up forestry as a profession. There are now some half dozen such schools in the States—which, by the way, cannot supply the demand for foresters fast enough—and it is proposed to establish in the University of Toronto a school that shall be second to none.

Educating men for a profession presumes that, when educated, these men will find employment, an opportunity of practising what they have learned and of earning their living by it. . . .

Few people really know what a forester is and what he is about. To your readers I would therefore say as emphatically as I may, that a for-ester is nothing less than a lumberman—an educated lumberman, a harvester of wood crops.

There is only one difference between forester and lumberman, namely, an added obligation on the former of replacing the crop which he has harvested. This he may do either by the mere manner of cutting the crop of Nature, or otherwise.

The relation of the forester to the limit holder, then, about which you ask, should be that of an adviser as to methods of securing a more thorough use of his limits and of a larger revenue without destroying their reproductive capacity.

Eventually foresters will be managers of timber lands and logging operations, carried on with a view to the perpetuity of timber supplies. Graduates of a forestry school are, of course, no more fitted to jump at once into such positions than young medical students are to be entrusted with the lives of patients; but they are prepared to acquire the necessary experience in a shorter time than those without the technical training, and this experience they will have to acquire in the logging camps and through employment in inferior positions under limit holders or government.

That there is nothing chimerical in the expectation that such men will be employed as soon as they are available is proven by the experience of the States, where not only the government, but private lumbermen and railroad companies do employ foresters. Even in Canada, only lately three firms have seen fit to place a value on such service.

The government, that is, the people at large, are, of course, interested more than the limit holders in anything that pertains to the future of the resources of the country, and the first employment of foresters should, and probably will, come from the government, first to secure better knowledge of its timber holdings, and then to prepare plans for their better management.

I know perfectly well that it is dangerous ground to suggest changes in existing methods of procedure with reference to the disposal and use of timber limits. I am, therefore, not going to express any views regarding such changes until I have more closely studied the situation. This, however, I may say, that whatever forest reservations the government has made or may set aside should as soon as practicable be placed under technical management, and for this service our graduates are to be specially fitted.

It goes without saying that no forestry can be practised where protection against fire is insufficient, and the solution of this problem must in every case precede the application of forestry methods. For this service, too, the forestry students will be available, and their better education will not be detrimental to their efficiency.

Finally, I may add, it is proposed to enter upon a broad University extension work, with a view of educating the people in appreciation of forestry principles, and, as far as practicable, the Faculty of Forestry will be ready to give advice regarding their application to farmers and limit holders.

Yours truly,
B. E. FERNOW,
Dean, Faculty of Forestry.

ROBERT LAIRD BORDEN INTRODUCES A CONSERVATION BILL

Official Report of the Debates of the House of Commons of the Dominion of Canada (1909), pp. 355-70.

Mr. R. L. BORDEN moved:

That in the opinion of this House it is advisable to appoint a select standing committee on natural resources who shall have authority to inquire into and consider and report upon all matters appertaining to the conservation and development of the natural resources of Canada, including fisheries, forests, mines, minerals, waterways and water powers, and to whom may be referred from time to time any report, document or matter touching the subject which they are appointed to consider.

Sir WILFRID LAURIER. I have no objection to my hon. friend going on with his motion, but I do not think the government can close the debate on it to-day.

Mr. R. L. BORDEN. My remarks will not be very lengthy. So far as the exact wording of this resolution is concerned, I shall be very glad indeed to accept any suggestion from the government or any hon. member of this House. My object is to point out that public interest in the conservation and development of the great natural resources of this country might be stimulated by action of parliament. We have at present a committee on agriculture. That committee has engaged for the most part in thoroughly non-partisan work and work which has been of great advantage to the people. We thoroughly realize that agriculture must be the principal basis upon which the future wealth of this country depends; but that consideration should not blind us to the further fact that we have, outside of agriculture, in the fisheries, forests, mines, minerals, waterways and water-powers of this country, very great resources, the extent of which we do not at present realize, and the development and conservation of these are of very great importance to the people.

Now, in speaking of 'development' and 'conservation' I believe that these two words should be the watchwords of the country with regard to its natural resources. Conservation does not mean non-user; on the contrary, it is consistent with that reasonable user of these great resources which is absolutely necessary for their development. And, on the other hand, development does not imply destruction or waste; it ought not to imply destruction or waste, but these great resources should be both developed and conserved, so that they may be of the greatest possible advantage to the present generation and may also be handed down as a continuing heritage to those who come after us in the work of upbuilding this Dominion and the British empire.

We have had a great many stimulating addresses throughout the country on the importance of these great resources. One might expect that the parliament of Canada would be one of the great forces in awakening public interest in our resources, and the consideration of means by which the development and conservation of these resources should be carried out. But owing, I believe, to some extent at least, to the fact that we have had no committee of parliament specially charged with the consideration of our natural resources, parliament has not taken the initiative to any very considerable degree, and the stimulus of public interest and public attention in respect of these matters has come to us almost altogether from outside sources. . . .

. . . If we could have committees such as the one I suggest, to take into consideration matters of great public interest, matters which perhaps for the time being, in the exigencies of the political situation, could not be taken in hand by the government itself, they might serve a very useful public purpose. The reports of such committees need not be acted upon immediately by the government of the day. For example, I believe that public attention should be directed to the pulpwood of this country. I realize what the conditions are in Quebec, the maritime provinces and other parts of the country. The people of this country do not understand that at the present time, while our producers are receiving for their pulpwood about $6 or $7 a cord labour bestowed upon it in the United States, when that pulpwood goes across the borders, make it worth $50 or $60 or $70. I realize that the subject is not free from difficulty; but it seems to me that a committee of this House, taking up such a matter as that, and bringing before the committee the men who are most strongly opposed to taking any step towards utilizing our pulpwood in our own country, and inviting them to state their reasons and to argue the matter out, could do a work for the conservation of the national resources of this country which could not be done by the government of the day. So, while men everywhere in Canada are lifting up their voices for the conservation and development of our natural resources, it seems to me that some initiative should come from parliament, and that the members of parliament, without regard to party, sinking for this purpose all partisan considerations, should take up this work and endeavour to accomplish something for the good of the country. It is purely in that spirit that I have brought this matter to the attention of the right hon. leader of the government and of this House. I am not concerned about the verbiage of the resolution, or whether the committee shall be appointed on the motion of an hon. member on this side of the House or an hon. member on the other side. But I would like to see something done, and I trust that the suggestion that I have taken the liberty of submitting to the consideration of the House will receive the favourable consideration of the Prime Minister and his colleagues and of hon. gentlemen on the other side of the House, and that in some manner it will be acted upon during the present session.

WORLD WAR I

INDUSTRIAL RESEARCH: A NATIONAL ASSET

George Bryce, 'The Crying Need of Industrial Research in Canada', *Transactions of the Canadian Institute*, vol. IX (1909-1912), 223-35.

CANADIANS, I fear, Mr. President, are disposed to be a self-satisfied people. We have not yet reached our jubilee as a Nation of the Empire, but we are inclined to think that we have done pretty well. It may be that the contrast between our condition before Confederation and our status at the present time is so great that we are apt to think more highly of ourselves than we ought to think. The student who fears the result of his examination is hilarious if he should make a bare "pass," the workman who has been receiving a low wage regards himself as rich if he is given a slight increase, and the Government which has had a deficit or a falling revenue is highly pleased if expenditure does not go beyond receipts. But excellence in each case means more than that. So, when we recall the homespun garb and the impassable roads, and the unsettled markets, and the poor school facilities which some of us knew some forty or fifty years ago, we are inclined to self-congratulation over our present circumstances and achievements. No doubt to-day Canada is the land of opportunity, but that is just because it is still far from what it may become.

I am a patriotic, and, in some respects, a proud Canadian, but to-night I cannot be a prophet of smooth things. . . .

It is surely with pain that we contrast the thorough preparation secured from the Gymnasium in Germany and the High Schools of Edinburgh, Glasgow or London, with what those of us who have been Educationalists for years have seen of hundreds of our poorly prepared matriculants, who present themselves for a University course.

An investigation into our factories, machine shops and business places all through Canada tells the same story, that the working lads coming from our schools have been very poorly instructed. We used to think the three Rs a very modest measure of acquirement for a lad leaving the public schools, but now we are quite familiar with his having not even that acquisition.

We cannot disguise the fact from ourselves, that, though Governments seem to make liberal donations to education, though many municipalities take pride in their public schools, though the inspectorates are well manned, yet there is in almost every province of the Dominion growing up a very considerable percentage of the young who are practically illiterate.

Now, this very lamentable state of things, which in the last forty or fifty years of our experience has been forming the standards of hundreds of our communities in all the provinces from the Atlantic to the Pacific, has produced a public opinion none too favorable to higher culture and the acquisition of a good sound education. The Mechanics in many cases do not value the reputation for efficiency. Men, as we have seen them—"handymen"—undertake to do work which they cannot do and "turn their hand" to anything that may present itself. A member of the Royal Commission had a stock question for carpenters:—"Could you build a winding staircase or a complicated house-roof?" Not one quarter of the witnesses could answer "Yes."

Teachers on permits without knowledge or facility make teaching a farce. Doctors have entered their profession who did not adorn it, and even, I am afraid, ministers innocent even of "Scant Latin and less Greek" were none too strong either in philosophy or general erudition.

I state these things because I fear that they indicate a serious imperfection of training, a carelessness about standards, and an unwillingness to surrender some of our fallacies, that may interfere with any effort to rouse our educational boards, our civic authorities, our cabinets and parliaments, to look on thoroughness and efficiency in education, labour and professional life, as absolutely essential to our Industrial success.

Complaints are made all through Canada that our schools do not fit the scholars for the factory, that apprentices are changeable and unreliable, that the apprenticeship system has broken down, that art as applied to Industry is not properly taught and that writing in the schools is very bad. These are all marks of imperfection and poor training. What are the consequences of these things in the Industries? They are these:—The Employer and foreman are poor judges and poor purchasers of the material needed; the management of the offices and shops is careless; the quality of the labour is poor; the business as a whole is badly managed, and the waste is enormous.

These are the things which the people who know have been telling us all through Canada; and we are bound to say that in older countries, where custom is strong and communities are better established, the efficiency in industry is greater. An observing writer has said: "The Manufacturers have not been men educated in the knowledge of the schools, but are men who know practically nothing of applied science and who in consequence forced their way to success through sheer fighting manhood and through the application of principles which they did not understand."

Many of the manufacturers think it sufficient to have a so-called "practical man," one not instructed, but simply an expert mechanic, who serves as "guide, philosopher and friend."

1. Thus the Manufacturer does not value true expert advice.
2. He shuts his eyes to the waste.
3. He settles down to a career of non-progressiveness.
4. He agitates for a higher duty on his products.

5. Dissatisfied, he turns his thoughts to making a Combination or combine—which is illegal.

The real remedy for many of his difficulties is Scientific Research. . . .

Thus thinking men are saying to-day—we need better elementary education, better High School training, more practical University Science, more men who know the principles and reasons of things. Especially do we need more Science in our Industries. Look at the wasted opportunities. Out of many letters, relating to from fifty to a hundred fields of Industry which I have received from keen sighted and intelligent scientific men in Canada, I may give examples of the tremendous waste of valuable things, and of unused opportunities. Nature has given us great resources in Canada and we do not know how to use them. . . .

What then is Research?

1. *It is a great National Asset.* Think of what it would be to have a hundred men of high attainments and practical skill working under favorable conditions in Canada upon the hundred problems to which we have referred. Yes, we have had them, but we did not set them to work on our National Science problems. Our Commission met Canadians highly educated and occupying places of scientific distinction in twos and threes in New York, Cornell (Ithaca), Johns Hopkins (Baltimore), Washington, Pittsburgh, Buffalo, Madison, Wis., Minneapolis, Kansas, Missouri, California, Washington State—our brightest minds.—From Toronto University alone there have gone to high educational positions in the United States hundreds of Canadians, and I have a list of graduates of the Guelph Agricultural College who have left Canada to hold high educational and research positions in 30 agricultural colleges and experiment stations, from the Atlantic to the Pacific in the United States. I am informed that in Institutions of Higher Learning and Scientific occupations in the United States there are no fewer than 600 graduates of Toronto University, and I know that McGill and Queen's are similarly represented.

One of the most brilliant of these wanderers said to me lately: "I am a Canadian; my wife is a Canadian; we are bringing up our little girl here as a Canadian. When I was in a Canadian University the only outlook I could see for myself at that time was as teacher of a High School. For that I did not care. I came here to be a Research professor." In harmony with this complaint one of my own students in Science, now a dean of Faculty in one of the most prominent Universities in the United States, lamented to me lately the few positions in Canada open to Canadians of higher grade. Even to Oxford, Manchester, Edinburgh, London, have our men of scientific mark been taken from us. These bright minds of ours are a national asset. We need them. We have no right to let them leave us. They are the Creator's gift to us for our higher development. Our Governments, our Universities, our private citizens of means, and our manufacturers should take hold of them, open positions for them, not specially for their own sakes, but because the field of profitable research requires them. . . .

If then Research is all this, how are we to secure it to our Country?

1. If it is a national asset and a benefit to all the people, then it is a fit subject for Government assistance. Probably the hundreds of brilliant Canadians who have gone abroad and are in the service of foreign nations could all have been saved to Canadian education and Canadian Manufacture by judicious Government action. If during our rising entrance upon manufacturing in Canada which has been very remarkable in the last forty years, the Government had understood and taken action, the result would be very different. . . .

Gentlemen of the Canadian Institute, Research is a practical subject. It is no dream or visionary fad. I have endeavored to describe it in its different phases. If Canadian Manufacturers are to succeed, this cannot be done by artificial bolstering up, or sleight of hand, or industrial cornering, or anything else except plain, intelligent hard work. I have pointed out how success may be obtained. It can only be done by Governments—Dominion, Local, and Municipal co-operating heartily in advancing Technical Education, by the co-operative association of Universities and Technical Schools, and it can be greatly assisted by the shrewd but interested support in co-operative plans of the Canadian Manufacturers. Besides, all these may be mightily stimulated by the gifts of rich and generous Canadians—and I am further sure that the Local Governments will pardon us if we should advise the wealthy men to take steps to escape the Legacy Tax by giving hundreds of thousands of dollars while they are still living, that they may see the fruit of their labours.

PLOUGHSHARES INTO SWORDS

H. H. Vaughan, 'The Manufacture of Munitions in Canada', *Transactions*, Engineering Institute of Canada, vol. XXXIII (1919), 1-5.

When the war commenced in August, Canadian Industries were suffering from a period of severe depression. Certain undertakings that were already under way were being completed but practically no new enterprises were being projected, the volume of business was small and values of all securities had fallen. This condition was, no doubt, principally due to the world-wide disturbance caused by Germany's decision to bring on a state of war in that year, but it was intensified in our case by the extraordinary amount of railroad construction in several preceding years, the great expansion which had taken place in our manufacturing capacity and on account of the general reaction following a period of great development.

During the opening months of the war, the sentiment regarding business conditions was decidedly pessimistic. The immediate prospect was one involving a complete suspension of all development work, a great demand for money in Europe and consequent stringency here and a practical stagnation in all our industries during hostilities. Few foresaw the length to which such a war could possibly extend with the corresponding demand for our natural products and I believe we can safely say that none foresaw our manufacturing capacity would not only be fully utilized but enormously increased to provide for the requirements of the Allies.

The first aid offered by Canada to the British Government was naturally military, and munition workers can claim no recognition in comparison with the magnificent contribution she has made in furnishing the troops that have served with such immortal credit to their country and have so nobly succeeded in establishing the freedom of the world. . . .

Second only to the help Canada rendered to the cause of the Allies in men was her contribution in the manufacture of munitions, a line of work in which the results that have been obtained were certainly not anticipated when the war commenced. From without, Canada would appear as a country whose wealth lay in her wheat fields, her mines and her forests, and whose manufacturing wealth was simply incidental to her local requirements, and it is strange to realize that such a country with her comparatively small population should, for a considerable period, have furnished over fifteen per cent of the total disbursements of the British Ministry of Munitions.

Without any desire to disparage the achievements of the Canadian Manufacturers, it must, however, be recognized that they enjoyed certain latent advantages which were not initially recognized. A lengthy period of prosperity had produced a large number of men who were used to attacking difficulties and overcoming them. A reasonably good supply of labor was available and, on account of the dullness in business in the United States, skilled assistance was readily obtained. Last, and probably most important, was the close connection Canadians enjoyed with the United States machinery manufacturers, which enabled them to obtain promptly information as to the machinery required and quick delivery when it was ordered. These advantages were not, however, appreciated when the work was commenced and in no way detract from the initiative that was displayed by those who acted as the pioneers in the work. . . .

The steel required the first consideration. This is required to conform to quite a rigid specification, which does not define the chemical composition but the physical requirements after heat treatment. The first difficulty experienced by the Committee was the specification that this steel should be acid open hearth. There was only one acid furnace in Canada and that was of small capacity and it was, therefore, practically imperative to induce the authorities to accept basic steel. Col Thos. Cantley obtained the suitable analysis from some acid steel in the possession of the Arsenal, made up a heat of basic steel to correspond with it and rolled it into bars. These were forged at the Arsenal, made up into shells and tested with satisfactory results. Colonel Carnegie went to England with two of the shells and word came back that basic steel that met the balance of the specifications would be accepted. I have no doubt that the authorities were realizing by that time that if they wanted shells they would have to accept basic steel, but this does not detract from the importance of the concession that the experiment justified, a concession that made the entire steel making capacity of the country available for munition work.

The permission to use basic steel did not conclude the steel makers' difficulties by any means. He still had to determine the exact quality of steel that would comply with the balance of the specifications which, during the first four months, gave him considerable trouble. Experience developed that a minimum about 0.42 per cent of carbon was necessary in order to meet the physical requirements but many failures occurred before the steel makers obtained sufficient experience to ascertain the exact grade required. The Nova Scotia Steel Company took the pioneer part in this work and were unsparing in their efforts to produce the proper steel as rapidly as possible, and they deserve great credit for their patriotic enterprise.

After the steel was secured, it next had to be converted into forgings. This work was handled in a small way at the Arsenal, but many difficulties were experienced by the firms who undertook to execute it on a manufacturing basis. Again the Nova Scotia Steel Company was one of the pioneers and the Canada Forge Company also took the work up energetically and rendered good service in obtaining successful production. An interesting example of the universal desire to assist in the work was afforded when the Nova Scotia Steel Company, who commenced forging on one of their large hydraulic presses, required additional capacity. The Canadian Pacific designed, made the patterns and castings, and constructed and shipped complete four 250-ton presses with 45-inch stroke and one 300-ton press with 36-inch stroke the first one in twenty days from the time the order was originally discussed and the last one ten days later.

WAR AND THE MOVEMENT FOR HOME INDUSTRY

Report of the Royal Ontario Nickel Commission (Toronto, 1917), pp. 3–4.

One of the early uses for which nickel-steel was found to be adapted was the manufacture of armour-plate for war vessels. France was early in the field in experimenting with nickel-steel armour-plate. Trials carried out in 1890 and 1891 by the Navy Department at Washington showed that with a covering of the new armour a battleship was well nigh invulnerable compared with vessels clad with the armour previously in use. The supremacy of the British fleet is synonymous with the maintenance of the British Empire, and popular feeling in Ontario was not long in drawing inferences and conclusions. If nickel-steel armour was the best, of course the British fleet would adopt it. After a somewhat prolonged trial, it did so. Popular feeling was gratified by the fact that the element which contributed so strongly to Britain's naval superiority was produced from Ontario mines, although as a matter of fact, New Caledonia nickel only was used in British armour-plate until 1904. It was known that the ore was mined and smelted in this Province, but that the refining took place mainly in the United States, and popular feeling began to ask "Why is nickel not refined in Ontario?"

It may not be possible to enumerate all the elements of this insistent and persistent inquiry, but analysis will reveal at least some of them. There is, first, the natural desire to have all the work on raw material which is produced here done at home, up to the point of turning out the finished article. Employment is given to Canadian workmen, Canadian chemists and Canadian experts. The rewards of this labour are spent in Canada and swell the volume of Canadian business. There is a feeling of impatience at seeing Canadians hewers of wood and drawers of water, while in another country, technical and skilled work is performed in refining an article of Canadian origin. It is felt that Canadian prestige would be enhanced by the establishment of an important industry of the kind, which would "build up Ontario." For some time after smelting began at Sudbury, low grade or "standard" matte only was made, containing say 40 per cent. of nickel and copper combined, and when the production of high grade or Bessemer matte, containing about 80 per cent. of the metals became the established practice, it was considered that a decided step in advance had been taken. But even Bessemer matte failed to silence the query "Why cannot nickel be refined at home?"

WAR REVEALS REAL REASON FOR INQUIRY

The outbreak of the great war made clear the most deeply seated and most potent of the feelings which underlay the inquiry. Nickel was a necessity in modern warfare; it was needed for armour-plate, for rifle-barrels, for heavy ordnance, bullet coverings, cartridge cases, automobile parts, and the whole catalogue of military and naval equipment. Not an ounce should go to the enemy! Every pound of Canadian nickel must be placed at the service of the Mother country and her Allies! Yet how to ensure this while the metal is refined in a foreign country, by a foreign company, with the countless opportunities of its passing into the hands of Germans or German sympathizers?

It is true that arrangements satisfactory to the British and Canadian governments were made to meet this situation almost immediately after war was declared; but a certain amount of uneasiness has remained, fed by newspaper articles and editorials, which was aggravated by the arrival at Baltimore in July last of the German submarine "Deutschland," bringing a cargo of dye stuffs and advertising its intention of returning with a cargo of nickel, and also by a subsequent repetition of the feat, in November. It is the fact of the British Empire being at war, and at war with a shameless and ferocious enemy, that gives special point to the desire to have our nickel refined at home. The plan adopted to ensure that no Canadian nickel shall find its way into German hands during the war was beyond doubt well calculated to accomplish that end; but it is asked, who can say that should another world-struggle involve our country or our Empire, a like happy condition will recur? Suppose the United States were to decide she needed for her own use the nickel now being refined there from Canadian ore. Canada might indeed restrain the exportation of matte, but this would not put her in possession of the refined nickel, were there no refineries here. The result might well be a shortage of nickel while the need was at its height, and a shortage of nickel might be a weakness sufficient to determine the issue of a war.

THE HONORARY ADVISORY COUNCIL FOR SCIENTIFIC AND INDUSTRIAL RESEARCH

Frank D. Adams, *The Need for Industrial Research in Canada*. Bulletin No. 1, The Honorary Advisory Council for Scientific and Industrial Research (Ottawa, 1918), pp. 1, 6-8.

One of the great facts which is being driven home by the present war is the striking part which scientific research and discovery is playing in this terrible conflict. It is, moreover, equally clear that this new factor will play a dominant role in the intense industrial competition which will follow upon the declaration of peace. Industry is the great basis of national prosperity, and if Canadian industry is to be placed in a position which will enable it even to hold its own in competition with the great nations of the world whose industries will be "speeded up" to the highest point, the Dominion must in this New Era strain every nerve to secure increased efficiency in its manufacturing by the introduction of the most advanced and scientific methods and the widest market for its manufactured products by the most advanced and modern methods of co-operative distribution. . . .

In its broadest sense research means simply the acquisition and application of new knowledge. Without new knowledge, no industry can continuously flourish. In the least organized industries new knowledge comes as the result of the accumulated experience of the worker. As conditions become more exacting and refinements necessary, the assistance of the technologist is required in seeking and providing scientific knowledge. In the largest and most progressive firms, staffs of men are provided to make and turn to account new scientific discoveries. It is indisputable that an industry must stagnate unless continually kept up to date by some such methods and a firm that effectively carries on research cannot but triumph over its less progressive rivals. . . .

The question may be asked—What is Canada doing to develop her industries by scientific and industrial research? Several of the larger universities of the Dominion, and some of the Departments of the Dominion and Provincial Governments, have done and are now doing important and valuable work in this direction. The volume of this work needs, however, to be greatly expanded, and it should receive more adequate financial support.

In order to further develop this important factor in our national life, the Government of the Dominion of Canada following the example of the Government of Great Britain, have appointed a Research Committee of the Privy Council, with an Honorary Advisory Council for Scientific and Industrial Research to advise them on all matters connected with this subject.

In order to train up in Canada a body of young men capable of carrying out industrial research and scientific investigation such as are engaged in this work in other countries, the Government has already, on the recommendation of the Research Council, established a series of studentships and fellowships which will be awarded to young men of ability and promise, thus enabling them to follow advanced courses of study which will qualify them to undertake this important work.

The Council has also taken a census of the industries of the Dominion, in order to ascertain the problems presented by Canadian industries at the present time, and has investigated for various industries a large number of questions and solved many difficulties which were presenting themselves in various manufacturing enterprises.

A number of important researches directed to the improvement of various manufacturing operations and the development of new industries are now being carried out.

On the Council's advice the Government established a Forest Experiment Station at Petawawa, Ontario, and has inaugurated a very important series of researches into the best methods of preserving the forests of Eastern Canada from the destruction that is at present overtaking them owing to the methods of cutting which are now employed, and to determine which of the methods of forestry practice developed in the older countries of Europe is best adapted to Canadian conditions and will be most effective for the preservation of our Eastern forests.

The Dominion Government in co-operation with the Governments of Manitoba and Saskatchewan, are also, on the advice of the Research Council, about to undertake the erection and operation of an experimental plant for the conversion of the low grade lignite fuels of southern Saskatchewan into a high grade domestic fuel having the general character of anthracite to supply the needs of the population of the eastern plains.

The Research Council has also secured the close co-operation, as Associate Committees, of the leading technical men of the Dominion in Mining and Metallurgy, the Chemical Industries, and in various industrial activities of the Pacific Coast, and is with them now engaged in developing its work for the furtherance of Canadian industry in a number of important fields.

There can be no doubt that after the war commercial competition will be much more intense than ever before, since every country will seek to increase its production and export, for the purpose of meeting the enormous debts which have been piled up. Those countries which improve the quality of their products while cutting down costs through the introduction and adoption of the best and most advanced methods which can be developed by industrial research—and who at the same time by the adoption of co-operative action can market their goods cheaply and on a large scale—will capture the competitive markets. In other words, as has been recently remarked, big business, progressive methods, and scientific research must come together. Syndicating businesses and organizing scientific education and research are the aspects of the same operation.

If Canada is to maintain and improve its position among the countries of the world it must do so by learning how to work up its abundant raw materials into the cheapest and best merchantable products by the application of scientific knowledge to this work in hand. More extended facilities for research and a greater number of highly trained men are needed now in preparation for the forward movement which Canada must make on the resumption of peace if she is to retain her place among the nations of the world. And above all the people of Canada must awake to the necessity of action in the matter of industrial research and recognize that if millions of dollars are being expended by governments and by individual companies in other countries for the development of industrial research, Canada cannot hope to achieve results unless she is willing to meet the necessary outlay.

AVIATION

WHEN FLYING WAS IN 'THE AIR'

Canadian Aviation, vol. VI (January, 1933), 3-4. Reprinted by permission of *Canadian Aviation*.

On March 31, 1933, the present agreement under which Federal aid is rendered to flying clubs will have run for a period of exactly five years, the time specified in the agreement.

While it is known that negotiations have been in progress for some time between representatives of the clubs and the Dominion Government with respect to future policy, it will probably be in order at this juncture to deal frankly with some of the more important aspects of the club scheme in order that an intelligent appreciation of any future course may be arrived at.

Most of our readers are familiar with the general provisions of the agreement, but for the benefit of others it might not be out of place to restate the exact conditions, in the main, under which the scheme, known officially as Standard Conditions, was inaugurated, authority being given under Order-in-Council, P.C. 1878, dated September 24, 1927. A club was required to:

(a) Provide its own flying field.

(b) Provide the Services of an Instructor and Air Engineer.

(c) Have at least thirty members willing to qualify as pilots.

(d) Have not less than ten members already qualified.

These conditions having been fulfilled, the Government undertook to give a club the following:

(a) An initial issue of two aeroplanes (on loan).

(b) A further issue of one aeroplane per year for each aeroplane purchased by a club.

(c) A grant of $100 in respect to each member qualified as an ab initio pilot.

(d) (A later provision) A grant not exceeding $100 in respect of each Commercial Pilot's License issued.

Keeping that information in mind, it may not be out of place to refresh our memory as to when and where the scheme began and, by following its progress, summarize for ourselves the measure of public approbation which it warrants.

In July, 1925, a scheme was launched in the Old Country, about which more will be said a little later, and in this, as in many other matters of good Government policy, we in Canada have been wise in following the lead.

In any event, early 1926 found matters beginning to take shape in

Canada. To name everyone who contributed toward the setting up of the Canadian scheme would be impossible. From many parts of the Dominion came the urge—the movement was "in the air" so to speak.

Of those most active in the early discussions one is safe in mentioning W. S. Lighthall, of Montreal. Also from Montreal there were Wing Commander (now Group Captain) J. L. Gordon, and an associate, the president of the Royal St. Lawrence Yacht Club. (In those days very few people could picture flying on anything except floats as we had no airports.) From Toronto support came from Wilf. Curtis, now president of the Toronto Flying Club, and others. Border Cities had already written history with one of the earliest aero clubs in Canada. Mr. Bell-Irving, known almost as a father of aviation in British Columbia, was an enthusiastic supporter in that province. Several other names come to mind but must give way to the demands of brevity.

The part played by J. A. Wilson, present Controller of Civil Aviation, is too well known to call for more than passing reference and we have not the temerity to think that justice could be done the "father of the flying clubs" in anything short of a major story. Those closely associated with him day by day have a true appreciation of the leadership he has given to the whole of civil aviation in Canada.

But, to focalize at the point where flying clubs were inaugurated in Canada, what was the actual situation with which we were faced?

Airports? There was no such animal, practically speaking. Air transportation was foreign to the average person's thoughts—something possibly for the hidden north country. Little thought was given to the possibilities of inter-city services by air. In brief, no ground facilities existed, without which flying could not possibly advance nor even start. It is now known that out of 80 municipalities queried at that time regarding airports, only two responded. "What was this new-fangled business, anyhow?" they might have asked. Pilots? They were imported from the Old Country. Practically no training facilities of any kind existed in Canada. Trained pilots were required and Canada did not possess the necessary machinery to meet the need.

At this point the flying club movement was launched, in brief, for the three-fold purpose of: (a) developing airports; (b) stimulating public interest in flying; (c) training pilots.

The results, widely known, but probably too little appreciated, will stand as a lasting tribute to everyone concerned with the successful operation of the clubs. We say "successful" advisedly because the operation of a flying club is a business as well as a flying operation and no new business was ever launched and carried through a more difficult period of economic conditions, than aviation during the past three years.

To the Federal Government must go due credit for producing a workable scheme rendering necessary tangible support; but even greater appreciation is due the various sources of co-operation and support thus engendered by such leadership. Keeping in mind the purposes of the scheme, a study of the results achieved, particularly in proportion to Government expenditures, will show the latter to be really more in the nature of an investment than an expenditure.

In scores of communities public-spirited citizens, many of them experienced war pilots, have given of their time, effort and money, to a degree perhaps too little appreciated; municipalities, excepting a few somnolent ones, were awakened to the importance of airport facilities and from coast to coast, from Sydney to Vancouver (we would say Victoria but for the silly notion still held by many Victorians that the city should not be disturbed by propeller noise). Some readers will remember that Summerside, P.E.I., once refused to let a railway station into their town. However, the town gravitated to the station! The lesson went home and today Summerside is very busy fixing up a fine airport. (Victorians, please note.); yes, from Sydney to Vancouver, in but four short years, there was developed a network of airports making possible and fairly practicable free intercommunication by air. These airports developed chiefly by the cities have established the practice, or the precedent, call it what you will, that makes smaller communities willing, even anxious, to support similar facilities when the need for them can be found.

What these facilities mean to the pilot flying across the Dominion must be experienced to be fully appreciated. Time alone and the daily use of scheduled air transportation, which is bound to come as surely as night follows day, will bring into the light of public appreciation the great national service rendered by those responsible for opening up Canada's network of airports.

When attention is drawn to the fact that Government-sponsored flying clubs were directly responsible for the development of 18 of our major airports, no more need be said in commendation of the movement from that standpoint alone. Without considering further results, that alone fully justified every dollar of Government expenditure on clubs. But let us turn to another point.

Not more than five or six years ago if an aeroplane succeeded in landing at your town without cracking up in somebody's pasture field, everyone turned out to see the strange contraption. A few of the really bold folk would go up provided they were willing to spend the necessary $5 or $10. Those were the good old days for barnstorming and let us say that we owe a great deal to the barnstormers—most of them—for introducing flying to countless thousands of people under conditions calling for utmost resourcefulness and good piloting.

Enter the flying clubs; the scene changes; fields are opened up all through the country; flying becomes a daily activity—a commonplace thing; newspapers carry more intelligent publicity (thank goodness there has been a decided improvement in that respect); spectacular aerial displays are staged; no one is hurt—as a rule; the public is amazed and possibly a little disappointed. Anyhow we have an entirely different public mind today toward flying. And by the way, one may believe it or not, but until the Air Force flight was taken with the Trans-Canada Air Pageant in 1931, several people—so they told us—did not even know we had an Air Force!

AVIATION REVOLUTIONIZES CANADIAN MINING

E. L. Chicanot, 'The Aeroplane Revolutionizes Canadian Mining', *World Today*, vol. LII (1928), 268-9.

In the era of civil aviation which opened up after the war Canada has not figured very prominently in an international way. This has not been because there has not been a steady and satisfactory progress in aeronautical affairs in the Dominion, but because development has been along lines essentially of domestic value and interest. The record of the post-war period is a noteworthy one, though of greater importance nationally than to the world at large, and in its accomplishment Canadian airmen have been involved in some of the most spectacular and hazardous flying, though this has been done in so unostentatious and routine a manner as to scarcely come to the attention of the Canadian public, much less receive notice beyond the confines of the country.

The peculiarity of Canadian conditions resulted in a development of aviation drastically different from that of any other country. The establishment and extension of passenger and mail services which has taken place elsewhere was not practicable in a country of so few, and such widely scattered centres of population. Instead from the very first the machine of the air was devoted to the greatest national service, the conservation and exploitation of the immense natural resources which constitute the country's wealth and her hope of future greatness. If Canada has not featured in trans-Atlantic and other stunt flying which has attracted international attention it is because she has been too thoroughly engrossed in her own work, setting her own world's records. No country, for instance, can approach Canada in the use of the plane in protective forest patrol. The Dominion record is unsurpassed in the field of aerial survey and mapping.

Another phase of aeronautics is developing in Canada which promises to become yet more important and of greater scope than these, one which has been Dominion pioneered and perfected and which she is going to make peculiarly her own. This is the use of aircraft in mineral exploration and development. Though Canada had a mineral production valued at £53,000,000 in 1927, and has produced some of the greatest mining camps in history, her mineral era is but beginning. But a relatively minute part of the country's tremendous area has as yet been prospected, one might almost say surveyed, and the interest exhibited in mining possibilities today by capitalists from many countries foreshadows immense developments in many far flung sections.

Before this can come about prospecting must be undertaken on a large scale and the minerals found. The search is naturally prosecuted in the wilderness, the movement being steadily further away from the facilities of modern transportation. Far more time is spent in travelling on foot with heavy packs or by canoe than is devoted to the actual search for mineral deposits. It has been keenly realized that this phase of the mining industry is out of line with modern development, and it is here that the assurance of a prosperous future has given the aeroplane its opportunity. It promises very thoroughly to revolutionize the work of mineral exploration in Canada.

Though it seemed extraordinary at the time it was quite along the lines on which Canadian aviation was developing that the first regular aerial service to be established should be from the edge of civilization into the wilderness of a new mining camp. It must have been a unique flying service in the world when inaugurated by enterprising ex-war pilots. It revolutionized altogether preliminary mining development and wrote the opening lines of an entirely new chapter of Canadian mining history. Primarily it substituted a journey of less than an hour spent in comparative comfort in the air for five arduous days of canoe paddling through a forest area, infested by mosquitoes and black flies. It actually did a great deal more.

From its base at Haileybury, on Lake Temiskaming, the company under took to drop passengers or express in any part of the Rouyn gold field where there was a lake, a condition easily met since the area is dotted with bodies of water of varying extent. It carried an average of more than thirty passengers a week, mining promotors, engineers, and prospectors; it supplied this camp so drastically cut off from civilization with fresh fruit and vegetables regularly; the ship of the air transporting over the virgin forest freight of every imaginable description—cats and dogs, dynamite, lumber, iron piping, ammunition, pneumatic drills, and gasoline, and on its homeward trips mineral samples for assay. According to authorities it set the progress of the new camp ahead by at least two years, and when at length after three years the railway reached it, more effectively bridging civilization and the wilderness, such reliance had come to be placed upon the air service that it continued to function, competing with the railway, and carrying out certain phases of transportation in which it had no rival.

It had constituted itself so essential a part of the Quebec field's development that when gold was discovered at Red Lake in Ontario and, following a rush, a new camp came into existence it seemed the most natural thing that a similar service should be established there, flying from the nearest point of railway contact over the wilderness to the scene of the new discovery. With the confidence inspired by the Quebec service it was perhaps an even bigger factor in the advancement of the Ontario camp in its first days. Flying boats took in passengers daily so that in record time hundreds of claims were staked out and the camp's progress got under way. The service has been consistently and satisfactorily maintained since and the experience in the Quebec field has been largely duplicated. The aeroplane is pushing this gold camp ahead as no other agency could.

When last year a much belated interest developed in the mining fields of Manitoba, which quickly resulted in a general development, the aeroplane was immediately called upon to play its part. A company was formed at Winnipeg with one plane at the outset which took passengers or express into any part of Manitoba's mineral area. As development progressed other planes were added and some quite remarkable work was done in the transport of mining machinery and equipment under extremely difficult and dangerous winter conditions. The service has quickly become recognised as a feature of Manitoba mining and the sphere of its activity is steadily extending with the expansion of the northern fields. This summer there are fifteen planes operated by the company in Manitoba's mineral belt, pushing the province's mining industry rapidly ahead.

These services in developing mining camps have been of immense value in more ways than one. They did pioneer flying in the remoter sections of the Dominion and through actual experience amassed a vast amount of valuable information on flying in out-of-the-way places, where facilities are of the most primitive and resourcefulness counts for so much. They were largely responsible, for instance, in developing and perfecting the ski-runner for taking off and landing on ice or snow in winter flying. They also produced the collapsible canoe which can be folded up and transported handily by plane, today considered indispensable to northern flying. They prepared the way for a development of yet greater scope in which the plane moves yet further back in the mining industry and enters upon the work of exploration and prospecting which leads to mineral discoveries. Though this is not entirely new, the work is now for the first time to be undertaken in an organized and comprehensive manner. Though practically nothing has ever been heard of it the plane has already done some pioneer work in mineral prospecting with such satisfactory results as to augur the greatest success for the broader work. Incidentally these expeditions, conducted in the most remote and inaccessible regions of Canada, involve flying under conditions as difficult and hazardous as any yet undertaken.

CANADA'S PLACE IN AN INTERNATIONAL AIR NETWORK

J. F. Grant, 'Definite Air Policy Required', *Canadian Aviation*, vol. VI (June, 1933), 8-9. Reprinted by permission of *Canadian Aviation*.

Has Canada any definite air policy? If so, has any concerted effort been made by the Canadian Government to attain a set objective?

These questions are interdependent, and the force of circumstances alone may soon require that a definite position be taken one way or another. No criticism can be laid at the portals of permanent officials in the Capital, many of whom have strived indefatigably to stimulate interest among our leading legislators in aviation. Having developed a long view of our future, and taking into consideration the advances being made in Great Britain and the United States, they appreciate the importance of plotting a course that will enable this ship to reach her destination without mishap.

Their enthusiasm and pleas fell on deaf ears. They fail to arouse any real response, however, which is rather natural at this time, it may be claimed, as the Dominion is beset with problems of a serious nature and her ministers are seeking every means to effect economies. Her fiscal, railway, unemployment, agricultural and certain industrial conditions demand immediate attention. This must be acknowledged. But, is the natural heritage of Canada to be sacrificed while thoughts are concentrated on the search for an outlet to the commercial impasse?

It is freely admitted that a number of civil aviation companies are daily performing innumerable feats of transportation throughout the Dominion, stimulated by mining activity in regions that cannot be reached with any degree of facility except by aircraft. The aerial map of this country presents a remarkable picture of lines, a veritable network, which extend from rail centres to chains of lakes in the hinterland. In addition, air mail services are operated through territory served inadequately by canoes or dog sledges. These efforts are individually and collectively remarkable, contributing much to the development of Canada and the happiness of her people. It is not enough, however!

There was a time when national unity was the sole aim and object of those responsible for the administration of this country. Such days have passed! This theory and policy was forced to disappear with the introduction of railroads and wireless in its initial stages, but the evolution of the automobile, the radio and the aeroplane has shortened distances, drawn individuals more closely together, and demanded international or world unity. This Dominion occupies a strategical position in the new world by reason of her geographical location, and unless some action is taken at once to establish her superiority, the advantage will be lost.

Full credit must be given to Great Britain and, in particular, to Imperial

Airways, through whose initiative great trunk lines have been created, first to India and then to South Africa. Singapore is the objective for next September, and Port Darwin, Australia, early next year. Some interest has been displayed by these enterprising Britons in Canada and her airways, but, through lack of any definite air policy and east-to-west air service in regular operation, it is generally believed that the country is sadly deficient in aerial transportation and oblivious to the advantages that it should bring her.

The result: Imperial Airways and Pan American Airways, one of the most active and enterprising aerial transportation companies in the world, are discussing ways and means of linking the continents of Europe and North America. London is the natural terminus in the east and New York in the west. Continuing, the line may be extended along routes already being flown across the United States to the Pacific Coast, with San Francisco the immediate objective. Japan and China, whose markets may be further expanded and developed, though the former country is anxious naturally to preserve those of the former Celestial Empire for herself, will be connected ultimately by air with North America, as the Far East is the ultimate terminus of this air route from England.

It will be noticed that Canada does not appear in this prospective picture, though one or more landings may be effected in British Columbia. Unless action is taken, and soon, she will remain permanently out of the picture. Montreal is the natural distribution centre for transatlantic mails. Canadian territory provides the shortest route to the Pacific and so to the Orient. This should not be forgotten, and every effort should be made to inform our friends in England of this position and of our desire to co-operate with them in the establishment of a through-service to the Far East.

Canada called the Imperial Economic Conference last year in an effort to promote and foster closer relations within the British Commonwealth of Nations. Subjects pertaining to aviation and air policy were discussed by the Air Communications Committee, of which Lieut.-Col. F. C. Shelmerdine, Director of Civil Aviation in Great Britain, was a member. An admirable report, pertaining to a transatlantic steamship-aeroplane service, was prepared and signed by representatives of the United Kingdom, the Irish Free State, Newfoundland and Canada. It would appear, however, that this report has been shelved.

Canada is anxious to co-operate with the Mother Country, from whose stock the larger proportion of her people are descended, but she must make an effort to protect her own interests. It seems that British aviation companies prefer to "play" with the United States instead of Canada, and there can be little doubt but that the 125,000,000 souls comprising the population of that country offer a greater incentive to the establishment of a transatlantic service than the 10 millions of this Dominion. Nevertheless, the thickly inhabited cities and towns of the United States can be reached with equal facility from Europe by way of Montreal, provided some means of conveying passengers, mails and express between the Canadian metropolis and the Atlantic seaboard is evolved.

A simple scheme was prepared by the Air Communications Committee at the Imperial Economic Conference, whereby the Strait of Belle Isle, Cabot Strait or Halifax would be linked with Moncton, depending on the season, and so with Montreal, but the decision of the Canadian Government to curtail all expenditure on aviation beyond that absolutely necessary to provide for an adequate mail service to isolated areas caused this to be abandoned, at least for the moment.

In the meantime, however, a commendable effort is being made to establish emergency landing fields across the length of the country, following the projected transcontinental air route, and to enlarge existing aerodromes. Labor is being provided through the unemployment relief programme conceived by the Departments of National Defence and Labor, a dual purpose thereby being served. But, unless something is done now to demonstrate that Canada is in a position to contribute something toward the establishment and operation of a short section of some thousand miles of an air line from England, the opportunity will be lost forever.

Readers of "Canadian Aviation" are urged to discuss the whole subject with Parliamentarians on any and every occasion. Once their interest has been aroused and some knowledge of the true situation is learned, they cannot help but be stimulated by the prospect of Canada as an integral unit in an international airway. Strong support must be forthcoming if the air future of Canada is to be set on a firm foundation, and little time lost in erecting the structure according to a definite plan.

THE AUTOMOBILE

THE GREATEST INVENTION SINCE THE LOCOMOTIVE

Official Report of the Debates of the House of Commons of the Dominion of Canada, II (1926), pp. 1997-8.

[C. G. Coote] The subject dealt with in this resolution is one of very great importance to this country. Canada is a land stretching 4,000 miles from east to west. We cover an immense territory. We have a population of nine million odd scattered over this large area. For that reason transportation is one of the greatest questions confronting us today. The greatest improvement in transportation facilities since the invention of the steam locomotive is the automobile, both freight and passenger. The greatest competitor that Canada has to-day is the United States. The United States has motor trucks available to her population at two-thirds the price at which they can be purchased by the people in Canada. The United States has one motor car for every six of her population, while Canada has one to every fourteen of her population. On account of our sparse settlement in this country, we really require more motor trucks and automobiles proportionally than the people of the United States. The only reason that I can see why we have only one car to fourteen of our population, and the United States one to every six is that cars are too expensive in this country and the people cannot afford to buy them. The Ford Times a year ago published this statement:

The development of the automotive industry is only a logical sequence of the demand for transportation facilities, which have always played a major part in opening up a land to its fullest possibilities. With vast unopened areas in our land of huge distances, proper railroad service could not be a paying or a practical proposition. The need for transportation still remains and is of prime importance in changing these waste spaces into productive areas. No country can rise to its full height of importance without adequate transportation.

What is the truth? Let us apply such facts as are available to the solution of this involved problem.

The automobile industry could never have attained its present tremendous totals over a period of 23 years had not its product more than justified itself economically.

Its proper use lengthens life, increases efficiency, stimulates general business and promotes the wealth and stability of the nation.

There we have in a paper published by the largest manufacturers of automobiles in Canada a very good argument as to why automobiles and trucks should be cheaper in this country—because they are so necessary to development and production. Because of the development of our social and economic life, cars to-day are a necessity for a great many of our people, particularly doctors, preachers, commercial travellers and farmers. It has been estimated that farmers in western Canada, or in Alberta, live on an average ten miles from a railway, and yet only about one-third of them own motor cars. While on a visit to British Columbia last year I noticed that practically all the fruit which was being delivered to packing houses in one of the large fruit centres of British Columbia was being delivered in motor trucks. I did not see one rig drawn by horses. These men have to pay practically 50 per cent more for their motor trucks than their competitors to the south of the boundary. In one town in my constituency this fall there were fifty-seven men delivering wheat to the elevator with motor trucks. Some of them were hauling the wheat a distance of twenty-eight miles. There are many others still hauling wheat with horses. I wish hon. members in this House could realize what a boon it would be to these farmers if they could afford to own motor trucks and deliver their wheat with them. It is impossible for a railway company to build railways within ten miles of all our settlers, and any man who has to haul his wheat, his cream and all his produce more than ten miles to market is certainly badly in need of a motor truck. For these and other reasons which I shall enumerate I think it is the duty of the House, without further delay, to see that some reduction is made in the price of motor trucks, so far at least as this can be attained through a reduction of the tariff. Henry Ford was quoted last year in the Ford Times as saying:

The great trouble with farming is that it involves too much unnecessary work. There is no reason why agriculture may not hope to come abreast of the other industries in the near future, if the farmer will turn his attention to modern industrial methods, instead of to the problem of borrowing money. There is no food scarcity. The problem is not one of how to increase production, and thereby pile up a surplus for speculators to play with, but how to simplify production and distribution so that less human energy shall be wasted in the process.

One of the ways to solve this farm problem is to reduce the price of motor trucks. I have never yet heard any suggestion in this House as to how it could be done unless we reduce the tariff. The low-priced automobile and the motor truck is the greatest boon which has come to farmers since labour-saving machinery was invented. Again I would quote from the Ford Times:

Autos Reduce The Farm Migration
Easy to Get to Town Now; Just a Case of Starting the Family Car
The farm telephone, the coming of labour-saving devices and the low-price auto are three of the greatest factors in checking the admittedly large migration from the farm.

Probably no mechanical invention has done so much as the low-priced automobile to lessen the monotony of farm life, particularly for people living on the prairies a long distance from the railways, and nothing has done so much to relieve the monotony of life for the farm women. Many of these people, prior to the coming of the automobile, were limited to their own farms. They are too far from town to drive there with a horse and rig. As I said before, approximately one-third of the farmers in Alberta are able to own motor cars, and I think the only reason the other two-thirds do not own them is that they are too dear at the present time. The Ford Times said recently:

Every sure enough farm needs three automobiles—any farmer with a family will vouch for that and that number is his goal.

Then it goes on to show that he needs a truck, a roadster and a Ford sedan to take him to town in bad weather.

I would be pretty well satisfied, Mr. Speaker, if we had on an average one automobile to each farm, and I should like to say to the editor of the Ford Times that there is only one reason why there are not more automobiles on the farm, that reason being that the Ford Company have kept the price too high.

A MENACE TO OUR RAILWAYS

Official Report of the Debates of the House of Commons of the Dominion of Canada, 1 (1926), pp. 478-80.

Mr. w. f. maclean (South York): I want to spend a few minutes in reviewing the present transportation problem in Canada, more especially in relation to the Canadian National Railways and certain other interests of the country. If we desire to arrive at a reasonable solution of our transportation difficulties in Canada I think we should consider the subject under two heads, first, transportation by land, and next, transportation by water. In regard to the first, we have of course the Canadian National Railways and the Canadian Pacific, these two systems providing the people of the country with freight trains and passenger services. Now, that freight train service may or may not change, but the passenger service in Canada is in process of a great revolution of which we cannot fail to take note. In this connection I would observe in passing that the Canadian people are not at all satisfied with the present passenger service and the suggestion is being made that there should be substituted for our present passenger trains, which are more or less lengthy and which run once or twice a day, the individual electric car, complete in itself, without any locomotive and running by its own motor. This car can carry up to seventy passengers and has baggage and express accommodation and accommodation for mails. It can make from thirty to fifty miles an hour and frequent trips throughout the day are possible. If our railways in Canada, both the Canadian National and the Canadian Pacific, wish to retain their passenger traffic they must use these small cars and give the people a more frequent service throughout the day. As regards freight trains, I shall deal with that question later.

   In the matter of land transportation there is another agency or service which is rapidly developing in Canada, expanding enormously, and it constitutes a menace to our railways; I refer to the competition of the automobile and the motor truck on our new highways in Ontario, Quebec and other provinces. The automobiles and motor trucks are securing nearly all of the local traffic by which the railways have so far been sustained, and where that competition is going to end I am at a loss to know. To show how efficient this motor service has become, I have only to say that many

Toronto business houses are able to have their telephone orders given to outlying towns filled in the space of a few hours or half a day. An order is telephoned say to the town of Kitchener from a house in Toronto and the reply comes back that the motor truck will be at the customer's door that afternoon or, if the order comes in too late, the next morning; and this obviates the use of a railway warehouse, besides cartage and so forth. It does away with the delay which is unavoidable when freight has to go through the railway freight shed. I know a good many men now living in Toronto who prefer to travel to Montreal by means of their costly but very efficient automobiles, and even the man with the little Ford or in the little motor bus is now competing with our railways. Where this competition is going to end I do not know, but it is already a serious proposition for the railways, and I am certain that unless the railways themselves adopt these new forces they are going to lose their main business, the business from which they derive their best revenue, that is, the business of local transportation in its various forms.

But there is something else that also threatens our railways. A very able American announced the other day—and he said that he had ample financial backing—that he and his associates were going to build a new right of way on a concrete foundation, that there would be a complete separation of grades, and that on this right of way they would run rubber tired cars and would give a transportation service that could be speeded up to one hundred miles an hour without any trouble. If I am to believe what the press say about it, that form of competition will be in operation within a year or two.

GOOD ROADS AND THE HOME

Canadian Good Roads Conference, 1921 (Montreal, 1921), pp. 5-8.

We have instituted a propaganda in Saskatchewan to get the people back to the farm, and the remedy for all the unrest in the world today, for Bolshevism—and in my opinion the British citizen has no use for Bolshevism—for the high cost of living, is to direct legislation towards the home; make conditions such that the home will be attractive to the man and his family; that the man may fit in his proper niche and carry out and solve his problems, whether he be living in western or eastern Canada.

What then is the thing that touches nearest to the home? I have tried many times to classify those things that touch nearest to the home and I have come back to this, that the thing nearest to the home is transportation, and the facilities we provide those in the home of getting out and seeing their neighbors; the facilities provided for the head of the home to get his product to market in order not to get 99 cents on the dollar for the labor he puts into his work, but to get 100 cents on the dollar for the labor he puts into his little institution, whatever that little institution may be.

So that I say the first consideration—especially out here in this western country, where the distances are great—towards making conditions in the home better is to provide for those homes a good utility highway that will serve the purposes that are in need at the present time. We believe out in Saskatchewan we should do that in order that we may get all those different peoples to come not only to understand our institutions, but that we should get them in the frame of mind where the other propaganda we may institute throughout the country to make British citizens out of them, may sink well in; that they may love their country because of what the country does for their home. That seems to be one of our first considerations.

A word about conditions we have been up against in that country and some of the problems that face us now for solution. I was born in London, Ontario, and was brought up in the wilderness in Huron county. I remember when I was a very young boy we went up there along the line road known as the London road; and when I go back to those days I find that settlement followed the highways; that the settlement gradually came in round the highway. In Saskatchewan and in this western country the conditions that obtained were absolutely opposed to that. From 1905 to the time of the war the great population that came into this country, came in all, as it were, in a day, and settled on the open prairie. Hundreds of families came in with us. Roads we knew nothing about. We did not know where they were. Roads were an after consideration. I tell you this for the purpose of accentuating the fact how necessary a thing to the home today in Saskatchewan is a good highway. And if we want to get at the essence of patriotism; to make these people love their country today; we will have to get down to business and spend immense sums of money not only on lateral roads but on good highways; on providing proper transportation for those people.

Our political institutions are built upon a well-known principle. If I outlined that principle briefly I should put it in this way: The essence of your interest is in your home. There is a little less foggy interest in your community. You have a little less foggy interest in your provincial situation, and a less foggy interest in your Dominion situation. That is the principle of our federal institution. We first built upon this principle in our highway problem; that our first interest is in the community in order that we may link up all the people in the community and help the community spirit. We have got past that now. We find we must branch out, and if we are going to make a community province we must endeavor to link those communities together. And we have got largely past that. Our great problem now is: If it is good for the home, if it is good for the community, if it is good for the province—if we are going to have a united Canada we must get greater in viewpoints; we must endeavor to reach out farther, and link up the different provincial units in order to have a concentrated British Dominion sentiment. That is the problem we have to solve; that is the problem we are trying to solve, and that is the problem towards which we are directing all our energies.

I am pleased to say I am carrying back to Saskatchewan two things that will help us to solve these problems. One—I am going back there with an increased British sentiment. Another thing I am going back with is a lot of valuable information that will be of use to me in helping to solve these problems, and in helping to make a greater Canada tomorrow than we have today. I hope these things obtain in your minds; and that when you leave this convention and go back to your different provinces, you will take those two things home with you; and I know you have that energy and that faith in your country to make the very best use of them possible.

AGRICULTURE BETWEEN THE WARS

MARQUIS WHEAT

C. E. Saunders, 'Cereal Breeding on the Dominion Experimental Farm During the Past Decade', *Trans. Roy. Soc. Can.*, vol. VII (1913), 151-5. Reprinted by permission of the Royal Society of Canada.

When in the year 1903 the experimental work in cereals and some other grains was removed from the Director's immediate care and organized into a separate Division (in charge of the writer of this paper) two principal tasks were immediately undertaken. The first was the careful and systematic study of the large mass of material which had been accumulated during the previous years by importation from foreign countries and by cross-breeding at Ottawa and some of the branch experimental farms. Though a good deal of selection had been done, and many varieties of grain, both new and old, had been rejected, the material had been accumulating at a rapid rate, and required not only thorough study but drastic elimination as well. The second task was to cross the best new and old varieties in as many different and promising pairs as possible. . . .

Beyond all doubt Marquis wheat was the most important discovery which the writer made in dealing with the descendants of the early crosses. Some account of the pedigree and achievements of this variety will perhaps be appropriate, in view of the world-wide attention which it has attracted.

Marquis wheat comes from a cross made in the year 1892 by Dr. A. P.

Saunders who was acting for part of the year as one of the Director's assistants. The parents of the new wheat were Hard Red Calcutta (female) and Red Fife (male). The cross was made on one of the branch experimental farms and the cross-bred seeds, or their progeny, were subsequently transferred to Ottawa. Here some selection was done, but the work was not carried far enough to separate out simple, fixed types. It was therefore a mixture, lacking in uniformity, which came into the possession of the writer when he took charge of the Cereal Division. By a careful study of individual plants selected from the plot, and especially by applying the chewing test to ascertain the gluten strength and probable bread-making value, radical differences in quality were found, and a few of the most promising plants were used as the foundation of new strains. These strains were propagated (each separately) for some years until they had been sufficiently studied to ascertain which was the best. This best strain was named Marquis. Its high bread-making strength and colour of flour were demonstrated in the baking tests made by the writer at Ottawa in the early months of 1907, and all the surplus seed was at once sent to the Experimental Farm at Indian Head, Sask. for propagation. . . .

It will be seen from the above account that we do not know the exact year when Marquis wheat came into existence; but it was probably between 1895 and 1902. It remained, however, mixed with other related strains until isolated in 1903. It was first grown in pure condition in 1904, when a few seeds were sown in a sheltered garden on the Central Experimental Farm. But its fine qualities were very imperfectly known at that time; and it was not until the baking tests of 1907 were completed that the decision was reached to send Marquis to Saskatchewan for trial under prairie conditions. The response of Marquis to its new environment was phenomenal. The year 1907 was decidedly unfavourable for most varieties of wheat owing to the prevalence of rust and of cool, wet weather. Marquis had a great advantage, because of its early-ripening habit and its ability to resist rust to a certain extent. It yielded more than any other sort, both in the plots and in the fields. In the plots it gave 32 bushels per acre, while the old standard variety, Red Fife, gave 12 bushels. In the field Marquis yielded at the rate of 42 bushels per acre, and stood far ahead of any other sort.

The following season Marquis was tried also on the Experimental Farm at Brandon, where it succeeded exceptionally well. In subsequent years it was distributed to farmers all over Canada. While it has given good results at almost all points, its greatest successes have been in the provinces of Saskatchewan, Alberta and Manitoba, especially in Saskatchewan.

Taking the average of the past six years (1907 to 1912 inclusive) Marquis has produced 35 per cent. more crop than Red Fife in the uniform trial plots at Indian Head. At Brandon in a test for five years (1908 to 1912 inclusive) Marquis has yielded 7 per cent. more than Red Fife.

The chief points in favour of Marquis for these provinces are its productiveness, its earliness in ripening (generally from 6 to 10 days earlier than Red Fife), its strength of straw, its comparative freedom from rust, the heavy weight per bushel and fine appearance of the grain, and the excellent colour and baking-strength of the flour produced from it.

The best field crops of Marquis on the experimental farms have been obtained at Brandon and Indian Head. In 1909 a field of 4½ acres at Brandon gave more than 52 bushels per acre. In 1910 a field of 5⅓ acres at Indian Head gave a little over 53 bushels per acre. Several very high plot records have been secured with Marquis, the most remarkable being at the rate of over 81 bushels per acre on a plot of one-fortieth of an acre at Indian Head in 1912. This probably constitutes a world's record for spring wheat. . . .

It is difficult to overestimate the value of this new wheat to the farmers of the prairie provinces. Without attempting to give any exact calculation, one needs only to mention that in the year 1912 there were grown in these three provinces about 183,000,000 bushels of wheat, a large proportion of which was Red Fife. If Marquis had been sown instead, the yield would have been on the average at least one-fifth more, and the wheat would have been as a rule of a higher grade. One-fifth more crop and a few cents better price per bushel would have meant a very large sum of money. In 1911 the advantage of Marquis would have been even greater than in 1912. I am happy to state that Marquis is now being so widely grown that the disasters of 1911 will not be repeated unless a still more unfavourable season should at some time occur.

THE PROBLEM OF RURAL DEPOPULATION

W. C. Good, *Production and Taxation in Canada, from the Farmer's Standpoint* (Toronto, 1919), pp. xi-21.

Of all the industries that contribute to human welfare Agriculture is undoubtedly the most important. And this is true despite the fact that others may be of more immediate importance in serving man's higher mental and moral life. It is true because Agriculture is more than the greatest and most fundamental of our primary industries: Agriculture also furnishes the human material—the men and women—for the other industries and vocations. It is a notable fact that the great majority of leaders in various walks of life come immediately or almost immediately from the farms, and that the country is the seed-bed of the whole population. Whatever may be the case in the future, city life has been, and is yet, self-extinguishing. Were it not for the influx of fresh and virile blood from the country, city-life would disappear from inherent weakness, and that much of civilization which is dependent thereon would disappear also. Rural life, therefore, is the permanent source from which all life springs: all families and all classes come more or less immediately from those most closely associated with Old Mother Earth.

This notable fact is not accidental. There are reasons for it. In the first place Agriculture (including, of course, the minor industries of lumbering and fishing) has almost a monopoly of *fresh air and sunshine*, two things of paramount importance in the building up of a strong manhood and womanhood. The farm also has the best opportunity of furnishing the freshest and most abundant supply of *good food*, equally important, with fresh air and sunshine, in the development of the rising generation.

In the second place, farm life and work is essentially *domestic*, requiring the co-operation of all members of the family. In this respect agriculture is perhaps unique. The city man's work is generally divorced from his home and family, and an early break-up of family ties and interests is encouraged, both by a separation of activities, and also by the proximity of multitudinous distractions and diversions. In fact it is extremely difficult to maintain home and family life in the city. In the country, on the other hand, the farm home is the centre of the farm work, and there is ample scope for all members of the family to co-operate in carrying on the work of the farm and home. Little children fill their places happily and usefully at a very early age, unconsciously learning many things, and growing in skill, ability and willingness for practical co-operation. No one who does not know intimately the possibilities of farm life in this respect can fully appreciate the tremendous advantages which agriculture possesses over other occupations in the education of children and in the development of some of the most important virtues through family co-operation. . . .

To those who live in Rural Canada with their eyes open, it is not necessary to explain, or dilate upon, the nature of our rural problem. To others I may say that the essential features of the problem are, first, that it has become profitable, indeed, almost necessary, for farmers to curtail production; and, second, that the satisfactions of farm life have not been sufficient to retain in the country the requisite number of people to maintain in proper condition rural institutions. Nor, while undoubtedly aggravated by, is the situation in any way justly attributable to war conditions.

Rural depopulation has been a marked feature of Canadian life for several decades past. . . .

As a matter of fact the campaign of educational work carried on under the auspices of our various departments of agriculture with such assiduity for the last thirty years has been powerless to stem the tide cityward. It has done much good but it has failed to meet the needs of the situation. It has been good so far as it has gone, but it has not gone far enough. It has touched only the *production* of wealth, and has ignored the question of *distribution*. Without equitable distribution production will halt. No man will sow where he cannot reap, unless he is enslaved; and if, all things considered, the rewards of other occupations are greater than those of farming, farmers will drift to other callings, and agriculture will suffer. Frank recognition of this fundamental truth would brush away many cobwebs of fallacy which now blind and confuse our minds; would clear the ground of unessentials, and enable us to perceive clearly the vital basis of the whole matter.

However, I do not wish to minimize the good results of education for *Better Farming, Better Business* and *Better Living*. Without it our plight would have been far worse. Every farmer should aim to utilize as much as he possibly can all technical information pertaining to the business of production. He should study soils, plant life, live stock and all the other multifarious things with which the farmer has to deal. He should keep in touch with the best farm practice, and he should inform himself as to the latest results of scientific investigation. He should discuss farm methods with his neighbors, and also gain others' experience by reading farm papers. All this is necessary in the revival of agriculture.

Of even more importance is *Better Business*, which consists of good farm management so far as the individual farmer is concerned, and co-operation so far as farmers generally are concerned. The problem of efficient management is one of extraordinary intricacy, which those not intimately acquainted with actual conditions may altogether fail to realize. Volumes have been written upon this aspect of farming alone, and there is no other industry that requires a greater degree of intelligence or better judgment. So far as co-operative methods go, the time has gone by when the farmer can live for, or to, himself. Other industrial classes are organized and he must organize. Individually he cannot now either buy or sell to advantage. Co-operation has become imperative.

In the revival of agriculture *Better Business* is of special importance because it need not wait for any political changes, or any general change in economic conditions. *Better Business* begins at home, and has made progress everywhere in spite of, or perhaps by reason of, the greatest difficulties. So far as it goes it will make for *Better Returns*, and thus fulfil the fundamental condition of industrial progress. Sir Horace Plunket, one of the greatest leaders in agricultural co-operation, says: "Better farming means the application of modern science to the practice of agriculture; Better Business is the no less necessary application of modern commercial methods to the business side of the farming industry. Better Living is the building up in rural communities of a domestic and social life which will withstand the growing attraction of the modern city. This three-fold scheme of reform covers the whole ground, and will become the basis of the country life movement to be suggested later. But in the working out of the general scheme there must be one important change in the order of procedure: *Better Business must come first.*"

MECHANIZATION AS A SOLUTION TO DEPRESSION AGRICULTURAL PROBLEMS

Andrew Stewart, 'The Economy of Machine Production in Agriculture', *Canadian Congress Journal*, vol. x (1931), 32-3. Reprinted by permission of the Canadian Labour Congress.

The economic welfare of Canada is so closely related to the conditions of the agricultural industry that the revolutionary changes taking place recently in that industry are of paramount importance. The development of the gasoline tractor, and, more recently, the introduction of the combine into Western Canada have resulted in radical changes in the technique of production, and the present depression through which agriculture is passing, has stimulated interest in the mechanization of farming. Two methods of meeting the existing situation are commonly under discussion, viz., rationalization and stabilization. Stabilization of prices is being advocated as a method of protecting grain producers from the adverse effects of the depression. Rationalization refers to a process by which producers may adjust the internal management of the farm to present circumstances and safeguard their farm business against similar occurrences in future. The former is a doubtful temporary expedient, the latter a permanent change calculated to secure stability for the industry by adaptation to the recent improvements in agricultural machinery.

Some improvements in farm machinery exert their influence on the existing farm unit. Such machines as feed carriers, mechanical milkers, manure carriers, stationary gas engines, etc., lighten the labor on the farm and save time. The use of improved machinery results in more efficient execution of farm operations. Manure spreaders permit of more economical utilization of animal refuse; silage cutters and feed grinders eliminate waste in feeding. Improved tillage machines and seed drills control weeds, secure a better seed bed, more uniform seeding at a more even depth and result in higher yields. Spraying machines for orchards and potato fields increase yields, and machines for dusting cotton and handling corn forage are instrumental in meeting emergencies occasioned by the attacks of the boll-weevil and the corn-borer. Modern haymaking machinery enables the farmer to take advantage of favorable weather and prevents deterioration of the crop; and dairy equipment—separators, testers, refrigerators, churns and butter-workers—improve the quality of the product.

By saving time and labor, reducing losses and increasing the production of better quality products on the individual farm, machinery secures increased returns to the operator.

Other improvements enable the available labor force to operate a larger acreage and can be used more economically on units larger than those previously existing. Where tractors, combines, corn pickers, cotton sleds, two-row cultivators, etc., are introduced, a change in the farm organization is necessary.

Equipment of this kind has resulted in an enormous saving in time and labor. A tractor operator with a five-bottom, 14" plough can turn over more land in one hour than the same man with a walking plough could cover in a day. Ten days of one man's time are required with a one-horse outfit to cultivate the same acreage that the four-row outfit can cultivate in one day. In 1830, with hand production methods, 32 hours of man labor were required to produce 10 bushels of wheat. In Montana an acre of land has been summerfallowed and a crop of wheat removed the following year with 2.5 hours of man labor. Modern machinery has reduced the labor of husking and cribbing corn 20 to 30 hours per acre. The labor in 1 ton of hay in bales was reduced between 1860 and 1894 from 35½ hours to 11½ hours.

This reduction in labor has resulted in a larger acreage operated per worker. Since 1850 the average acres of improved land per worker in the United States has increased steadily from 30 acres to 49 acres in 1925, and the figures for Canada show that between 1881 and 1891, acres of farm land per worker increased 95%, improved land per worker 105% and crop acres per worker 109%.

This tendency has increased the productivity of those employed in agriculture. The American farm worker produces about three times as much as do similar workers in important European countries.

Not only may the farmer increase his physical volume of production by the use of machine methods, but, where the farm organization is adapted to the new equipment, operating costs per unit of product may be reduced. According to North Dakota figures "the combine method saves approximately $1.75 per acre when 600 acres are straight combined and about $1.25 when the crop is windrowed and picked up."

The ability to save labor, extend the crop acreage, increase production and at the same time reduce costs enables the individual farmer to secure higher net income. C. D. Kinsman says of conditions in the United States: "In general the farm operators in the States having a high utilization of power per worker are shown to have a correspondingly high net income. This circumstance would indicate that the extensive use of power and labor saving equipment, if effectively employed, is extremely profitable." That Canadian producers have also profited by the adoption of machine methods is indicated by the fact that whereas the average value of goods produced by each farm worker amounted to $509 in 1901, this had increased to $1,340 in 1921, or by 163%.

The relatively high standard of living found among agriculturists on this continent, in comparison with conditions in European or Asiatic countries is maintained largely through the benefits of improved machinery.

Grain farming is pre-eminently adapted to machine methods of production and conditions in Canada favor that type of agriculture. Approximately two-thirds of the agricultural land devoted to field crops is in the prairie provinces, where topography, climate and soil are conducive to extensive methods. These conditions are accentuated by the relative abundance of land, and the small population which makes labor scarce and necessitates producing for distant markets.

For these reasons agriculture in Canada has developed through the utilization of machinery and a steady increase in the size of farms. Past history and present experience demonstrate that success in mechanized farming can only be achieved by adapting the farm to the improved equipment.

Canadian agriculture is passing through a transition period to-day. The rapid increase in the efficiency of inanimate power machines, and the combine, which tractors have made possible, are slowly revolutionizing grain production on the prairies and the effect is being felt in all phases of the industry. Sales of tractors and combines demonstrate their growing use, and to secure the advantages of these machines reconstruction of farm organization is necessary. It has been authoritatively stated that successful combine operators in Saskatchewan are those who adjust their farming methods to the use of the machines, and the prime necessity for economical operation of both tractors and combines is a larger acreage than is found on the average horse and binder farm.

The figures of the 1926 Census of the three prairie provinces indicate that the movement to increase the size of farms is proceeding rapidly....

The evidence leads to the conclusion that the enlarging of the family-sized farm will continue until the maximum acreage that can be operated from one point is reached. When that time arrives, and during the process, managers with a business bent will seek to enlarge their operations by the type of organization which permits of division of labor.

To secure the adjustments, which increasing mechanization necessitates, with the minimum of loss, requires further investigation of many problems, including capitalization and methods of financing; the relative economy of different sizes of machines; the economical farm units for the available equipment; the organization of these units and the combinations of machinery which secure the greatest economy.

Increasing mechanization of agriculture in Canada is inevitable, but its major effects will be most evident in certain areas. Grain-growing regions provide the most favorable conditions, but the economical utilization of large machinery is limited by topography and, to some extent, by climate. For these reasons, the adaptation to machine methods of production will be most apparent in the level, open-prairie regions of Western Canada. This will lead to a concentration of live-stock farming in the park land areas, and where the topography is rough or broken.

CONCLUSION.

The history of agriculture demonstrates that operating costs can be reduced, production per worker stimulated, standards of living raised and national wealth increased, by the adaptation of farm organization to improvements in equipment, and the increased size of farms made possible by machine methods of production in agriculture.

AN AGRICULTURAL CORPORATION

G. L. Smith, 'The Grievous Plight of Canadian Agriculture', *Saturday Night*, June 4, 1932. Reprinted by permission of *Saturday Night*.

Agriculture, the foundation upon which the whole of Canada rests, is in bad shape. Again and again in years gone by it has had to be patched up, and while it may, with repairing, weather the present storm, eventually it will require complete rebuilding because it never went down to a sound footing in the first place. Each depression weakens the structure, each calls for a longer period of recuperation. Reconstruction cannot be long delayed and fortunately is not only possible but a definite path is suggested by the more recent trend in industrial development. . . .

. . . Nearly half of our population resides on farms and more than a quarter of the remainder are employed in industries that are handling or processing farm products or are manufacturing things for the farmer to buy.

And agriculture, the giant supporting this burden, is sick. This very sickness, however, may prove a salvation because at such times we are often forced to adopt certain long overdue corrective measures that lead eventually to permanent good health.

There have been previous depressions. There was one just after the war, another just before it and a third in the 'nineties of the last century. In fact as far as Canadian farmers are concerned, the past is largely made up of bad times with only an occasional profitable period when a large war sent the prices of food stuffs soaring. Money made then helped to finance the depression following. But it only helped, the account was never balanced.

If Canadian farmers had to buy back the fertility they have taken out of their soil since this country has been settled, or if in Ontario they were only called upon to restore buildings, fences, and other equipment, well over ninety per cent. of them could not do it. While we on this continent have been inclined to look down on the European peasant, we have to admit that his soil is as rich to-day as in his grandfather's time and his buildings are in good repair. Though he has been farming intensively ten times as long as we have been here, his plant has not been milked or even neglected.

Starting off with free or low-priced virgin land we were able to live in much better style than the man across the Atlantic though even with our immense initial advantage we were unable to put him out of business. We paid little attention to the basis of all farming operations, the soil, and as a result our yields per acre, especially in the West, are but a fraction of what they are in Denmark, Belgium, Holland and France. Our cost of production, therefore, was always high and as the cheap land vanished and the fertility became depleted, it began to go higher.

While actual costs vary with locality, crop and management, it is generally admitted that wheat, hogs, beef cattle, milk and most other farm products cannot be grown profitably at present prices in this country and yet no sane observer can see any prospect of materially better values in the near future. In the meantime farmers are living on their capital, chiefly the fertility of the land and the improvement in the ways of fences, buildings and equipment supplied during one of those rare periods when something over a bare living was being made.

But both these resources, already strained by the depression which followed the war boom, are getting low. A motor trip through almost any section of rural Canada reveals the fact that probably less than $100 in repairs has been spent by the average farmer in the last five years and any business man knows that depreciation on frame and part frame buildings, which could not be replaced for at least $6,000, must amount to several times that amount in a single year. Houses and barns have gone unpainted, fences are falling to pieces, roofs are leaking, machinery has been patched with hay wire, and commercial fertilizers, which have never had more than a limited sale among specialty farmers, though used universally in Europe, are not being purchased.

Spasmodically, too, the fundamental fault of Canadian agriculture, excessive cost of production, has been attacked. Machinery has been installed, and the output per man raised, but this development also seems to have fallen down with grievous results to the manufacturers of the machines. There was nothing wrong with the new type of farm implements; the trouble lay in the fact that they were simply grafted onto the old agriculture. Farming was never reorganized to accommodate them. . . .

. . . Eliminating waste in costs of distribution will help, but this alone is not enough, there will have to be a lowering, a drastic lowering, in the cost of production.

As ordinary co-operation does not seem to have worked, the most natural thing is to turn to a solution among our highly-organized urban industries, where costs are reduced by mass production, expert direction and proper location, and where the general business is regulated through trade associations.

In the last 50 years there has been a remarkable industrial development in this country. Individual railroads, mills, foundries, banks, stores and practically everything but the farms have been grouped together. Experts who under the old system would have had to confine their efforts to the management of one small store, and in addition to the duties they liked and were specially qualified to carry out, would have had to do other routine work as well, are now in charge of chains. Manufacturing and distributing charges are only a fraction of what they once were. But the size of the farm has shown little change. Is there any real reason why the system which has proven so successful in the cities should not prove just as successful along the concession lines?

Suppose we select ten typical Ontario farms and merge them into a single unit. This will give us practically a thousand acres, with the good level land in large blocks and rough pasture areas more or less together. In Russia I understand the plan is to put the villagers into apartment-houses but we Christians while willing to love our neighbors prefer more insulation than a six-inch wall. In our plan we will allow each farmer in this company we are forming to retain his house and about an acre of ground about it, but the remainder of the farm will be thrown into a common pool with the absolute ownership vested in a joint-stock company.

Actual valuation of the land would be fixed by a committee and shares in the company based and issued accordingly. Fencing and lanes would be adjusted immediately and the whole block farmed as a single unit. At first barns and other buildings would remain as they were in order to keep capitalization down to the lowest practical level, but gradually as they wore out one or two central structures would take their place. In the same way the old orchards would be operated as long as practical but all new planting would be confined to one spot, the best orchard land on the whole thousand acres.

Each original owner would become a managing director in the new company, receiving dividends on the amount of stock held and also a salary based on the work done. Each would have certain specific duties, those most fitted for the raising of feed, naturally taking charge of that end of the business, and those with a liking for poultry, the chicken end, and so on. With buildings, orchards, and some long-term crops scattered there would not be the reduction in costs that would be effected eventually, but there would be a very direct saving at the start. On your average hundred-acre farm today, there are three horses, a binder, mower, rake, and other farm implements, usually of the smallest size. Some of this equipment is only used ten days in the year. The horses spend 75 per cent. of their days in the pasture or stable, and the tractor, which we now find on every third Ontario farm is used even less than the horses. In the small fields close to ten per cent. of the time is taken up in actually turning machinery around.

When the farms are merged most of this wastage would be eliminated. About half the horses could be dispensed with and tractors used to supplement the work of the remainder in the rush season by operating in two shifts, 16 hours a day. As the original machinery wore out, and in most cases this would not be long, it would be replaced by the modern, wide machines, and two shifts adopted during harvesting and seeding, in order to get something like maximum results out of these machines. Costs of growing feed on these new farms could be reduced fully 25 per cent. right at the start and still further as consolidation and development went on.

Your average individual farmer spends an hour on the road daily. Under company farming, one large truck and possibly a small one would handle all transportation. Supplies like coal, cement, lumber and fertilizer would be purchased in carlots and at carlot prices. By being responsible for only one end of the business, and that the one for which he had the most ability and liking, there would be an opportunity for greater efficiency and expansion. Regular hours, the thing that has attracted more country people to the city than anything else, could be adopted except perhaps during the rush season, although in this case, two shifts might serve the purpose.

Advantage could be taken of the latest labor saving devices because on a farm this size there would be a chance of making profitable use of machinery. Surplus milk and other products could be manufactured into less perishable things right on the farm or at least in plant controlled by a group of these company farms. The trouble with the small-sized holding today is that there is a little of this and a little of that with not enough of one thing to fully employ a man. One jumps from one job to another with loss of time and hurried work. The new farm would allow concentration.

A BRIEF GUIDE TO FURTHER READING

There are very few studies in the history of Canadian technology and fewer still that deal with technology and society. The following brief list is meant simply to suggest the kinds of materials in which the interested student may find further information of interest.

GENERAL

Brown, J.J. *Ideas in Exile: A History of Canadian Invention* (Toronto, 1967).

Craig, Gerald, ed. *Early Travellers in the Canadas* (Toronto, 1955).

Innis, Harold A. and A.R.M. Lower. *Select Documents in Canadian Economic History*, 2 vols. (Toronto, 1929, 1933).

Kranzberg, Melvin and Carroll W. Pursell. *Technology in Western Civilization*, 2 vols. (New York, 1967).

Ouellet, F. *Histoire économique et sociale du Québec, 1750-1850* (Montreal, 1966).

Séguin, Robert-Lionel, *La Civilization Traditionelle de l''Habitant' au 17e et 18e Siècles: Fonds Materiel* (Montreal, 1967).

TRANSPORTATION

Aitken, Hugh G.J. *The Welland Canal Company: A Study in Canadian Enterprise* (Cambridge, 1954).

Berton, Pierre. *The Last Spike: The Great Railway 1881-1885* (Toronto, 1971).

————. *The National Dream: The Great Railway 1871-1881* (Toronto, 1970).

Currie, Archibald W. *The Grand Trunk Railway of Canada* (Toronto, 1957).

Ellis, Frank. *Canada's Flying Heritage* (Toronto, 1961).

Glazebrook, G.P. de T. *A History of Transportation in Canada*, 2 vols. (Toronto, 1964).

Guillet, Edwin C. *The Story of Canadian Roads* (Toronto, 1966).

Kingsford, William. *The Canadian Canals: Their History and Cost* (Toronto, 1865).

Stevens, George R. *Canadian National Railways*, 2 vols. (Toronto, 1960-62).

MANUFACTURING AND NATURAL RESOURCE INDUSTRIES

Bartlett, James H. *The Manufacture, Consumption, and Production of Iron, Steel, and Coal, in the Dominion of Canada, with Some Notes on the Manufacture of Iron and on the Iron Trade in Other Countries* (Montreal, 1885).

Denison, Merrill. *Harvest Triumphant: The Story of Massey-Harris* (Toronto, 1948).

Donald, W.J. *The Canadian Iron and Steel Industry* (Boston, 1915).

Fauteux, Joseph-Noël. *Essai sur l'Industrie au Canada sous le Régime Français*, 2 vols. (Québec, 1927).

Innis, Harold A. *The Cod Fisheries: The History of an International Economy* (Toronto, 1940).

————. *The Fur Trade in Canada: An Introduction to Canadian Economic History* (New Haven, 1930).

————. *Settlement and the Mining Frontier* (Toronto, 1936).

Jones, Robert L. *History of Agriculture in Ontario: 1613-1880* (Toronto, 1946).

Kilbourn, William. *The Elements Combined: A History of the Steel Company of Canada* (Toronto, 1946).

Le Bourdais, Donat-Marc. *Metals and Men: the Story of Canadian Mining* (Toronto, 1957).

Lower, A.R.M. *Great Britain's Woodyard. British America and the Timber Trade, 1763-1867* (Montreal, 1973).

————. *Settlement and the Forest Frontier in Eastern Canada* (Toronto, 1936).

Martell, J.S. 'The Achievements of Agricola and the Agricultural Societies, 1818-25', *Bulletin of the Public Archives of Nova Scotia*, vol. 2, no. 2 (Halifax, 1940).

Nelles, H.V. 'The Politics of Development: Forests, Mines and Hydroelectric Power in Ontario'. Unpublished Ph.D. thesis, University of Toronto, 1969.

Richardson, William G. 'A Survey of Canadian Mining History'. Unpublished M.A. thesis, University of Toronto, 1973.

Salle, Benjamin. *Les Forges Saint-Maurice, 1699-1763* (New York, 1916).

Tessier, Mgr Albert. *Les Forges Saint-Maurice: 1729-1883* (Trois Rivières, 1952).

ENGINEERING AND URBAN TECHNOLOGY

Burpee, Lawrence J. *Sandford Fleming, Empire Builder* (London, 1915).

Cooper, John I. *Montreal; A Brief History* (Montreal, 1969).

Due, John F. *The Intercity Electric Railway Industry in Canada* (Toronto, 1966).

Gowans, A. *Building Canada: An Architectural History of Canadian Life* (Toronto, 1966).

Keefer, T.C. *Philosophy of Railroads*, H.V. Nelles, ed. (Toronto, 1972).

Master, Donald C. *The Rise of Toronto, 1850-1890* (Toronto, 1947).

Richie, T. *Canada Builds, 1867-1967* (Toronto, 1967).

Shanley, Walter. *Daylight Through the Mountain: Letters and Labours of Civil Engineers Walter and Francis Shanley*, Frank N. Walker, ed. (Montreal, 1957).

Shaw, Charles A. *Tales of a Pioneer Surveyor* (Don Mills, 1970).

Young, C.R. *Early Engineering Education at Toronto, 1851-1919* (Toronto, 1958).